MINOR PROPHETS

MINOR PROPHETS

H. A. IRONSIDE

Revised Edition

Introductory Notes by
John Phillips

LOIZEAUX
Neptune, New Jersey

First Edition, 1909
Revised Edition, 1999

A Publication of Loizeaux Brothers, Inc.
A Nonprofit Organization Devoted to the Lord's Work
and to the Spread of His Truth

Unless otherwise indicated, Scripture quotations are taken from
the King James version of the Bible.

Library of Congress Cataloging-in-Publication Data

Ironside, H. A. (Henry Allan), 1876-1951.
Minor prophets / H. A. Ironside:
introductory notes by John Phillips.—Rev. ed.
p. cm.
ISBN 0-87213-411-3 (pbk.: alk. paper)
1. Bible. O.T. Minor Prophets—Commentaries. I. Title.
BS1560.I68 1999
224'.907—dc21 98–20506

Printed in the United States of America
10 9 8 7 6 5 4 3 2 1

CONTENTS

PREFACE

TO THE REVISED EDITION

H. A. Ironside's commentary on the Minor Prophets was first published in 1909. As might be expected in an exposition of prophetic Scripture, the author examined Bible prophecy in the light of then-current events and wove his observations into the commentary. Decades later some readers find certain of these references a bit puzzling.

During preparation of this revised edition we considered the possibility of eliminating or modifying observations that might be considered particularly dated. Ultimately we decided to retain these portions unchanged, believing that they provide valuable insight into the author's thinking and the way he examined current political events in the light of God's Word. The fact that none of Dr. Ironside's conclusions were subsequently invalidated indicate that there is much we can learn from his careful approach.

As the author stated in the first edition: "I have sought to press the practical application as giving important teaching for a remnant people in a day of decline, while not neglecting their dispensational bearing. This, I am persuaded, is what is greatly needed at the present moment."

The Publisher

AUTHOR'S NOTE

After many months of intermittent labor, I have been, through grace, enabled to complete this volume. Now I send it forth with the earnest prayer that God may use it—imperfect in many respects as I know it to be—to the glory of His great name and the blessing of many of His people.

Everywhere we have found the same great facts emphasized: Humanity at its best is altogether vanity, but grace abounds over all our sin and failure.

If at times the notes seem pessimistic and unduly burdened with a sense of moral failure, it is not intentional but rather an evidence of human frailty and imperfection. For the prophets, rightly read, should lead to the brightest optimism. They confront us with evil only so that we may judge it in ourselves. And they always point beyond sin to the glad morning without clouds, when the Savior we wait for shall come down like rain on the mown grass, His kingdom like the clear shining after the storm has passed.

Evil is transitory and has sway only for a moment. The good will endure forever, when the last remains of sin will be banished to the lake of fire, and there shall be new heavens and a new earth wherein dwelleth righteousness.

> Wherefore, beloved, seeing that ye look for such things, be diligent that ye may be found of him in peace, without spot, and blameless. Ye therefore, beloved, seeing ye know these things before, beware lest ye also, being led away with the error of the wicked, fall from your own stedfastness. But grow in grace, and in the knowledge of our Lord and Saviour Jesus Christ. To him be glory both now and forever. Amen (2 Peter 3:14,17-18).

AUTHOR'S NOTE

INTRODUCTION
THE PROPHETS
MEN SENT FROM GOD

BY JOHN PHILLIPS

The appearance of a prophet always marked a period of apostasy and rebellion in Israel. The prophets raised their voices in loud protest against the prevailing idolatry, corruption, and blindness of their times, calling the nation back to God. It is a mistake to think that a prophet's primary function was to foretell the future. The prophet did that of course, but he was first of all a man with a message from God for his own generation, a "forthteller" rather than a "foreteller." Often the prophets were statesmen with both insight and foresight, clearly seeing the end of the dangerous religious and political experiments of their contemporaries.

The prophets often failed to understand all of their own utterances, for the burdens they delivered sometimes had a double fulfillment: an initial and partial fulfillment close to the time the words were uttered, and a later, more complete fulfillment, at a remote date. They usually spoke from the standpoint of their own people. The Gentiles being mentioned only to the extent that the other nations were to come into conflict with, or to be blessed through, Israel. Their themes were many and varied but, apart from the initial, immediate, and partial fulfillment of their predictions, their prophecies focused on two future events, the first and second comings of Christ. The prophets themselves probably could not distinguish between those two comings and often too a message would be given only to be enlarged upon at a later date either by the same prophet or by another.

Three of the prophets directed their messages to Gentile nations: Obadiah, Jonah, and Nahum: the first to Edom and the other two to Nineveh. It often happened that the prophet was unpopular with the people to whom he delivered the message of God, and sometimes he was bitterly persecuted for his preaching, his message being considered subversive to the national interest and the prophet himself, a traitor. The prophets were the moral conscience of their age.

Bible Prophecy is Unique

The Bible is the only book which challenges unbelief by foretelling the future, staking its authority on the ultimate, certain, and complete fulfillment of its detailed predictions. It has been said that there were some 109 Old Testament predictions literally fulfilled at Christ's first coming, and that of the 845 quotations from the Old Testament in the New Testament 333 refer to Christ. There are some 25 prophecies concerning the betrayal, trial, death, burial, and resurrection of Jesus uttered by various prophets over a period of some five hundred years. These prophecies were literally fulfilled although the chance would be one in 33,554,438. If the law of compound probabilities is applied similarly to all 109 predictions fulfilled at Christ's first coming, the chance that they could accidentally be fulfilled in the history of one person is one in billions.

The writing prophets belonged to three main periods of Hebrew history, either before, during, or after the Babylonian captivity. Note that the dating of many of the prophets' ministries cannot be given with absolute certainty therefore the dates given in the Profiles are approximations. There were, of course, other prophets besides the writing prophets, notably Elijah and Elisha. Others include Enoch, Nathan, Micaiah, and Huldah, a prophetess. Moses, Samuel, and David also must be counted as prophets. From the days of Samuel it would seem that schools were set up for the training of prophets, but the Holy Spirit by no means restricted Himself to those schools when He called a man to the prophetic office.

THE WRITING PROPHETS

B.C.	PREEXILIC	EXILIC	POSTEXILIC
830-819	Joel		
784-772	Jonah		
764-755	Amos		
755-714	Hosea		
739-692	ISAIAH		
736-700	Micah		
648-620	Nahum		
634-625	Zephaniah		
619-610	Habakkuk		
627-575	JEREMIAH		
592-572	Obadiah		
593-559		EZEKIEL	
605-536		DANIEL	
520-504			Haggai
520-489			Zechariah
436-416			Malachi

Background of the Prophets

The political and religious conditions of the times of the prophets are constantly reflected in their writings, so those conditions need to be studied as part of the background of the prophetic books. The empires of Egypt, Assyria, Babylon, and Persia overshadow the whole prophetic era, whereas Greece and Rome also color the visions of Daniel. Lesser kingdoms such as Moab, Edom, Syria, Philistia, Ammon, Phoenicia, Elam, and Ethiopia are also pictured on the prophetic page. The power struggles of these several nations form the historical background against which the prophets poured out their warnings, their wooings, and their woes; and consequently something should be known of them. This is true especially of Assyria and Babylon, the empires that terminated the monarchies of Israel and Judah, and of Persia, the nation that brought about the restoration of the Jews to their homeland.

Assyria

From the reign of Sennacherib on, Nineveh was the capital city of the Assyrian empire and, as we are told in the book of Jonah, it was a great city. The Assyrians were fiendishly cruel, their kings often being depicted as gloating over the tortures inflicted on conquered peoples. They pressed their wars with the utmost ferocity, uprooting whole populations as a policy of state and deporting them to remote parts of their empire. The leading men of conquered towns were given over to torment and were horribly mutilated before being put to death. It is no wonder that fear of Assyria fell on all her neighbors.

Babylon

The Assyrians were succeeded on the world scene by the Babylonians. God gave to Nebuchadnezzar a sweeping mandate over the other nations of the earth, including Judah. Nation after nation fell as the invincible Babylonians swept westward. Egypt was defeated in the famous battle of Carchemish on the Euphrates in 605 B.C., and with that, nothing could halt the conquerors. Jerusalem fell and the Jews were deported as warned by Jeremiah and his contemporaries. Tyre was sacked, and Egypt handed over to Nebuchadnezzar by God in payment for this service. Many lesser kingdoms felt the weight of the Babylonian arm, and for some seventy years the Babylonian empire reigned supreme, the Jews tasting complete captivity to their Gentile captors.

Persia

The Babylonian empire was ended by the Medes and Persians, with Persia emerging soon afterward as the supreme Gentile power. Cyrus the Great (whose name had been mentioned by Isaiah long before he was born) was a humane ruler. He issued a decree ending the Babylonian captivity of the Jews. Daniel, carried away to Babylon during the first deportation by Nebuchadnezzar, lived through the entire captivity period and on into the Persian era. He lived to see Judah restored to partial sovereignty and, in vision, saw Persia fall and Greece come into focus only to fall in turn before the Romans. His piercing eye saw still farther into the future than that, for he saw to "the time of the end." Such were the prophets, and they are unique in the history of the world. Their words still ring with authority as they bring a message for us even today.

Hosea

A PROFILE

HOSEA
PROPHET OF THE BROKEN HEART AND BROKEN HOME

BY JOHN PHILLIPS

Hosea (755-714 B.C.) has been called "the Jeremiah of the Northern Kingdom," for like Jeremiah he was called to weep and suffer. He deals with the condition of Israel just before the fall of Samaria. His terrible statement in 13:16 is but a reflection on the typical savagery of the Assyrians: "Samaria shall become desolate; for she hath rebelled against her God: they shall fall by the sword: their infants shall be dashed in pieces, and their women with child shall be ripped up." Hosea's contemporaries were Amos, Isaiah, and Micah. He prophesied in the days of Uzziah, Jotham, Ahaz, and Hezekiah of Judah, and of Jeroboam II of Israel.

Contrast of Amos and Hosea

Amos and Hosea are a study in contrasts. Amos thundered out the righteousness of God; Hosea wept out the mercy of God. The first took the heathen nations into his prophecy; the second limited his utterances to Israel, with an occasional reference to Judah. The style of Amos is clear and lucid, his illustrations being drawn from the countryside. Hosea's style is simple but just as clear as he pours out his heart in short, sharp sentences, his broken home giving him ample illustration to convey the truths that were heavy on his heart.

Structure of Hosea

The book of Hosea is organized according to two tragedies: the tragedy in Hosea's homelife and the tragedy in his homeland.

I. The Tragedy in Hosea's Homelife (1–3)
   A. The Signs: Reflected in the Children (1)
   B. The Sins: Reflected in the Wife (2)
   C. The Salvation: Reflected in the Husband (3)
II. The Tragedy in Hosea's Homeland (4–14)
   A. The Polluted People (4–7)
   B. The Punished People (8–10)
   C. The Pardoned People (11–14)

The Background of Hosea

Hosea was commanded to marry a woman named Gomer, who soon proved unfaithful to him. The children she bore were a source of sorrow. The first child, a son, Hosea owned as his own; the second, a little girl, he called Lo-ruhamah ("not beloved" or, as Baxter suggests, "she-that-never-knew-a-father's-love"). This child he disowned. The third child he likewise disowned, calling him Lo-ammi ("not my people" or "no child of mine"). Each step of the tragedy in his homelife is related to the tragedy in his homeland, for Gomer represented Israel, and her children, the people of the nation. Hosea's patience and pleading with the wife who broke his heart was a parable of God's love and longing for Israel. Even when Gomer forsook him to play the harlot, Hosea's love followed her, and at last he found her dishonored and deserted and, it would seem, in slavery. He purchased her (3:2) but refused to restore her fully until a time of chastening had passed. The whole sad story of domestic tragedy and heartache taught Hosea that Israel's sins were as adultery and harlotry in the sight of God.

The Burden of Hosea

Hosea set himself the sad task of translating all this into a passionate wooing of and warning to Israel. The sins of the nation were many: swearing, lying, killing, stealing, adultery, drunkenness, idolatry, backsliding, pride, treachery, insincerity, forgetfulness, ingratitude, covetousness, craft, love of sin, oppression, highway robbery, and anarchy. All of these sins are reflected in Hosea's pages. The pagan priests aided and abetted murder (6:9), and the government was unstable. One faction urged compromise with Assyria, and another insisted on an alliance with Egypt (7:11).

Hosea's pleadings went unheeded, for Israel had "sown the wind" and would "reap the whirlwind" (8:7). Throughout the book, the rumble of the gathering storm can be heard. But God is love too and that theme is ever present. Hosea tells us that sin hurts God; it not only breaks His laws but it breaks His heart. Thus we find that there is a promise of ultimate salvation lightening the ever-darkening sky. "I will heal their backsliding, I will love them freely: for mine anger is turned away" (14:4). Hosea illustrates the "love that many waters cannot quench."

CHAPTER ONE

THE PROPHECY OF HOSEA

Hosea, whose book is the first of the so-called minor prophets, began his prophetic ministry when Amos was prophesying to Israel and served almost as long as Isaiah did in Judah (see Amos 1:1 and Isaiah 1:1). During the long reign of Jeroboam II, king of Israel, and the reigns of Uzziah, Jotham, Ahaz, and Hezekiah, kings of Judah, there was much to rebuke in the two nations. Hosea seems to have confined most of his direct messages to Judah, speaking rather *of* the ten tribes than *to* them. But the scope of his prophecy embraces both nations very fully. In fact, no other messenger, including Daniel, gives so complete an outline of the ways of God with His earthly people as does Hosea. When read in connection with the visions of Daniel, each throws much light on the other.

Of Hosea's personal history it has not pleased God to give us any details, except in relation to his marriage and children. His father's name is given as Beeri, but neither the prophet's tribe nor the place of his birth is mentioned. *Hosea* means "help" or "salvation." With a single vowel point added, it becomes *Hoshea*, "salvation of Jah." *Beeri* is said to mean "The well of Jehovah." The two names together remind us of the Lord's words to the woman of Samaria, to whom He offered living water from Jehovah's well that would result in her salvation (John 4).

HOSEA 1: The Blood of Jezreel

"The beginning of the word of the Lord by Hosea" was a command for the prophet himself, directing him to do what would naturally be offensive and what must have greatly tested his heart.

Like Isaiah, Hosea and his family were to be signs for Israel. He was told to unite himself in marriage to a woman devoid of character—a harlot—thus signifying the wretched condition of unfaithful Israel, who nevertheless remained the object of Jehovah's love, despite their iniquity, and the filthiness that was in them. What more wonderful picture could we have of grace, not only to the undeserving, but to those who had deserved the very opposite? It is important to remember that grace is not merely *unmerited* favor, but it is favor in spite of *merited* judgment.

This is the marvelous lovingkindness of our God—that He finds the objects of His love not among the righteous and the holy but among sinners lost and ruined, deserving nothing but judgment. We are stained with guilt and polluted by sin, having left His way and become unprofitable. Nevertheless, He sets His love on the wretched and redeems them to Himself. Jehovah's dealings with ancient Israel picture His ways of grace with believers now. "All these things happened unto them for examples, and they are written for our admonition upon whom the ends of the [ages] are come" (1 Corinthians 10:11).

In obedience to the voice of the Lord, Hosea "went and took Gomer the daughter of Diblaim" as his wife; thus giving to her who previously had no standing the place of honor of a wife in Israel. With her he had several children. Having died to her old sinful life (of which she might well be ashamed) she gives children to the one who has set his love on her and given her his name and protection. It is easy to see in all this a lovely illustration of the words of the Holy Spirit in Romans 6:21-22:

> What fruit had ye then in those things whereof ye are now ashamed? for the end of those things is death. But now being made free from sin, and become servants to God, ye have your fruit unto holiness, and the end everlasting life.

Also in Romans 7:4: "Wherefore, my brethren, ye also are become dead to the law by the body of Christ; that ye should be married to another, even to him who is raised from the dead, that we should bring forth fruit unto God."

Hosea had to bear the shame of having married a woman of low character, but he did not have to die for her. How different it was for our blessed Lord Jesus. He not only came where we were in our sin and shame, but on Calvary's cross He was made sin for us so that we might become God's righteousness in Him. There He purchased us with His own precious blood, "that he might redeem us from all iniquity, and purify unto himself a peculiar people, zealous of good works" (Titus 2:14). Hosea's kindness to Gomer is only a faint picture of Jesus' all-conquering love and Jehovah's undying affection for Israel, His earthly bride. For the cross was where the price was paid for both the heavenly and the earthly people.

When Hosea and Gomer's first son was born,

> the Lord said unto him, Call his name Jezreel; for yet a little while, and I will avenge the blood of Jezreel upon the house of Jehu, and will cause to cease the kingdom of the house of Israel. And it shall come to pass at that day, that I will break the bow of Israel in the valley of Jezreel (Hosea 1:4-5).

The name *Jezreel* itself speaks of blessing, yet here it is used to express judgment. *Jezreel* means "sown of God," and in Hosea 2, as well as 1:11, it is used quite differently than here in 1:4-5.

God was about to cast Israel, the northern kingdom, out of His sight among the Gentiles, to chasten them for their iniquities. He had redeemed them in grace and brought them to Himself; but they had proven false and treacherous. Therefore they would have to learn by judgment what they had not learned by lovingkindness. He connected their destruction with "the blood of Jezreel," which is most significant.

The reigning house of Israel had gained the kingdom through the "blood of Jezreel." For Jehu had become the instrument for the destruction of Ahab's house at Jezreel, and Jeroboam II was his descendant.

Yet there is more connected with Jezreel. Remember that Jezreel was originally the inheritance of the righteous man Naboth. In 1 Kings 21 we learn that this Naboth "had a vineyard which was in Jezreel." Ahab coveted the vineyard and sought to buy it so that he might turn it into a garden. Naboth rightly refused to sell his inheritance, saying, "The Lord forbid it me, that I should give the inheritance of my fathers unto thee." Sullen and depressed, Ahab "laid him down upon his bed, and turned away his face, and would eat no bread." The proud and willful monarch could not stand the thought that someone as insignificant as this Jezreelite should thwart his wishes. Jezebel, his heathen wife, however, wrote letters in his name, saying, "Proclaim a fast, and set Naboth on high among the people: And set two men, sons of Belial, before him, to bear witness against him, saying, Thou didst blaspheme God and the king. And then carry him out, and stone him, that he may die" (1 Kings 21:9-10). The ungodly plot was duly perpetrated. False witnesses swore away the life of the righteous one, and "they carried him forth out of the city, and stoned him with stones, that he died" (13).

His inheritance was declared forfeited, and Ahab went down to take possession of it. But on the way he was met by Elijah the prophet, who was sent with a message of judgment. Jehovah had been watching, and He commanded His servant to declare to the godless king that his doom was sealed and his house would fall. The blood of Jezreel would be his ruin, for, "Thus saith the Lord, In the place where dogs licked the blood of Naboth shall dogs lick thy blood, even thine" (19). And Elijah prophesied against Jezebel as well, "saying, The dogs shall eat Jezebel by the wall of Jezreel" (23). All this was literally fulfilled. Ahab was slain in the battle of Ramoth-Gilead, and we read, "So the king died, and was brought to Samaria; and they buried the king in Samaria. And one washed the chariot in the pool of Samaria; and the dogs licked up his blood; and they washed his armour; according unto the word of the Lord which he spake" (22:37-38). This happened in the area of Jezreel, Ahab's summer home.

Ahab was succeeded by his ungodly son Ahaziah, who died after a fall; then Ahab's other son, Joram, or Jehoram, as he is sometimes called, took the throne. Jehu, having been anointed king of Israel by Elisha the prophet, made it his first task to put Joram to death. Joram had "returned to be healed in Jezreel of the wounds which the Syrians had given him, when he fought with Hazael king of Syria" (2 Kings 9:15). Jehu and Joram met on the plot of land that had belonged to Naboth the Jezreelite; Ahaziah king of Judah was also there (21). "And it came to pass, when Joram saw Jehu, that he said, Is it peace, Jehu? And he answered, What peace, so long as the whoredoms of thy mother Jezebel and her witchcrafts are so many?" Joram attempted to flee, but Jehu pierced him through with an arrow and, in fulfillment of the word of Jehovah, cast his bleeding corpse into the plot of Naboth (24-26). Ahaziah too was struck down, but fled to Megiddo to die (27). It was against the house of Ahab the Lord's vengeance was to fall in Naboth's portion of Jezreel!

Here too Jezebel met her dreadful fate, as the prophet had predicted. "When Jehu was come to Jezreel, Jezebel heard of it; and she painted her face, and tired her head, and looked out at a window." As she taunted Jehu calling him a regicide, he called for anyone who was on his side to throw her down. At once several eunuchs took hold of her and "they threw her down, and some of her blood was sprinkled on the wall, and on the horses: and he trode her under foot." Afterward Jehu sent his servants to bury her, but they found that dogs had devoured her in the portion of Jezreel, as the Lord had spoken (30-37).

The ruling dynasty (Jehu's) in Hosea's day had therefore come to the throne through this blood of Jezreel. Sadly, though, they had failed to learn from this solemn lesson of God's hatred of sin, and His abhorrence of idolatry in particular! Therefore this same valley of Jezreel would be the scene of *their* judgment. And it was only a few years later in that very spot (called then Esdraelon) that the Assyrians defeated Israel and her captivity began.

Dispensationally, all this is filled with vital truth. Israel, according to Isaiah 5, is Jehovah's vineyard. So the vineyard of Jezreel speaks of Israel. The Jews were "sown of God" in the land of Canaan to be Jehovah's portion. But they hired false witnesses against the Lord of the vineyard, the righteous One, who would not give the enemy His rightful inheritance. By wicked hands they killed the Husbandman and claimed the vineyard as their own. Because of this, the Gentile oppressor was permitted to overturn the kingdom, and power was transferred to the nations. The awful plea, "His blood be on us, and on our children" (Matthew 27:25) has been terribly answered, as the blood of Jezreel foreshadowed. In the very place where they killed the Lord of glory, their blood has been poured out as wine bursting from the winepress, and they have been devoured by the dogs—the unclean Gentiles.

Have the Gentiles, on their part, learned from the dreadful lesson of the blood of the seed of God? Far from it. Proud and indifferent to God's claims on them, they have gone their own ways, and refused to pay attention to His Word. Therefore they too shall be cut off, and God will avenge on them the blood of Jezreel.

Coming back to the literal application of the passage in Hosea, we note that Jehovah was about to "break the bow of Israel in the valley of Jezreel" (Hosea 1:5). Because they had not taken to heart the fact that Ahab's evil dynasty was destroyed because of sin but had walked in the same unholy paths, the ten tribes were to be carried into Assyria. This prophecy, as we well know, came to pass about fifty years later in the days of King Hoshea, who was imprisoned by Shalmaneser the Assyrian ruler, and his people taken captive.

In the next verse we learn that a daughter was born to Gomer and Hosea. In obedience to the word of God, she was called *Lo-ruhamah*. The name means, "Not having obtained mercy," and it describes the present state of Israel since they have been cast out of their land. On Judah the Lord would still have mercy and would save them from their enemies. They had not yet openly revolted, as had the ten tribes (7).

A third child, this time a son, was named *Lo-ammi*. This name means "Not My people," for the Lord now declared, "Ye are not my people, and I will not be your God" (9). They had broken the covenant entered into long ago at Sinai and ratified in the plains of Moab. From the beginning they had been rebellious; therefore on the basis of merit they could claim nothing. So God gave them up for the time being and refused to own them as His people. This Lo-ammi sentence remains unrepealed to the present day. At the Babylonian captivity, Judah also came under this judgment, and all Israel has been in its shadow ever since. This accounts for the omission of the name of God in the book of Esther, which illustrates God's providential care over the Jews while they are scattered among the nations, and when He cannot publicly identify Himself with them.

According to the Hebrew arrangement the first chapter of Hosea ends with verse 9; the two verses that follow serve as the introduction to chapter 2. They speak of mercy still unrealized, and tell us that though all is lost on the basis of works, God still has in reserve boundless stores of grace that the Jews will enter into and enjoy in the latter day.

> Yet the number of the children of Israel shall be as the sand of the sea, which cannot be measured nor numbered; and it shall come to pass, that in the place where it was said unto them, Ye are not my people, there it shall be said unto them, Ye are the sons of the living God. Then shall the children of Judah and the children of Israel be gathered together, and appoint themselves one head, and they shall come up out of the land: for great shall be the day of Jezreel (10-11).

It will be observed that, in justifying from Scripture the present work of God in showing mercy to the Gentiles, this is one of the passages to which the apostle Paul appealed in Romans 9:25-26; while his brother-apostle Peter applied the same words to the present remnant of Israel in 1 Peter 2:10. Both Jew and Gentile stand now on the same ground before God; therefore the same passage may well apply to both, for the salvation of either is on the ground, not of legal works, but of pure grace.

The reference to the sand of the sea in Hosea's prophecy carries us right back to the original covenant of pure grace made with Abraham and confirmed by the oath of El Shaddai. God will not renounce the promise made to the fathers, however great the failure of the children. A numberless host of reunited Israel and Judah will yet be brought into blessing—never again to be abandoned—in the very land pledged to Abraham, Isaac, and Jacob and stained with the blood of Jesus. This is not the return that took place under Cyrus. Very few from the ten tribes came back at that time, and all were driven out of their land because of the rejection of Messiah when He came, in accordance with prophecy, to offer Himself as King. When the Lord's set time has come, they will return from all the places where they have been scattered. They will no longer be divided but will be one happy, united people, under one Head, the once-rejected Jesus—the Christ of God. That will be the true day of Jezreel, when the field of blood will become again the vineyard of Jehovah, and they shall be sown of God in the land of their fathers, never to be uprooted again.

HOSEA 2: The Valley of Achor

God's ways of grace and rule are marvelously blended in Hosea 2:1, which follows closely on the promise in the last two verses of Hosea 1. Continuing with the previous verses' assurance of future restoration and blessing, Jehovah cries, "Say ye unto your brethren, Ammi; and to your sisters, Ruhamah." This is faith's anticipation of the time when the *Lo* ("not") shall be removed, and the Jews will again be owned as God's people who have obtained mercy. This, of course, looks for its fulfillment in the millennium, when "all Israel shall be saved"(Romans 11:26)—that is, the *remnant* of Israel which will then become the righteous seed for the millennial kingdom (see Romans 9:27-29; Isaiah 10:20-23). But it becomes true even now whenever a soul of either Israel or the Gentile nations turns to God in repentance, trusting the once-rejected Messiah.

In order to lead Israel to this place of self-judgment and abhorrence of her past ways God searchingly outlines her grievous sin of turning away from Him in Hosea 2:2-5. As a wretched harlot—worse than that, an adulteress—He had to put her away. For after all the love and grace lavished on her, she had turned from Him to idols in spiritual harlotry.

Because of this He will see that she eats the fruit of her own actions. His dealing with her in His holy and righteous way is solemnly portrayed in verses 6-18. This is in full accord with Jeremiah's words, "Thine own wickedness shall correct thee, and thy backslidings shall reprove thee: know therefore and see that it is an evil thing and bitter, that thou hast forsaken the Lord thy God" (Jeremiah 2:19). This is how God makes sin serve His purposes. If His people do not refrain from evil but persistently take their own course and refuse to obey His voice, then they must be taught by their own sin the lesson they would not learn from His words of warning and admonition.

Israel had forsaken Him for idols: she would be given up by Him for a time and left to the idols of her own choosing for her correction. And in her troubles she would find no one to answer her (Hosea 2:7). Brokenhearted and world-weary at last, chastened and disciplined by her experiences, she would cry, "I will go and return to my first husband; for then was it better with me than now." Amazing the grace that, after such heartless abandonment on her part, would yet cause God to open His arms to her again in the day of her genuine repentance.

This same love and grace is found by every weary sinner and every failing saint when they seek God's face, confessing the sin and shame of their evil ways. No transgression is too great for Him to pardon; no evil-doing is too much for His mercy, if there is a humbling before Him, and if the sinner testifies to God's righteousness and his own unworthiness.

Movingly Jehovah points out the blindness of Israel concerning the true source of all her past blessings. "She did not know," He says, "that *I* gave her corn, and wine, and oil, and multiplied her silver and gold, which *they* prepared for Baal" (2:8, emphasis added). The treasures He bestowed so lavishly she had poured out on the altars of her shame! Therefore, He would withhold His favor until she learned that her false gods could bring her no good, but only sorrow and impoverishment. All she valued would be stripped from her until she learned that in Jehovah, whom she had so dishonored, was all blessing to be found. She had attributed His gifts to her idols, saying, "These are my rewards that my lovers have given me." But, bereft of all, she would learn that she had been deluding herself and dishonoring Jehovah. (For another striking example of this see Jeremiah 44:15-22.)

When at last her lesson has been learned, she will receive the grace Jehovah has had in store for her, which will be fully revealed when she repents. This is the precious and tender theme of the balance of the chapter.

> Therefore, behold I will allure her, and bring her into the wilderness, and speak comfortably unto her [Hebrew, "speak to her heart"]. And I will give her her vineyards from thence,

> and the valley of Achor [trouble] for a door of hope: and she shall sing there, as in the days of her youth, and as in the day when she came up out of the land of Egypt (Hosea 2:14-15).

God loves to remember the days of Israel's first betrothal to Him, when she followed Him into the wilderness, into a land that was not sown; when she was holy to the Lord, and her heart was fixed on Him alone. Those happy days of her first love will be renewed. Once more He will charm her and draw her away from the scenes of her captivity and dishonor. Alone with Him in the wilderness of the people (see Ezekiel 20:35), He will plead with her face to face. He will restore her vineyards of joy, and the valley of Achor (of trouble) will become a door of hope. Achor was the scene of Achan's judgment, as recorded in Joshua 7:24-26. Defiled by her unholy departure from God and her coveting of accursed idols, Israel's blessing will begin when the sin that has troubled her is judged and put away. Then, restored to Him from whom she had wandered so long, she will sing (or perhaps "respond") as in her early days when everything was new, as in the days when she came out of Egypt.

The application to the individual soul is simple and natural. For the backslidden child of God who has learned the folly of abandoning the eternal lover of his soul and returned to God, the joy of early days will be restored, and communion, long lost, will be enjoyed once more.

In the day of Israel's restoration, she will be called the wife of Jehovah. It is important to notice the difference between her place and portion and that of the bride of the Lamb in Revelation 19 and 21. The first is earthly; the other, heavenly. The former is not called a bride, because she is a restored wife who had long wandered from her husband. The latter is presented as the bride for the first time at the marriage supper of the Lamb in Heaven. In the millennium, the Lamb and His heavenly bride will reign over all redeemed creation. On the earth, the restored wife of Jehovah will have her place in the land of Palestine. The new Jerusalem above is the capital city of the first; the rehabilitated Jerusalem on earth is the capital of the second. Then will the words be fulfilled,

> And it shall be at that day, saith the Lord, that thou shalt call me Ishi ["my husband"]; and shalt call me no more Baali ["my lord," or "my master"]. For I will take away the names of Baalim out of her mouth, and they shall no more be remembered by their name (Hosea 2:16-17).

These will be the days of Isaiah 54:6, "For the Lord hath called thee as a woman forsaken and grieved in spirit, and a wife of youth, when thou wast refused, saith thy God." Then the land will become the land of Beulah, and both land and people will be unmistakably Jehovah's.

To this joyous period the prophets devoted much attention. It is the day of the glory of the kingdom, when Jesus will be declared "the blessed and only Potentate" (1 Timothy 6:15) by the world that once rejected Him.

It will be a time of universal spiritual light and blessing. But more than that, the curse will be lifted from the ground, and the lower creation will be brought into the liberty of the glory for which it has groaned so long (Romans 8:22).

> In that day will I make a covenant for them with the beasts of the field, and with the fowls of heaven, and with the creeping things of the ground: and I will break the bow and the sword and the battle out of the earth, and will make them to lie down safely (Hosea 2:18).

All this will come about when the Son of man is exalted and all creation rejoices in His beneficent rule (see Psalm 8). Isaiah 11 strikingly pictures the blessings of that halcyon time, the true golden age, to be ushered in by the return of the Lord Jesus, who will shepherd the nations with a rod of iron (Psalm 2; Revelation 19).

Nor shall Israel ever be unfaithful again. The tarnished history of the past will be forgotten—or remembered only to emphasize the grace that restored her. "And I will betroth thee unto me forever" is Jehovah's word, "yea, I will betroth thee unto me in righteousness, and in judgment, and in lovingkindness, and in mercies: I will even betroth thee unto me in faithfulness: and thou shalt know the Lord" (Hosea 2:19-20). These words do not refer to the church, but to literal Israel. When the fast-approaching end of the "times of the gentiles" comes, Israel will be grafted into the olive tree of promise, restored to God and to their land, and made the inheritors of the promises assured to the fathers. A careful reading of such portions as Romans 11; Jeremiah 30–31; Ezekial 36:22-38; 37 should make clear to the least-instructed reader that God has not cast off His ancient people forever. When He restores them, it will be in pure grace on the basis of the new covenant, sealed already with the blood of His Son. Nothing will ever destroy that hallowed union or again divorce the earthly spouse from Jehovah.

A lovely millennial picture concludes Hosea 2.

> And it shall come to pass in that day, I will hear, saith the Lord, I will hear the heavens and they shall hear the earth; And the earth shall hear the corn, and the wine, and the oil; and they shall hear Jezreel. And I will sow her unto me in the earth; and I will have mercy upon her that had not obtained mercy; and I will say to them which were not my people, Thou art my people; and they shall say, Thou art my God (21-23).

This passage may be a little plainer if we read "respond to" or "answer" in place of "hear." In the imminent day of Messiah's glory, Heaven and earth will be united in the blessing of "the times of restitution of all things, which God hath spoken by the mouth of all his holy prophets" (Acts 3:21).

The heavens, in which will dwell the glorified saints who have been raised or changed at the coming of the Lord, will respond to the joy of a redeemed earth, just as God Himself will respond to them. It will be a scene of blissful communion, never again to be broken, despite Satan's last effort to mar and ruin what God will have done (Revelation 20:7-10).

The earth, freed from the primeval curse, will no longer produce thorns and briers, but will respond with overflowing supplies of corn, wine, and oil. The desert will rejoice and blossom as the rose. No more by the sweat of his face will man eat his bread with weariness; but, as though an animate thing, the earth will ungrudgingly yield her treasures for the redeemed of the Lord.

To Jezreel all will likewise respond. Israel will be sown as the seed of God in the very land that had once been stained with the blood of the righteous One—and afterward, in awful retribution, with their own blood. There they will take root and triumphantly spring upward, and the people once called Lo-Ruhamah will become Ruhamah. Likewise the Lo-Ammi sentence will be forever repealed and they will be called Ammi. In joyous response they will lift their eyes and hearts to Jehovah's throne, and with deepest reverence and self-abandonment they will exclaim, "My mighty One!"

This shall be the closing scene of the day of Jezreel. No more will sin and sorrow, war and desolation, sweep the plains of the field of blood. Rather, it will become the scene of unmingled joy and blessing when Jesus is acknowledged as the sovereign Lord.

HOSEA 3: Israel's Present and Future

This chapter, brief as it is, becomes of vast importance when we understand God's ways in regard to the earth and His earthly people, Israel. It is, one might say, the Romans 11 of the Old Testament. And when read in connection with that passage, it sheds much light on the mystery of Israel's present anomalous condition and the predictions concerning her future glory.

Once more the prophet's relationship with his wife is used as an illustration. She who had been previously called a harlot is now regarded as an adulteress. The difference in application is readily apparent. Israel, utterly unworthy before Jehovah took her up in His wondrous grace and sealed her union with Him by covenant, had proven more unworthy still. She was likened then, not only by Hosea but other prophets also, to an adulteress—a woman who seeks strangers instead of her husband.

The language used by the King James version in Hosea 3 is significant. The prophet is not told to love *his wife*. She had forfeited all claim to that relationship. She is simply called "a woman," and he adds, "beloved of her friend"; that is, one who had chosen another in place of her rightful spouse.

Hosea's love for so unworthy and worthless a creature was to be a picture of "the love of the Lord toward the children of Israel," who, professing themselves to be in covenant relation with Him, yet "look to other gods and love [the sacred raisin cakes]." The latter expression is the correct reading in place of "flagons of wine" (KJV), which has no specific reference to idolatry. The cakes expressed the idolatrous relationship they were sustaining (see Jeremiah 7:18; 44:19). This was how they honored her who in that day bore the title "Queen of heaven"—a title that in apostate Christendom has been given to Mary the mother of our Lord in direct defiance of Scripture.

Gomer (for I do not doubt that she is indeed the "woman" the passage speaks of) seemed to have entangled herself in such a degrading situation that only by paying a redemption price could she be released. So the prophet "bought her to [himself] for fifteen pieces of silver, and for an homer of barley, and an half homer of barley." This was the price of a common slave, thus illustrating the words of Isaiah, "Ye have sold yourselves for nought; and ye shall be redeemed without money" (Isaiah 52:3). I take "without money" to mean that they had no money to redeem themselves, so had to be redeemed by someone else. Jehovah had tenderly entreated them through Isaiah to "return unto me; for I have redeemed thee" (44:22). Though the price was paid at Calvary's cross, Judah and Israel are wayward still, and the marriage covenant has not been renewed.

Hosea said to Gomer, "Thou shalt abide for me many days; thou shalt not play the harlot, and thou shalt not be for another man: so will I also be for thee" (Hosea 3:3). These words indicate a period of testing, undefined in duration, before she would be restored to conjugal privileges.

The application is made by the Holy Spirit in the closing verses:

> For the children of Israel shall abide many days without a king, and without a prince, and without a sacrifice, and without an image, and without an ephod, and without teraphim: Afterward shall the children of Israel return, and seek the Lord their God, and David their king; and shall fear the Lord and His goodness in the latter days (Hosea 3:4-5).

These two verses succinctly set forth the Jews' whole state for this entire dispensation, as well as the future blessing that will be theirs in the day when the kingdom is displayed in power and glory. The "many days" of verse 4 run throughout the whole present period until the fullness of the Gentiles is completed.

Ever since the destruction of Jerusalem by the Romans in A.D. 70 the Jews have illustrated the truth of this prophecy. They have been scattered throughout many nations, "without a king, and without a prince." The Davidic scepter has departed from Judah and the lawgiver's staff from between his feet (Genesis 49:10)—solemn witness of the fact that Shiloh (the One to whom the scepter belongs) has already come, only to be rejected by them. Therefore they have been left without a sacrifice, for their temple has been destroyed and their altar profaned. From nation to nation, and from city to city, they have wandered through the centuries; an often-hated people, despised by man and without means of approach to God on the basis of the law they have broken.

Ritual and Talmudic lore have in large measure taken the place of God's appointed ordinances and the authority of the Torah (the law) among them. But from year to year they have to confess in anguish, as they beat their breasts, "Woe unto us, for we have no mediator!" The smoke of sacrifice ascends not to Heaven. The blood of atonement is not sprinkled within the veil of any earthly sanctuary. And blindness in part having wrapped them in judicial darkness, they do not know that the Lord Jesus' one offering on the cross has taken away iniquity and purged sin, because eternal redemption is found in that precious blood.

Not only are they without a sacrifice, but they are without a priest also—"without an ephod"—for all records have long been lost. Though many survive who are in the direct line of priesthood (as shall be revealed in the day of their restoration), they cannot now trace their genealogy. Even if they could, there is no temple in which to officiate. Meanwhile the heavenly Priest ministers in the sanctuary above, but their eyes are blinded, and they do not know Him.

It might naturally be supposed that, being denied all the consolations of the religion of their fathers, they would have fallen again into idolatry. However, we learn that they were to live "without an image" and "without teraphim." The Babylonian captivity cured them of idolatry. Since then, *that* at least has not been one of their national sins. They have no means of access to the true God while they revile and refuse His Anointed. On the other hand, they do not follow idols but wait, like the redeemed wife of the prophet, until the day when they will again be publicly acknowledged by Jehovah.

When the present dispensation is ended and the church has been translated to Heaven, God will once more take the Jews up in grace and fulfill the promises made to the fathers. After passing through the unparalleled tribulation of the latter days—as predicted in Jeremiah 30, Daniel 11–12, Zechariah 12–14, and by our Lord Himself in Matthew 24—they shall "return, and seek the Lord their God, and David their king; and shall fear [or the Hebrew may be rendered, 'shall hasten to'] the Lord, and his goodness." This will fulfill all that the prophets have looked forward to; when Israel's wanderings will be over, their sins blotted out, themselves renewed, and the kingdom confirmed to them. In that day Jesus will be King over all the earth, sitting on the throne of His father David and reigning in glorious power and majesty. It would seem too, from a careful comparison of this passage with the latter part of Ezekiel's prophecy, that a lineal descendant of David's line (called "the prince") will rule the restored nation under the authority of Him whose capital city will be the new and heavenly Jerusalem, the "city which hath foundations, whose builder and maker is God" (Hebrews 11:10).

So shall the years of Israel's mourning be ended, and the day of Messiah's glory have arrived; for the two synchronize. There can be no full blessing for Israel and the earth until the tragedy of Calvary is repented of, and Jew and Gentile unite in confessing their sin in crucifying the Lord of glory and killing the Prince of life.

Till then, the unhappy condition delineated in the next chapter must continue—except the curse of idolatry has been done away, as we have seen.

HOSEA 4: Joined to Idols

The statement we have just been considering—that Israel should remain many days without an image or idol—seems all the more remarkable when we remember the gross idolatry into which they had fallen when Hosea was divinely called to declare God's view of their condition. Idolatry was then their characteristic condition; and from it, as from a parent-stem, sprang all the other evils for which the prophet was called to rebuke them.

Because truth had departed, and with it mercy and all knowledge of God, Jehovah had a controversy with the inhabitants of the land. His holy eye saw only swearing, lying, murder, theft, and adultery instead of holiness and fidelity to Him. The covenant entered into at Sinai had been broken in every point. Not one of the ten commandments remained sacred to them. For all this the Lord set His face against them in His righteous sovereignty, as He had warned them He would through the lips of the lawgiver himself (Hosea 4:1-3).

So utterly fallen and wretched were they that none was fit to reprove another. All shared a common guilt. The leaven of idolatry openly introduced in the wilderness, though secretly carried from Egypt and even from beyond the Euphrates (Joshua 24:2), had been working unjudged until the people had become utterly corrupted. How true it is that, "Evil communications corrupt good manners" (1 Corinthians 15:33). They had become like those who "strive with the priest"; that is, they persistently refused to submit when the mind of God was made known (Hosea 4:4).

The lesson for us is a solemn one. Someone has well said that evil never dies of old age. Sin unjudged among the people of God becomes like a spreading leprosy or a cancerous sore, ever working and extending its disfiguring effects until the whole mass becomes defiled.

With Israel, at least at first, it was not ignorance that led to their downfall, though light refused inevitably results in darkness. They were like those who fall in the daylight, even their prophets doing likewise. Therefore they needed to be cut off (5).

"My people are destroyed for lack of knowledge." Such was Jehovah's lament. But the lack of knowledge was the result of their own refusal to listen. He had impressed His truth on them, but they would accept none of it. So He added, "Because thou hast rejected knowledge, I will also reject thee, that thou shalt be no priest to me: seeing thou hast forgotten the law of thy God, I will also forget thy children" (6). Light rejected results in deeper darkness than ever, as well as great distress, and rejection from God.

Often in the history of the church, a similar state has existed, and always the issue is the same. In the sixteenth century God raised up Martin Luther to sound, with clarion voice, the battle cry of the Reformation, "The just shall live by faith!" But the majority of the professing church had no ear for the message and sank into deeper superstition and folly. Later, the Wesleys and their colaborers were ordained of God to revive the lifeless profession of their day with a call to repentance. But the majority refused to listen, and formalism became more formal and ritualism gained its harvest of lost souls. At the beginning of the nineteenth century, the truths of the unity of the body of Christ and the presence of the Holy Spirit were recovered. Yet the apostles of what were incorrectly called, "the new doctrines," were ridiculed, abused, and criticized. As a result, Christendom is rapidly sinking into apostasy, and the presence of the Holy Ghost is unknown in many places. The Scriptures are rejected as God's revelation and put on a par with human writings, while pride and arrogance are the order of the day. The Lord's words are having a severe and awful fulfillment, "If, therefore, the light that is in thee be darkness, how great is that darkness!" (Matthew 6:23)

Is the reader one to whom light has come, but you are afraid or unwilling to obey? Remember that when you act according to God's will as revealed through His Word, your path shines brighter and brighter until the perfect day. On the other hand, revealed truth willfully ignored or, still worse, refused, has a hardening effect on the conscience. I have known of people who had learned from Scripture certain truths that, if acted on, would have delivered them from worldly ways and worldly religious associations and given them freedom to go to the rejected One, bearing His reproach. They hesitated, however, because of possible worldly loss, or of probable family difficulties. Seeking an easier path than the one marked out in the Book, they argued down their consciences and quenched the Spirit of God. Look at the sad result! Stripped of spiritual power, deprived of their strength, they regard the truths they once enjoyed as dead letters. Their consciences are calloused, and their testimony for God is over. In vain they may talk of and try to make sacrifices along other lines, but this will not do for Him who has said, "To obey is better than sacrifice, and to hearken than the fat of rams" (1 Samuel 15:22).

Israel's sad history may well be a warning to us of the dire consequences of resisting the truth. "As they were increased, so they sinned against me: therefore will I change their glory into shame" (Hosea 4:7). Prosperity had not turned their hearts to Him but away from Him, so He would deal with them according to their deeds. Because they delighted in their sin and ignored God's word, He would give them up to destruction; priest and people would suffer together. In their self-gratifying path, they would learn the costly lesson that there is nothing satisfying apart from following God. Their unholy ways would only "take away the heart," and they would stumble and fall "because they have left off to take heed to the Lord" (8-11).

They were ready to ask counsel of their idols, but were too proud and self-sufficient to turn to Him to whom they owed every blessing! It has often been observed that when people get away from God they can be most meticulous about self-imposed rites and superstitious observances, while counting it a hardship to obey the voice of the Lord. The same is true regarding faith. Those who find it difficult to trust the simplest statement of the Holy Scriptures can accept with amazing ease the most remarkable hypotheses and notions of unbelieving theorists. And so it was with Israel at this time. Nothing that their idolatry demanded was too much for them, but they could not tolerate the law of Jehovah. "Therefore," said He against whom they had so openly transgressed, "the people that doth not understand shall fall" (12-14). These things are among those "written for our admonition." Oh, for grace to *learn* and act accordingly. This is what the prophet wanted to impress on Judah. "Though thou, Israel, play the harlot, yet let not Judah offend" (15). Sadly later on we find the southern Kingdom in the same apostasy as the northern kingdom.

Because Israel had repeatedly regressed spiritually, "like a backsliding heifer," God would, as it were, give them their way. They would be like a lamb feeding in a large place, left free to go to all lengths but with certain judgment coming. For though they thought they were pleasing themselves, they were like lambs fattening for the slaughter. The word had gone forth, "Ephraim is joined to idols: let him alone" (16-17).

Nothing can be more sobering than this last phrase. It is as though God had exhausted every possible means for their recovery, save one: to give them up to learn by bitter experience what they would not take to heart in any other way. The New Testament equivalent is being delivered "unto Satan for the destruction of the flesh, that the spirit may be saved in the day of the Lord Jesus" (1 Corinthians 5:5). When a soul proves utterly stubborn and willful, God may at times say of him as of Israel, "He is joined to his idols." Further reproof or brotherly correction is useless. Let him be severely alone, until he learns at Satan's hands how far he has gone from God and how low he has fallen. Observe: It is only after the failure of all other means to recover the wanderer that God so deals with souls. It was when His patience had come to an end, as it were, that He gave up Ephraim. From the beginning He had tolerated them, ministered to them, chastened, entreated, and disciplined them; but all had been in vain. They were set on having their own way. Finally, because He loved them too much to give them up forever, He said, "Let them alone." Now they were where they would learn by sad experience the full result of leaving the Lord. They would be given up to their own hearts' lusts until they would "be ashamed because of their sacrifices" (Hosea 4:18-19).

How deep the love that breathes through all this unhappy description. How tender the grace that persisted to the end in seeking the restoration of those so worthless and so undeserving!

And for us too, it is precious to know that His grace is unchanging; and if saved by that precious blood of Christ, we are the objects of that

> Faithful and forbearing love
> That never turns aside.

Surely, nothing should have so powerful an effect on our ways as the fact that our waywardness has not, *cannot*, quench His love. No change in us results in any corresponding change in Him. Therefore we are urged, "Grieve not the Holy Spirit of God, whereby ye are sealed unto the day of redemption" (Ephesians 4:30). It is not to grieve Him *away*, as people often mistakenly insist this means, for then the words would be in the nature of a threat instead of the force of a tender entreaty. How corrupt the soul that would take advantage of love so immeasurable in order to follow its own bent, thus disdaining the Spirit of grace!

HOSEA 5: I Will Hide Myself

This chapter is full of searching truths for the people of God in all ages, which we of the present permissive times will do well to lay to heart. It may be part of a single discourse, of which the previous chapter is the introduction and the balance of the book the remainder; or the various sections may have been penned at different intervals, as the prophet was led of God to write them. In either case, the moral value is the same, and the object is also the same throughout—namely, to bring the backslidden people into the presence of God so that they may be restored in soul and savor sweet communion with the everlasting One.

Priests, people, and the royal house were all addressed in Hosea 5:1 and told that judgment was coming on them. It had not yet come; but it was like an angel of wrath with drawn sword facing their way, and nothing but repentance could cause that sword to be sheathed.

In vain they had been rebuked by Him, to whose eyes all things are naked and open. Their iniquity was always before Him; but though He had sought their recovery so long, they persistently refused to "frame their doings to turn unto their God." A malignant demon, "the spirit of whoredoms," seemed to possess them, and they did not know the Lord (1-4).

And this was not the worst of it. Despite their wretched condition, they were puffed up with pride. "The pride of Israel doth testify to his face." Because of this they needed to be punished. "Therefore shall Israel and Ephraim fall in their iniquity; Judah also shall fall with them" (5). Failing to learn from her sister's sin, Judah had followed in the same path. She too would be cast out of the land under the judgment of God.

The sentence of Lo-Ammi, referred to in the first chapter, cannot be changed. Even though they *seemed* to have a desire for God, they would not find Him, for they had hated knowledge and despised all His reproof.

When people refuse light, the light is withdrawn, and they are given up to judicial darkness. This is what we read in Hosea 5:6: "They shall go with their flocks and with their herds [for sacrifice] to seek the Lord; but they shall not find him; he hath withdrawn himself from them." This would fulfill the word spoken through Moses many years before: "I will hide my face from them, I will see what their end shall be: for they are a very froward generation, children in whom is no faith" (Deuteronomy 32:20).

Notice, God would not forget them, nor would they be completely cast out of His presence. Rather He would withdraw from them, leaving them to spiritual famine and desolation until they realized their true condition and confessed it before Him.

In the present dispensation of grace we have examples of similar dealings. Consider Jesus' encounter with the Gadarenes (Mark 5:1-17). Finding them determined to go their own way, He left them for a time, but was welcomed by them on His return to the Decapolis (Mark 7:31-37; Gadara being one of the cities of the Decapolis). And indeed this incident pictures to us His rejection when He came at first, but points too to the day when He will return in glory and be welcomed.

Until repentance comes, God will not publicly manifest Himself on their behalf. They may have continued in their pride to produce illegitimate children and boast of progress and expansion, but all their achievements were empty, for the Judge was at the door (Hosea 5:7).

From verses 8 to 14, the prophet seemed to have the invading army in sight. "The day of rebuke" was almost upon Israel. They blew the trumpet and sought to defend themselves; they attempted an alliance with Assyria. But their efforts were futile; it was but leaning on a broken reed. God had become like an enemy—to both Ephraim and Judah He would be a destroying lion from whose power no one could deliver them.

But note that in all this God was still seeking their blessing. "I will go and return to my place, till they acknowledge their offence, and seek my face: in their affliction they will seek me early" (15).

The Spirit of Christ was very clearly speaking through the prophet in this verse. The same conditions of Hosea's day also prevailed when the Lord Jesus came to this earth. True, idolatry was no longer an issue; but pride, arrogance and self-will abounded. Jesus came to His own, but His "own received him not" (John 1:11). Therefore He had to say, "I will go and return to my place." If they had no room for Him here, the Father had a seat for Him on His throne. So Jesus left their house desolate and went up on high, where He waits for them to acknowledge their offense. The great tribulation—the time of Jacob's trouble—will result in a remnant seeking His face with contrite hearts. Then He will no longer hide Himself but shall appear as their Deliverer in glory.

HOSEA 6: What Shall I Do Unto Thee?

The opening verses of Hosea 6 connect intimately with what we have just been considering, while the balance of the chapter is another appeal to the consciences of Ephraim and Judah.

Nothing could be more suited to the lips of the restored remnant than the expression of these first three verses:

> Come, and let us return unto the Lord: for he hath torn, and he will heal us; he hath smitten, and he will bind us up. After two days will he revive us: in the third day he will raise us up, and we shall live in his sight. Then shall we know, if we follow on to know the Lord: his going forth is prepared as the morning; and he shall come unto us as the rain, as the latter and former rain unto the earth.

This is the cry of the returning remnant, who have learned to know the Lord in the smoking furnace of tribulation, and who now ask the way to Zion, returning with chastened spirits to the One they so long despised. The awakening in Zechariah 12 closely correlates with what we have here in Hosea. They recognize that it has been God who has torn and smitten them, but their faith turns them toward Him for healing and growth. After two days of solemn searching of their consciences, leading to repentance, He revives them on the third day. This day corresponds to the day the water of separation was sprinkled on the unclean person so that he might be declared clean on the seventh day (Numbers 19). Thus they who once were defiled by the dead are made to live in His sight. So when God descends in glory like showers of rain on the grass, they will find revival and blessing, with daily growth in the knowledge of God in His kingdom throughout the age to come.

However, though this will indeed happen when they are made willing in the day of His power, they were far from being in that happy state when the prophet Hosea was sent to them. We see the lovely millennial picture for only a moment before the Spirit of God continues to address their wretchedly fallen condition, and tenderly plead that they turn from their sins.

There had once been what seemed like a desire to be true to God, but it had proven to be fleeting. "O Ephraim," He cried, "what shall I do unto thee? O Judah, what shall I do unto thee? for your goodness is as a morning cloud, and as the early dew it goeth away" (Hosea 6:4). Like Ephesus of a later day, it was for only a brief season that they clung to their first love. The tender feelings of those early days, when they followed Him into the wilderness, had been short-lived indeed. Their love had vanished like the dew when the sun rises in its strength. Because of this, in place of sending prophets to encourage their spirits, the Lord had been obliged to send them a message like that afterwards given by John the Baptist, who layed the ax to the root of the trees, which in their pride rose up to such heights (5). The distinction might be made that the prophets of old were more like men sent to prune away all excess, endeavoring to trim the branches with a view to fruitfulness. But all their efforts were futile, so John came to lay the ax to the *root* of the trees. Everything must come down. Recovery was hopeless. The first man (Adam) could bring forth nothing for God; he must be superseded by the Second (Romans 5:12-21). This is the great difference between the closing books of the Old Testament and the opening message of the New.

Mere outward correctness and attention to forms and ceremonies would not do for God. He says, "I desired mercy, and not sacrifice;

and the knowledge of God more than burnt offerings" (Hosea 6:6). Isaiah similarly declared the emptiness of ritualistic observances when the heart was far from the Lord (for example, see Isaiah 58). God must have reality. All else is but hollow mockery in His sight.

In Hosea 6:7 God accused them of transgressing the covenant. God had made known His will to them, but they had violated His every command, following the lust of the flesh, the lust of the eye, and the pride of life (1 John 2:16). They dealt treacherously with the One whose servants they professed to be.

And Gilead, so greatly favored naturally, had become a city of iniquity and stained with blood (Hosea 6:8). A priestly city, it should have been holy to the Lord. But these godless clerics were as troops of robbers, plundering those they should have led in the right way and living in uncleanness, instead of in God's holy ways. The leaders of the people caused them to decline, and led them astray from the paths of truth.

Who can fail to see the same ungodly conditions developing now in Protestantism? The open debauchery of the well-named Dark Ages was checked by the light of an open Bible, which made people ashamed of what they once dared to revel in, in the darkness and ignorance of Romanism and medieval times. But now Satan's supreme effort is to poison minds by the unholy speculations of faithless clergy who give free rein to the filthiness of the spirit. They use their positions as leaders in the church to enrich themselves while starving the true flock of Christ and poisoning those who, while bearing the name of Christians, are destitute of divine grace! How terrible the end will be when false religion is judged in the day of the Lord's anger!

And how ineffectual was the warning voice of old—and of today. The majority went recklessly on their way, heedless of God's solemn rebuke. "I have seen an horrible thing in the house of Israel: there is the whoredom of Ephraim, Israel is defiled" (10).

Verse 11 can be interpreted two ways. For Judah, a harvest has been appointed when they will be returned from captivity. This might mean that God will get His harvest, despite human failure, when He restores His people to Himself. But since only Judah was mentioned, while the guilt of both had just been proclaimed, I conclude the harvest referred to here is that awful judgment yet to be reaped because of the rejection of the Messiah. Judah must pass through this, as we have already noticed, just prior to their restoration and blessing. The ten tribes, as such, had no part in the rejection of the Lord Jesus. It was not on them that the rabid elders invoked the curse when they cried, "His blood be on us, and on our children!" Consequently, for Judah a terrible harvest is yet to come. They sowed the wind; they shall reap the whirlwind, when the vials of the wrath of God are poured out on the prophetic earth.

HOSEA 7: A Cake Not Turned

Judgment is God's mysterious work. He had no desire to punish the people He had taken into covenant-relation with Himself, even though they had violated the covenant from the beginning. On the contrary, He had always offered them blessing and restoration, dependent on their repentance. But when He would have healed Israel—had they shown evidence of self-judgment—He had to say "the iniquity of Ephraim was discovered, and the wickedness of Samaria: for they commit falsehood; and the thief cometh in, and the troop of robbers spoileth without" (Hosea 7:1). His holy eye could detect no sign of contrition for all their offenses; they persisted in sin and lawlessness, despite every plea to stop. In their sinful security they did not consider that God would remember all their wickedness, until "their own doings" had surrounded them, so that their iniquity was openly before His face. Their rulers delighted in the debauched state they had fallen into, taking an unholy satisfaction in the dishonesty and wickedness prevailing (2-3).

In verse 4, a most significant picture is presented for our contemplation. "They are all adulterers, as an oven heated by the baker, who ceaseth from raising after he hath kneaded the dough, until it be leavened." The leaven of unrighteousness had long been secretly working in the nation, but now it was energetically and openly corrupting the whole. Satan's effort had been only too successful. Idolatry, having been early introduced and never thoroughly judged, had permeated the entire nation. To this passage the apostle Paul doubtless would have directed the minds of the Corinthian saints when he wrote, "Know ye not that a little leaven leaveneth the whole lump?" He also stressed the same serious principle when writing to the Galatians (l Corinthians 5:6; Galatians 5:9).

Leaven, in Scripture, rarely typifies that which is good; it usually signifies some form of evil. Here we see all Israel leavened with the unholy system of idolatry, with its corrupting influences doing its deadly work for centuries. Once the leaven is added to the dough, the baker knows it will act according to its nature; he sleeps through the night, but the oven is prepared for the morning. The oven was to be the furnace of judgment.

In Christendom we see the same thing. The Lord Jesus warned of the leaven of the Pharisees, of the Sadducees and of the Herodians. They seem to speak of hypocrisy, false teaching and worldliness. And we are alerted to the leaven of malice and wickedness in 1 Corinthians 5:8. But there is no hint in all Scripture of the leaven of *grace*. We can infer then that just as in Israel the leaven of idolatry was introduced when they made the calf in the wilderness (and, being never fully judged, worked on until it had permeated the whole nation), so in the church's early history was the leaven of error added to the food of the people of God. It too has never been dealt with, but is rapidly leavening the whole lump. It is identical to the mystery of iniquity the Holy Spirit warns us about in 2 Thessalonians 2, which will soon be led by Babylon the great and the antichrist.

Believers are charged to "purge out, therefore, the old leaven," whenever it is revealed in their assemblies (1 Corinthians 5:7). If, however, the majority are already so corrupted that there is no obedience to the Word of the Lord, those who would be vessels "unto honor, sanctified, and meet for the master's use" must purge themselves from the unholy mixture. They must separate themselves from that which is opposed to the holiness that is appropriate in God's house. And they must find their fellowship with those who "follow righteousness, faith, charity, peace" and "call on the Lord out of a pure heart" (2 Timothy 2:16-22).

For Israel there was no hope. The entire nation was symbolized by the king who was drunk with the wine of fleshly exultation and allied with the scorners. Their own hearts were like the oven of the baker, who could sleep while the leaven worked and the fire was prepared to heat the oven for the baking of the coming day. Therefore, they themselves would work out their own judgment, because there was no one who called out to God (Hosea 7:5-7).

> Ephraim, he hath mixed himself among the people [as one with the nations]; Ephraim is a cake not turned. Strangers have devoured his strength, and he knoweth it not: yea, gray hairs are here and there upon him, yet he knoweth not. And the pride of Israel testifieth to his face: and they do not return to the Lord their God, nor seek him for all this (8-10).

This passage emphasizes their lack of awareness of their true condition. Indifferent to their actual state before God, they are like a cake placed on the coals and forgotten by the baker until, left unturned, it is all burned on one side. Taking no heed to the prophet's warnings, the majority went carelessly on their own way. They took for granted that all was just as it should be, when, in reality, everything was all wrong. This apparently unconscious backsliding is a sad characteristic of many today. Away from the Lord, yet professing and even presuming that all is well—how many are like this cake not turned! This one-sidedness tells the tale to an observant, anointed eye, revealing that something is radically wrong in many a case. Often saints make much of the truth as a matter of doctrine while becoming utterly negligent about walking in that truth from day to day. They are like a cake not turned, all brown on one side and raw dough on the other. Doctrinally, they may be very particular. Practically, they are loose and unconcerned.

At other times the case is just reversed: much is made of experience, with little or no heart for what is slightingly termed "dry doctrine." But it is as necessary to "hold fast the form of sound words" (2 Timothy 1:13) as it is to seek to live in a godly way. In fact, doctrine is the root of all practice; and our experience will prove faulty if it is not the result of knowing the mind of God as revealed in His Word. Let us never forget that truth and practice go together, even as position and condition must never be divorced.

Ephraim's first grave mistake was in mixing himself among the unbelieving people. God had called Israel to dwell apart, and not be counted among the nations. Nothing but evil ever resulted from mixing with those from whom they had once been separated. It was "the mixed multitude" who first caused them trouble in the wilderness, and started their murmuring and longing for Egyptian food instead of the bread from Heaven (a type of our Lord Jesus Christ come down in grace to meet His people's needs, see Exodus 16; Numbers 11; and compare with John 6).

This associating with godless people was also the ruin of Samson, the mighty Nazarite, who gave up the secret of his strength when he lay in the lap of Delilah (Judges 16). How many a valiant servant of God has become as weak as other men in a similar way ever since!

We can trace the same evil practice all through the history of the chosen race, until at last it ended in their being cast out by the Lord in judgment. In exile they mixed among the nations until they had their fill of the society of the strangers who devoured their strength and brought them to desolation.

The lesson is a beneficial one for us because we too have been called with a higher calling and are commanded to walk apart from a godless world and a corrupt church. Indifference to this separation of the clean from the unclean has had a debilitating effect on the testimony and experience of thousands. Yet we learn so slowly. Oh, that we had hearts to cling to the Lord, heeding His word, "Come out from among them, and be ye separate" (2 Corinthians 6:17).

It is as futile to try to reform what is not of God by joining it in fellowship as it would be to try to teach sparrows to sing like a warbler by placing a canary in a cage with them. The only result would be that the canary would lose its song, while the sparrows would chirp on as before. Sadly, many a once joyous saint has lost his song by mixing among the people of the world and the worldly church! Such a person may boast of his open-mindedness and be as unaware as was Ephraim of the true state of affairs. The spiritually-minded, however, shake their heads in sorrow as they say, "Strangers have devoured his strength, and he knoweth it not: yea, gray hairs are here and there upon him, yet he knoweth not" (Hosea 7:9).

Gray hair is the sign of departing strength; it tells the tale that its owner is going downhill—age and frailty are coming on. But Ephraim, like many other backsliders in heart, was oblivious to the true condition of affairs. In such a case others may notice the gray hairs "here and there upon him"—the carelessness here, the indifference there, a growing fondness for worldly companionship, less and less time spent in prayer and over the Word of God, increased love for that which is light and frivolous, and a growing fondness for unprofitable conversation. Contrast this attitude with that of 1 Timothy 4:15-16.

Accompanying this lack of interest in spiritual things, will invariably be found an assumption of easygoing superiority. "The pride of Israel testifieth to his face" (Hosea 7:10). But there will be no turning to God and seeking His mind until that person is broken by discipline.

Ephraim, "like a silly dove"—without regard for Him who had carried them in His bosom—had turned to Egypt and then to Assyria for help when the hour of trial came (11). But the Lord loved them too much to permit them to find anything stable in the world and its empty pomp and show. So He would cast His net over them, like one taking a bird in a snare. He could not allow those who were in covenant relationship with Him to go on in their own way for long (12).

They had sinned against Him, though He had redeemed them. Having drifted away from God, they had "forgotten that they were purged from their old sins" (2 Peter 1:9). With supreme indifference to their true condition they blamed Him for what had come upon them as though they themselves were blameless. Consequently, God charged them with speaking lies against Him. "I sometimes think," the devout G. V. Wigram once said, "that God has been hard with me, when I forget how hard I have been with God!" This is always the tendency of a heart unexamined before the Lord (Hosea 7:13).

They had continued this way for many years, neither seeking Him when alone in the privacy of their own homes nor when gathered in what should have been a solemn assembly—but was really a time of godless festivity. "They howled upon their beds," not in repentance for their evil ways but over the Lord's discipline. Jehovah had indeed trained them to confide in Him, and strengthened their arm against their adversaries; but in return they thought ill of Him, turning to any recourse other than God. So incorrigible is the human heart, even that of a saint, when away from God. Therefore they must be left to sound deeper depths of sorrow and disaster, like the incestuous man of 1 Corinthians 5, who was delivered "unto Satan for the destruction of the flesh, that the spirit may be saved in the day of the Lord Jesus". Their princes would be destroyed, and they themselves would become a laughingstock to their Egyptian allies, on whom they had vainly depended (Hosea 7:14-16).

Surely, the way of man is not in himself. It is not in man to direct his own steps. This is why we need brokenness of spirit and self-judgment before God, so that He may lead us in the paths of righteousness for His name's sake.

HOSEA 8: A Vessel Wherein Is No Pleasure

God seemed to almost exhaust figurative language in describing the sad condition of His deluded people, their hearts set on wandering from Him who was their only real good. He had already used the expressive symbols of an adulterous wife, a wine-inflamed drunkard, a backsliding heifer, troops of robbers, a leavened mass, a cake not turned, a silly dove, and a deceitful bow. In Hosea 8 He warned that because of their sins they will be scattered among the nations as "a vessel wherein is no pleasure" (8).

This was the logical result of the Sinai covenant, where the nation pledged to obey all the words of the law, which promised blessing to all who kept it but invoked a curse on the violators of its precepts. According to this chapter, Israel had broken it at every point. Therefore, on that ground, they had no rights to claim. God still had wondrous resources of grace yet to be disclosed, which the final chapter of Hosea makes abundantly clear. But the nation would only enjoy these blessings when the people acknowledged their sins and gave up all pretension to merit.

The prophet, figuratively speaking, sounded the trumpet to summon the whole congregation into the presence of the Lord so that they could face the reality of their condition as a people who have transgressed the covenant and trespassed against the law (1).

In the second verse, we glimpse a possible hint of future restoration: "Israel shall cry unto me, My God, we know thee." But it seems more likely to imply their ignorance of their true condition. With amazing audacity, they cried, "My God, we Israel know thee" (RSV), all the while persisting in their folly. Having cast off the thing that is good, they were driven before their enemies. They set up kings after their own heart and made princes without asking Jehovah's counsel. Idolatry too flourished everywhere, and the temple service became a mockery (3-4). They professed to know God, but their works denied Him.

How tragically easy it is to fall into the sad condition depicted here. How many today talk of being the people of the Lord while all the time condoning sin and living in disobedience to the Word of God. While Jesus walked the earth He had this to say: "The scribes and the Pharisees sit in Moses' seat: All therefore whatsoever they bid you observe, that observe and do; but do not ye after their works: for they say, and do not" (Matthew 23:2-3). They could preach to others fairly well according to the law, but their practice was the true indicator of their soul's condition—and how far they were from God! Again, it should always be remembered that while it is of prime importance to be doctrinally correct, a merely correct position is a poor thing if there is not a corresponding rightness of soul. Neither one can be neglected without loss. But nothing can be worse than priding oneself on "maintaining divine ground" while the life is defiled and the heart is disobedient to the truth.

The soul that turns from the living and true God to idols, of whatever nature, will learn at last what it is to be forsaken when help is most needed. The calf of Samaria cast them off. As with the priests of Baal in Elijah's day, they cried, but no one answered, or even heard them. How could it be otherwise, when they had placed their trust in the work of their own hands (Hosea 8:5-6).

Having sown the wind, therefore, they had to reap the whirlwind, as many a soul has done before and since. Yet how slow we are to learn! *Theoretically*, all saints know that there can be no real blessing apart from walking with God. But *experientially,* how easily most of us are lured aside, and led after other gods when some opportunity seems to present itself for profit or advantage! But finally all realize that the only result of such sowing is disappointment and sorrow. "The bud shall yield no meal: if so be it yield, the strangers shall swallow it up" (7).

Apply this to every area of life, and you will find that there are no exceptions. Apparent success may seem to follow disobedience, but "the end is not yet." We may imagine that God and His Word can be disregarded, but we will prove in bitterness of soul that it is an evil thing indeed to choose our own path.

How many brokenhearted wives could testify to the truth of this principle. How often unhappy husbands become a living illustration of it. God has plainly forbidden unequal yokes. The Word is clear, and the young saint has it driven home on the conscience. But then one who seems promising as a suitable life partner crosses the path. Admiration develops into affection. Affection ripens into love. A proposal of marriage is made. Then begins a period of doubt and vacillation. God's Word is plain enough, but its clear precepts are forgotten. Pleasant qualities are remembered. The fact that the other party is unsaved is glossed over. A willingness to go to the meetings of Christians and listen to the Scripture is magnified into a persuasion that a work of God has begun in the soul. Finally the young saint—only too readily—is drawn into the snare. An unequal yoke is entered into, and a lifetime of regret follows. In by far the majority of cases, the seeming interest in divine things passes away with the first few weeks of married life. Then even if open opposition is not developed, a cold, studied indifference ensues in regard to eternal things that no kindness or consideration can cover up. Thus the child of God is doubly wretched: the sense of disobedience finally comes home to an awakened conscience, and the realization dawns that the unsaved and unconcerned spouse, if not converted, will be separated for all eternity from the saved one.

In many other ways the same sad law is fulfilled, whether in business, social, or religious life. Oh that we might learn from what God has so plainly put before us in His Word, and from the unhappy experiences of thousands, the danger of trifling with conscience and with the truth that sanctifies the obedient soul.

Because Israel refused to obey His Word, God finally had to say, "Israel is swallowed up: now shall they be among the Gentiles as a vessel wherein is no pleasure" (8). This describes in one verse their history for over two thousand years. Driven out of their land, scattered among all nations, they have been like a vessel in which God could take no delight. What a contrast to the One who came to save them! "This is my beloved Son, in whom I am well pleased" (Matthew 3:17), was the Father's announcement when, at Jesus' baptism, He offered Himself as the One who came to "do always those things that please [the Father]" (John 8:29). He is the vessel of God's pleasure. Israel has become a vessel in which there is *no* pleasure. How marked the contrast!

It was futile for Israel to turn to Assyria or any of the surrounding nations. There could be no help for them while under the curse of the broken law. Like a wild ass, they had shown the untameableness of their nature. They did not know how to obey. So they would suffer under the power of the Gentile oppressor, whom God had made a "king of princes"—that is, Nebuchadnezzar, king of Babylon, to whom the Gentile dominion was first fully entrusted (Hosea 8:9-10; compare Ezekiel 26:7). God was evidently bypassing the Assyrian.

Ephraim had made many altars to sin by offering sacrifices to demons and not to God. His sin should return on his own head (Hosea 8:11).

The essence of all Jehovah's controversy with His people is declared in verse 12: "I have written to him the great things of my law, but they were counted as a strange thing." They were responsible to act in accordance with the written Word. They had failed to do so. Therefore the Judge was at the door. As with them so it is with Christendom—never more apparent than at the present time—God's Word is despised and regarded as nothing everywhere you turn. The end cannot now be far off.

Having despised the Word, it was useless to bring offerings and to sacrifice and eat flesh before the Lord. He could not accept worship from a disobedient and disloyal people. He remembered their sins, and had to deal with them because of their rejection of His law. Morally, they would return to Egypt, as in fact a remnant actually did in the last days of Jeremiah.

"For Israel hath forgotten his Maker, and buildeth temples." They had cast His commandments behind their back yet built temples where a pretended worship was offered. History repeats itself. These words might well describe what is so prevalent today. But the day of the Lord is coming; and, as of old, a fire will be sent forth from

God that will consume all the empty works of proud people when the hour of Jehovah's wrath strikes (13-14).

Remember, responsibility always increases as God's truth is revealed. How serious then the present moment, and how serious must be the results if truth is held in the mind but does not change the life!

HOSEA 9: The Days of Visitation

Even an utterly worldly person is relatively happy compared to a child of God whose heart has strayed from His heavenly Father. This is what the opening verse of Hosea 9 emphasizes. "Rejoice not, O Israel, for joy, as other people: for thou hast gone a whoring from thy God." Nations who had never known the Lord might go on with a measure of rejoicing in their ignorance and superstition; but for Israel, that could not be. Having once been the object of His lovingkindness, the ones to whom He had revealed Himself as the one true and living God, they could never be happy in their sin again.

The memories of past joys, of hours and days when the soul delighted in God and found precious food in His Word, make the backslider all the more cheerless as he fills his life with restless, unhappy experiences. And what a mercy to us that it is so! How grateful we should be to our God and Father that we cannot be in the enjoyment of true peace and genuine happiness while out of communion with the One to whom we are indebted for every good we have.

It is true that the soul away from Him may find a certain excitement and exhilaration in the follies of earth. But they are only the "pleasures of sin for a season" (Hebrews 11:25), and cannot be compared to those precious realities of which the psalmist wrote, "In thy presence is fulness of joy; at thy right hand there are pleasures for evermore" (Psalm 16:11).

So, of fallen Israel we read that the floor and the winepress would not satisfy them, and the new wine would fail. Nor would they dwell in the Lord's house, but they would return to Egypt, and feed on unclean food in Assyria. Having despised the service of the Lord, they would be cut off from His temple, and not eat of His sacrifices (Hosea 9:4).

Then Hosea pressed home the question, "What will ye do in the solemn day, and in the day of the feast of the Lord?" (5) Scattered among the heathen, they would think of past blessings and remember that it was time for a solemn feast day, but they would be cut off from its privileges. What then would they do, and how would they be able to satisfy their souls?

How seldom do the people of God think of these things as they should! Enticed by the world, fired by unholy ambition, and stimulated by pride, believers often allow themselves to be drawn away from the simplicity that is in Christ! Soon those who once enjoyed sweet fellowship with like-minded saints are widely separated. Those who once earnestly reflected on Christ's love and suffering for them as they sat at the table of the Lord, now drift away in darkness. What must be their feelings when, on the Lord's day, they recall amid scenes of worldly religiosity (or of irreligious worldliness) the sacred times once spent before the Lord with holy joy! To remember that, at the very hour when they are engaged in something that cannot have the Lord's approval, former friends are communing together at the feast Christ's loving heart instituted—surely in such tender memories there must be mingled a grief and a remorse not easily overcome.

This would be the nature of Israel's memories as the appointed seasons for the Passover, the day of atonement, and the feast of tabernacles came round and they were scattered among strangers, unable to participate in privileges once held so lightly. Gone from their land, and ravaged by Egypt (illustrative of that world from which the believer has once been delivered), their precious things would be a prey to their enemies. And they themselves would be wounded by thorns and nettles—pierced through with many sorrows (6). What a desolate, graphic picture of what every backslidden soul must endure.

In all this, Israel would be reaping only what they had sown. They had said (and in solemn irony they are reminded of it), "The prophet is a fool, the spiritual man is mad." This is how they had tried to quiet their consciences because of the multitude of their sins. Now, when all these things came to pass, they would know that "the days of visitation are come, the days of recompense are come" (7).

The watchman of Ephraim, who had sought to turn them from their evil way, was with God. But they had said, "The prophet is a snare of a fowler in all his ways," because of their hatred against the house of his God (8). It is so easy to denounce one who faithfully rebukes sin and strives to stop the deterioration of the soul. The leaven of Gibeah's wickedness (the record of which we have in the last chapters of the book of Judges) was still at work among them after all these centuries. Sin never dies a natural death; it must be thoroughly *judged.* Like leaven, it is stopped by fire—by judgment, *self*-judgment or God's judgment. When a person indulges in sin or permits its presence, it continues working though often imperceptibly, until it is judged by one's self or by God's people or by God Himself. This is the sober lesson of this chapter. Doubtless the Israelites addressed here had forgotten all about the days of Gibeah; or perhpas they would have pleaded that the trouble at Gibeah happened centuries before they were born, so there was no point in concerning themselves with it. But God's holy eye saw deeper than this. He saw that the self-will and corruption demonstrated at Gibeah were still rampant among them and called for brokenness and self-judgment before His face. But they ignored this. Therefore God would have to judge them and remember their sins (Hosea 9:8-9).

This is somber truth that may very well disturb us in the present season of the church's deep failure and ruin. Are we not a part of that house of God set up in responsibility on earth? Do we feel in our hearts how dishonored God is in that house, and consider that we may be a part of the problem? May God give grace to both reader and writer to let this truth penetrate the heart and awaken the conscience, thereby leading to a godly discernment as to what opposes the holiness of God's house, and self-judgment because of the part one has taken in assisting that opposition. It is easy to judge others. We are called upon to judge ourselves, and true self-judgment will lead one to review his downward path. This requires an awakened conscience, and it is the very opposite of ecclesiastical pretension and spiritual pride.

In verse 10 God lingers lovingly over the early history of His people, when He found Israel like grapes in the wilderness—precious fruit for Himself in a dry and thirsty land. But how soon did that early freshness disappear. It was not long till "they went to Baal-Peor, and separated themselves unto that shame." Balaam's wicked counsel was only too literally followed when he "taught Balak to cast a stumblingblock" before the separated nation (See Revelation 2:14). The daughters of Moab accomplished what all the enchantments of the false prophets could not do; "and their abominations were according as they loved" (Hosea 9:10). Let the reader carefully study the whole account in Numbers 22–25, and 31:16, compared with Revelation 2:14.

From the very beginning, Ephraim had proven himself untrustworthy. Therefore, his glory would fly away like a bird, and the people would be bereaved until no one was left. "Yea," said God, "woe also to them when I depart from them" (Hosea 9:11-12).

It should always be borne in mind that the Spirit of adoption, the indwelling Spirit who seals all true believers in the present dispensation of grace, will never depart from those whom God has marked as His own—no matter how much they may fail. However if they do fail, the Holy Spirit is grieved, communion is interrupted, and the Lord ceases to use them when waywardness becomes characteristic.

Ephraim, once "planted in a pleasant place," could no longer be blessed with children. "Fruitfulness" is what the name *Ephraim* signified. They would become fruitless and barren however; or if children were born, they would only be appointed to death (13-14). Communion with God and fruit for God go together. Where the first is lacking, the desired result will be absent as well.

Gilgal was once the first step in the promised land, the place where the Israelites set up the stones of remembrance after crossing the Jordan on dry ground and circumcised themselves once more in consecration to the holy One of Israel (Joshua 4–5). Now it was only a testimony to the people's wickedness. Therefore the One they had so dishonored would drive them from His house and disown them. When He says "I will love them no more," it is not that His heart or purposes had changed, rather that He would no longer openly work on their behalf. He would give them up to their enemies as One who, as far as they could see, loved them no longer (Hosea 9:15).

In this way Ephraim would belie his name. Stricken by God's judgment, "they shall bear no fruit." And even if they produce fruit, God's hand would be against them for destruction. This is how God would vindicate His holiness: by casting them out of His sight so that they might become wanderers among the nations (16-17). Moses had warned them of this from the beginning; but they had given no consideration to what should have always been before them if they had had eyes to see, ears to hear, and a heart to understand. Therefore they would have to learn by discipline because they had despised the word of the Lord.

Are we, with so much greater light, any wiser than they? Let us search ourselves before Him whose eyes are like a flame of fire and answer as in His own holy presence.

HOSEA 10: An Empty Vine

After reminding Israel of its early relationship with God when He found them like grapes in the wilderness, He pronounces solemn judgment against them as an utterly failed testimony: "Israel is an empty vine, he bringeth forth fruit unto himself" (1).

The lesson of the vine is an important one, which we would do well to trace through both Testaments. In Psalm 80:8-11 we have a most significant statement:

> Thou hast brought a vine out of Egypt: thou hast cast out the heathen, and planted it. Thou preparedst room before it, and didst cause it to take deep root, and it filled the land. The hills were covered with the shadow of it, and the boughs thereof were like the goodly cedars. She sent out her boughs unto the sea, and her branches unto the river.

This was Israel in God's mind—His testimony in the earth. They would have remained such, had there been humility of mind and submission of heart that led to confident dependence on Him. But the very opposite of this was developed, as we well know and as Scripture makes abundantly clear. Therefore, "the boar out of the wood doth waste it, and the wild beast of the field doth devour it"

(Psalm 80:13). God came looking for fruit, but gazing on His vine, He found only wild grapes (see Isaiah 5). They had become, as described by Hosea, "an empty vine"; there was no fruit for the Lord. All was for self.

Therefore, the vine of the earth was set aside, its enclosing wall broken down, and it will be fully judged in the awful vintage yet to come (Revelation 14:18-20). Meanwhile, after rejecting the empty vine, God has brought in a vine that will always bear fruit. The Lord Jesus, the Man of God's purpose, told His disciples that He was the "the true vine" (John 15). He took the place of Israel to maintain a testimony for God in the earth. In matchless grace, He connects His redeemed with Himself: "I am the vine, ye are the branches." Empty branches, with no vital link, may intrude among the branches as belonging to the vine; but as there is no living connection with the vine there will be no fruit. Such are false professors who are cut off and cast away as withered branches, whose end is to be burned. The fruit-bearing branches are purged that they may bear *more* fruit. Indeed, God the Father is glorified when they bear *much* fruit!

It will be seen from this that the vine refers to the earth. It is God's testimony in the world; once committed to Israel, now maintained by Christ through His beloved people in this world. The empty vine has been set aside in judgment. The true Vine has taken its place and shall never be set aside, for it is Christ Himself and His people in Him.

This tenth chapter of Hosea concludes the proof that Israel had indeed fallen into the sad condition described in the first verse. All hope of recovery was gone for the present. They must pass through affliction, tribulation, and consequent repentance before they could be raised up again. When they are, they will be like branches in the living Vine, linked with their once-rejected Messiah as God's testimony in the millennium. No longer will they be under the old covenant, dependent on their ability to keep the law (which they failed to do from the start), but they will abide under the new covenant of God's pure grace toward them, unmerited and sovereign.

The opening words of Hosea 10:2 give the root-trouble in a very brief sentence, "Their heart is divided." This was the cause of all subsequent sorrow and failure. They did not cling to the Lord with their whole heart. They were double-minded and therefore unstable in all their ways. A single heart for God's glory is the prime necessity for a holy life. This they had neglected. Therefore they had to eat the fruit of their own sowing.

To walk with God with a divided heart is utterly impossible. He is not asking for the first place in the heart either—as people often put it. He is far too exclusive for that. His word is, "My son, give Me thy heart"—the whole heart, with no reservation whatsoever. Only when this is done will a person's walk and ways be in accordance with God's mind. Here Israel failed, as their idolatrous altars testified. And when God chastened them for their sin, instead of admitting His righteousness in dealing with them in this way, they sought to make a covenant with the nations so that they might escape their deserved discipline. Having no prince to save them, they made desperate efforts to secure an arm of flesh elsewhere on which to lean; but God would not permit that (3-4).

The inhabitants of Samaria, who for so long had "feared the Lord, and served their own gods" (2 Kings 17:33), must now be made to tremble "because of the calves of Beth-aven," which they had relied on (Hosea 10:5). For at last, after so long a trial, God had written "Ichabod" over the whole northern kingdom. The glory had departed. Therefore they would be carried as a gift to the king of Assyria so that Ephraim might receive shame and Israel be ashamed of his own counsel. Thus Samaria's king would prove as powerless as the foam upon the water, which seems for a moment substantial and real but in the next moment has vanished away (6-7).

The eighth verse looks to a far greater fulfillment than to the Assyrian victory of old. The expressions used connect it with the awful overthrow of all established order in the last days, as described concerning the sixth seal of Revelation 6. At that cataclysmic time "they shall say to the mountains, Cover us; and to the hills, Fall on us." This will be the time when they will receive from the Lord's hand double for all their sins and will realize, in bitterness of soul, their folly in departing from the living God.

Again He reminds them, as in the previous chapter, that they had sinned from the days of Gibeah. The evil perpetrated then had never been thoroughly judged; rather, like leaven, it had worked throughout all the years since, permeating the mass. God therefore must chastise them because of His yearning desire to bless them. He loved them, so He had to discipline them for their sins.

The expression, "When they shall bind themselves in their two furrows," (10) is translated in a variety of ways and seems ambiguous. The Revised Standard version says, "When they are chastised for their double iniquity." Might "their double iniquity" be the "two evils" of Jeremiah 2:13? They had forsaken Him who is the fountain of living waters, and had hewed out broken cisterns for themselves. The prophet Isaiah similarly charged them with two transgressions—the rejection of God's Anointed, and the pursuit of idolatry.

The positive result of the disciplinary ways of the Lord is beautifully portrayed in Hosea 10:11-12. These verses are somewhat parenthetical, appearing before the subject of their sin and its punishment is continued in the closing verses of the chapter. Both Judah and Ephraim, as compliant oxen, will submit to God's yoke and delight to tread out the corn when they have learned their lesson. This will only happen, however, when they sow in righteousness and godliness. Then they shall reap in mercy. The fallow ground must be broken up by the power of the Word ministered in the energy of the Holy Spirit. Only when this occurs will they seek the Lord and He will come and rain righteousness upon them. For us, all this has its present application, if we have hearts to bow to it.

For Israel and Judah, though such blessing is in store, the last three verses describe their unhappy state until they are made willing to serve the Lord in the day of His power. Plowing wickedness, they went on reaping iniquity and eating the fruit of lies because their trust was not in God, but in their own way and the multitude of their mighty men. Consequently, breaking up and spoiling, instead of repairing and restoring, would be their portion (See Isaiah 58:12). Bethel, which had become the center of their idolatry, would prove their undoing because it testified to their apostasy. Judah, we know, was preserved for a time, and a light shone for David's sake until Messiah would appear. The king of Israel, however, was utterly cut off and the throne overturned, never to be re-established until He shall come whose right it is to reign. Then the breach between Israel and Judah will be healed, as predicted by all the prophets, when the refreshing times will come from the Lord. No longer will "an empty vine" describe the earthly people; but as a flourishing vine they will take root and produce fruit-laden branches, to the praise of the glory of Jehovah's grace.

HOSEA 11: Bands of Love

"When Israel was a child, then I loved him, and called my son out of Egypt" (1). It is plain, from a consideration of Matthew 2:15, that God had in view His own Son, our Lord Jesus Christ, when Hosea uttered these words. Matthew wrote clearly and unmistakably of the holy Babe's sojourn in the land of Egypt: "That it might be fulfilled which was spoken of the Lord by the prophet, saying, Out of Egypt have I called my Son."

Yet a careful reading of the first few verses of Hosea 11 will make it equally clear that the prophet himself had none other than the nation of Israel in mind when he spoke the words quoted by Matthew. He was thinking of Israel's past deliverance from Egyptian bondage when Jehovah loved him and called him as His son.

Is there then contradiction between Hosea and Matthew? On the contrary, there is the most perfect agreement, which another passage at once make clear. In 2 Corinthians 3:17 we learn, in connection with the entire chapter, that the Lord is the Spirit of the Old Testament. He is everywhere presented to the anointed eye. So the apostle wrote by divine inspiration when he declared that Hosea's words prophetically foretold the coming of God's Son out of Egypt. In wondrous grace He would, as it were, begin His earthly pilgrimage as His people began theirs. As a Babe whose life is sought by Herod, He was carried over the route taken by Jacob when driven by famine to Egypt. And from that land, from which His people had been delivered when oppressed by Pharaoh, He later returned to Palestine. In this way He would be identified with them in their wanderings so that they might understand how the Holy Spirit spoke of Him when He said, "In all their affliction he was afflicted, and the angel of his presence saved them" (Isaiah 63:9).

Called out of Egypt, He was always the One in whom the Father found delight. How blessedly opposite He is to Israel! Redeemed by power from Egyptian tyranny, they went far from Him, though He called them in tenderest love. Turning away, they sacrificed to Baalim, and worshiped images of man's design (Hosea 11:2).

Yet He had taught Ephraim to take his earliest steps, holding his arms and directing his way. But like ungrateful children they soon forgot Him to whom they owed so much. They did not realize that it was He who had healed them. Tenderly, He recalled those early days when He "drew them with cords of a man, with bands of love," delivering them from the yoke and providing all that they needed for their sustenance and enjoyment (3-4).

What saint cannot see in such lovely words the story of his own deliverance from sin and Satan, when first brought to the knowledge of Christ! Long enslaved in something worse than Egyptian bondage, how unspeakably precious was the earliest revelation of His grace to our souls, when He drew us to Himself from our wickedness and waywardness by the bands of love. These were indeed the "cords of a man"—the Man Christ Jesus, who gave Himself a ransom for all! Let us examine our hearts concerning what response we have made to a love so deep and tender. What is the Baal that has lured some of us so far from Him who once was everything to our hearts, when we took our first steps out into the wilderness? Rest assured, fellow believer, until every idol is destroyed, we will never rediscover the freshness and joy of those early days.

Once set free from Egypt, Israel as a nation could never return there. Because of their sins however they were given into the hand of the Assyrians. This is a precursor to the awful last days, when the sword will fall on them, "because of their own counsels" (5-6).

Such must be the bitter fruit of forgetting their God and taking their own foolish and sinful way. From the start they had been "bent to backsliding" from Him, though He had called them again and again to repentance. But they persisted in their folly until there was no remedy (7).

Yet His yearning heart caused Him to cry "How shall I give thee up, Ephraim? . . . my heart is turned within me, my repentings are kindled together" (8). He could not bear to desolate them like the cities of the nations on whom His wrath had fallen without any mixture of mercy. Zeboim and Admah (see Genesis 14:8) were two of the cities of the plain blotted out when Sodom and Gomorrah fell beneath His judgment (Deuteronomy 29:23). Moses warned Israel of a similar doom if they failed to keep His holy law. So they were righteously under that awful sentence. But God in His sovereignty declared, "I will not execute the fierceness of mine anger, I will not return to destroy Ephraim: for I am God, and not man; the Holy One in the midst of thee: and I will not enter into the city"—that is, to utterly consume it (9).

It is wonderful to realize that God, once He has given His word in grace, will never repent or permit people to be cursed whom He has blessed (as He made known to Balaam). Yet He reserves the right to turn from His wrath, however richly deserved, and bestow His lovingkindness on the people of His choice when they repent. Therefore, though He rightly could have destroyed Ephraim, He chose in grace to preserve a remnant who will yet praise His glory in the land of their fathers. "They shall walk after the Lord," in the day that "he shall roar like a lion," causing His once-blinded people to tremble at His word. He shall "set his hand again the second time to recover the remnant of his people, which shall be left, from Assyria, and from Egypt, and from Pathros, and from Cush, and from Elam, and from Shinar, and from Hamath, and from the islands of the sea" (Isaiah 11:11). At His call they will come, weeping because of their sin yet rejoicing in His love, "as a bird out of Egypt, and as a dove out of the land of Assyria," to be placed "in their houses," never again to be removed, according to the word of Jehovah (11).

This verse completes another distinct division of Hosea's prophecy, which extends from their first call out of Egypt to their restoration to the land and to God in the days of the millennial kingdom.

The last verse of Hosea 11 is properly the introduction to chapter 12, and brings in a new subject, which closes with the end of chapter 13. When Hosea prophesied, the sins of Judah were not yet so obvious as those of the ten tribes whom Jeroboam had led astray from the very beginning, turning them away from Jehovah, and setting up the golden calves for their worship. Israel had been idolatrous from the first, and all their kings had followed in the steps of

"Jeroboam the son of Nebat, which made Israel to sin." Therefore God pronounced sentence on them earlier than He did on Judah, saying, "Ephraim compasseth me about with lies, and the house of Israel with deceit." There had never been any response to the many warnings and entreaties sent them by the Lord.

The situation with Judah, though, was different. With them, decline was a matter of slow and sometimes thwarted progress. That's why we read, "But Judah yet ruleth with God, and is faithful with the Most Holy" (12, literal translation). Up to the time when Hosea prophesied, there was still a measure of devotion to Jehovah in Judah. Moreover, revival after revival followed the prophets' fervent calls to repentance. However, as the years went on, they too became less and less responsive to the voice of God, until they lost all concern for His holiness. Hypocrisy therefore developed especially in Judah: "This people honoureth me with their lips, but their heart is far from me" (Mark 7:6; see also Isaiah 29:13). This is the danger where doctrine is right and outward form correct, while the heart is away from God. Let every child of God beware of this (See Luke 12:1).

HOSEA 12: The Balances of Deceit

As already noted, a new section of Hosea's prophecy began with verse 12 of the previous chapter, in which God exposed the hidden corruptions of Ephraim.

Like the royal preacher of Ecclesiastes, Ephraim had sought in vain for something to fill the heart apart from God. He had been feeding on wind and following the desolating wind of the east, discovering for himself that "all is vanity and vexation of spirit" when the heart is estranged from the one true source of all good (Ecclesiastes 1:14). Endeavoring to make a league with the powerful Assyrians, whom they dreaded, and sending oil (as a bribe, evidently) into Egypt to buy the help of their old enemy, they sought to avert the awful day of judgment. But they were following lies and desolation. No human ingenuity could turn aside the day of the Lord's dealing with them for their sins (Hosea 12:1).

With Judah too He had a dispute; for the encouraging word spoken in 11:12 (KJV) did not necessarily imply that God was fully satisfied with them. The seed of Jacob, as a whole, were emulating the crookedness of him from whom they sprang. So they too must be judged according to their ways (12:2).

In verses 3-6 Jacob himself is described as a picture of the people descended from him. A supplanter from his birth, he displayed his defrauding spirit from the womb by grabbing his brother's heel (Genesis 25:26). Nevertheless grace had come in, and in his distress he clung to God (or, "He behaved himself princely with God") thus making good his new name, Israel—a prince with God. When unable to struggle any longer, he hung onto the One he had striven against. This was the power in which he prevailed—when he wept and made supplication to Him. It was what another has called "the irresistible might of weakness"—clinging to Him who is mighty, even as the apostle declared, "When I am weak, then am I strong" (2 Corinthians 12:10). This was the secret of Jacob's prevailing with God, who had found him in Bethel when he was a fugitive and a wanderer because of his sin. "There he spake with us" implies that the word of the Lord to Jacob on the night when a stone was his pillow was also intended for all his house to the end of time (Hosea 12:4). Whatever their failings, God's eye would always be on them: "Even the Lord God of hosts; the Lord [Jehovah—the eternal, the unchanging One] is his memorial" (5).

Oh that Israel would learn from all these things to turn to their God, keep justice and mercy, and wait on Him continually (6).

Instead of this, they had followed Jacob's early ways. So God likened Ephraim to a merchant in whose hand are the balances of deceit (7). He is really a Canaanite—for such is the word translated "merchant." So unconscious was he of wrongdoing when he took advantage of the need or greed of his victim, that he congratulated himself on his increasing wealth. As his store grew day by day, swollen with ill-gotten gains, he said, "In all my labours they shall find none iniquity in me that were sin" (8).

However dark the picture has been from Hosea's day to now, the Lord has never utterly cast off the nation whose God He was "from the land of Egypt" (9). In pure grace He will yet restore them to their ancient land, fulfilling all His promises and bringing them into the full enjoyment of the true feast of tabernacles. With their toil ended, their lessons learned, and their warfare finished, everyone will dwell beneath his own vine and fig tree, with no one to make them afraid (Zechariah 3:10).

With this purpose in mind, God had spoken by His prophets, multiplying visions and using parables. He tried to press on the people's consciences their serious condition as well as encourage them with the blessings repentance would bring (Hosea 12:10). In reading the message of these prophets, it is important to bear in mind the instruction given to us in the New Testament: that no prophecy of Scripture is of its own interpretation, but all must be read in view of the ways of God, as expressed so fully by both Hosea and Daniel. The goal of all the prophecies of these men of God is to bring in the day of the Lord and establish the kingdom in glory on this earth. They look to the time when Israel will return in heart to Jehovah and confess their once-rejected Messiah as David's Son, for whom they have waited so long.

The ministry of the prophets was to lay bare the true state of affairs. So they uncovered the iniquity of Gilead. Vanity was written on all. In Gilgal, where once the reproach of Egypt had been rolled away, they sacrificed—but not to Jehovah. Altars were everywhere, like heaps of stone piled in the furrows of the field, but not to His glory (11). So they would find their symbol once more in Jacob. Because of his deceit, he fled into the land of Syria and there kept Laban's sheep so that he might purchase his wife by hard work (12). When the Lord's set time had come to bring Israel out of Egypt, it was by a prophet He did so. By a prophet he led them through the wilderness, preserving them in all their trials (13). The same kind of ministry must be experienced again before they would be delivered from the bondage of their sins and brought into the enjoyment of the promised inheritance.

Instead of heeding the word of the Lord, however, and humbling themselves before Him when He sent His servants to them, "Ephraim provoked him to anger most bitterly: therefore shall he leave his blood upon him, and his reproach shall his Lord return unto him" (14). God-sent ministry, heeded and obeyed, leads to growth and blessing. But when the Spirit's testimony is rejected, it increases the guilt of him who hardens himself against it and makes his condition far worse than before. It is always the case that light refused makes the darkness all the deeper. This is why we need a tender conscience, quick to respond to every word from God.

HOSEA 13: In Me Is Thy Help

The opening words of Hosea 13, which are really a continuation of the message begun in the last verse of chapter 11, remind us forcibly of God's word to Saul when he disobeyed His voice (see 1 Samuel 15:17). "When Ephraim spake trembling, he exalted himself in Israel; but when he offended in Baal, he died" (Hosea 13:1).

These words give us the spiritual history of thousands who have begun well but ended badly because of failure to cling to the Lord with singleness of heart. As we trace the biographies of many of the kings of Judah, we see the same thing illustrated. It is different with the kings of Israel because *not one of them* began with God at all. All of them were idolaters; and of the entire number, Jehoahaz is the only one who ever sought the Lord—and he did that only when in deep distress (2 Kings 13:4). Among Judah's rulers, however, many started out well. Of them it was often said, "as long as he sought the Lord, God made him to prosper." With most of them though, failure eventually marred their testimony, bringing sorrow and trouble in its train.

When God first took up Ephraim, he was "little in his own sight" (1 Samuel 15:17) and he "spake trembling" (Hosea 13:1); that is, realizing in some measure his weakness and insufficiency, he was humbled when the word of the Lord came to him. God says, "To this man will I look, even to him that is poor and of a contrite spirit, and trembleth at my word" (Isaiah 66:2). Such was Ephraim in his early days. When this was his condition, "he exalted himself in Israel; but when he offended in Baal, he died." How disappointing that this sentence ever had to be penned! How much happier it would have been for Ephraim, as for untold thousands more, if they had never left their first love! These things are our examples, and from them God would have us learn not to trust our own deceitful hearts, but to walk humbly before Him, in reverence and godly fear. In no other way will we be preserved from a moral and spiritual breakdown. Self-confidence is always the prelude to severe and crushing defeat.

It is generally true that, after the first step is taken away from God, each succeeding one becomes easier and easier. Twinges of conscience are less frequent; the strivings of the grieved Holy Spirit attract less and less attention as the heart becomes hardened through the deceitfulness of sin. So was it with Ephraim. "And now they sin more and more," said the prophet, as he proceeded to describe the gross idolatry that pervaded the land and all classes of people (Hosea 13:2). Consequently they would be carried away in judgment. "They shall be as the morning cloud, and as the early dew that passeth away, as the chaff that is driven with the whirlwind out of the floor, and as the smoke out of the chimney" (3). In this way the Lord was about to purge His threshing floor.

But, as so frequently declared, He did not intend to make a full end of them, the people of His choice. On the contrary, He remained the only true God, the Lord who had been their God from the land of Egypt. The day would come when they would worship Him alone and know no God besides Him, for He only was the Savior of Israel. In the wilderness—that dry and thirsty land—He had sustained them until their heart was "exalted." When they were filled with all good things, though, they had forgotten Him. Therefore, He who had given them all these mercies would be to them as a leopard by the way, and as a bear robbed of her cubs, who would rip them apart and tear into them like a lion. The wild beast was appointed to devour them (4-8).

In the images used here, it would seem that we have more than a hint of the character of the Gentile empires that would successively oppress Israel. If we compare the passage with Daniel 7, we will see more than a mere coincidence in the lion being used as the symbol of Babylon; the bear, of Medo-Persia; and the leopard, of Greece. The generic term, "the wild beast" or, "the beast of the field," is possibly a veiled reference to the last beast, the "dreadful and terrible" Roman empire that for many years persecuted Israel (Daniel 7:7). Though it is now fallen, it will be revived as the first beast of Revelation 13, when the endtime comes and the great tribulation concludes the sufferings of Jacob.

According to Hosea 13:9 Israel alone was responsible for all that had befallen them and for all that would yet come upon them. "O Israel," God said, "thou hast destroyed thyself; but in me is thine help." Their self-will had been their ruin; but He still waited to save, ready to bare His arm for their deliverance if there were any sign of repentance. "I will be thy king: where is any other that may save thee in all thy cities?" He asked, possibly referring to Israel's last king, Hoshea. They had trusted in him, but now he was a prisoner in the hands of Shalmaneser, king of Assyria (2 Kings 17:1-4). They had asked for a king, to be like the nations around them; God had granted their request, but where was the power of their king and his judges? The people had been trusting in a bruised reed.

It may seem strange, so many centuries after the establishment of the monarchy and at the close of the history of the ten tribes as such, that God would rebuke them for the sin of asking for a king in the days of Samuel. However, the same spirit of independence that led them to want a king (when Jehovah Himself was their King), still persisted among them; for *that*, judgment would fall. How somber are the words, "I gave thee a king in mine anger, and took him away in my wrath" (Hosea 13:11).

God will often allow His children to have what they want when their hearts are away from Him. He will give them their requests but send leanness into their souls. It is much better, in all our prayers and supplications to bend our will to His, saying, "Thy will be done." He knows so much better than we possibly can what is best for us. And when hearts submit to Him He will reply, not according to our faulty petitions, but according to His own lovingkindness and wisdom. When we assert our will, though, He often has to answer our prayers in judgment, and we may have years to regret our folly in not having left all our affairs in His hands.

To all his other failures Ephraim added this, that he kept his iniquity "bound up" and his sin covered (12). Whenever anyone does this, God's hand must be on them in discipline: "He that covereth his sins shall not prosper" (Proverbs 28:13). On the other hand, the moment everything is out in the light and sin is judged and confessed, God Himself provides a covering, and the evil is gone from His sight forever. "Blessed is he whose transgression is forgiven, whose sin is covered. Blessed is the man unto whom the Lord imputeth not iniquity, and in whose spirit there is no guile" (Psalm 32:1-2).

Because of Ephraim's persistence in covering his own sin, he must suffer like a woman in childbirth. Hosea then switches to another simile, comparing Ephraim to an unwise son, remaining where his presence can only be most embarrassing and foolish. So he persisted in his folly when warned and begged to stop (Hosea 13:13).

The last two verses of this chapter continue to declare the terrible extent of the disastrous judgments the people of Israel must undergo. But before these somber scenes are depicted, a precious word of grace—like a rainbow of hope in the gloomy, wrath-filled sky—is seen in verse 14. He who was about to visit them in His anger spoke of mercy and kindness, giving a promise of the final triumph of His love. "I will ransom them from the power of [sheol]; I will redeem them from death: O death, I will be thy plagues; O [sheol], I will be thy destruction: repentance shall be hid from mine eyes."

What could be more wonderful than such a promise in the midst of so grave an indictment? In wrath God will remember mercy. He will yet appear as the Redeemer of His chosen, plundering death and sheol (synonymous with Hades, the unseen world of spirits—not Hell nor the grave) of their prey and saving all who turn to Him in brokenness of spirit, confessing their guilt. He will never swerve from His purposes of grace; they shall abide forever in His goodness and mercy.

For centuries Israel has been like a dead man, buried among the nations, wandering like a shade in sheol. But the hour is not far off when the closing message to Daniel will be fulfilled (as well as the prophecy of the valley of dry bones in Ezekiel 37).

> At that time shall Michael stand up, the great prince which standeth for the children of thy people: and there shall be a time of trouble, such as never was since there was a nation even to that same time: and at that time thy people shall be delivered, *every one that shall be found written in the book.* And many of them that sleep in the dust of the earth shall awake, some to

everlasting life, and some to shame and everlasting contempt (Daniel 12:1-2, emphasis added).

This is also the testimony of the older prophet, Isaiah (26:19). "Thy dead men shall live, together with my dead body shall they arise. Awake and sing, ye that dwell in dust: for thy dew is as the dew of herbs, and the earth shall cast out the dead." These passages will have their glorious fulfillment when the remnant of Israel and Judah are awakened from their death-sleep, and come forth at the call of God to return to Zion with singing and with everlasting joy.

Literally too there will be a wondrous fulfillment when "All that are in the graves shall hear his voice, And shall come forth; they that have done good, unto the resurrection of life; and they that have done evil, unto the resurrection of damnation" (John 5:28-29). "Blessed and holy is he that hath part in the *first resurrection*" (Revelation 20:6, emphasis added).

It would be nice to close our chapter with this precious reminder of the grace of our Savior-God. But it is necessary to be reminded that the day of Jehovah's power and Messiah's return has not yet come. So we return once more to consider the sad condition of Israel and the dark days awaiting them before the glory dawns.

As we ponder the words of Hosea 13:15-16, the rainbow of hope seems to fade away; the dark clouds of doom gather heavier and heavier above the land of promise. "Out of the throne proceeded lightnings, and thunderings, and voices" (Revelation 4:5), announcing the dreadful storm about to burst on those who, having eyes to see, saw not, and having ears to hear, heard not the ominous rumblings of the approaching day of wrath until it was too late to find a hiding place. An east wind from Jehovah "shall come up from the wilderness," drying up all the springs of hope and fountains of joy, and ruining all the stored treasures (Hosea 13:15). Desolation would wrap Samaria in midnight gloom, "for she hath rebelled against her God." Therefore they would fall beneath the avenging hand of the bloodthirsty Assyrians, who would spare neither age, sex, nor condition (16).

All this was fulfilled when Shalmaneser marched his hordes through the land. There will be another, more dreadful one when the last Assyrian sweeps down like a resistless flood, stopped only by the breath of the Lord. This will take place when they are restored to the land of Palestine in unbelief, following the rapture of the church and prior to the establishment of the Messiah's kingdom.

With this, the body of the prophecy closes. The next and final chapter is a tender call addressed to the backslidden people, exhorting them to return to their Lord, who is their only good and their only hope.

HOSEA 14: Restoration and Blessing

The same yearning tenderness that led the rejected Messiah to weep over Jerusalem as He said, "If thou hadst known, even thou, at least in this thy day, the things which belong unto thy peace" (Luke 19:42), can be felt throughout this final chapter of Hosea. This is one of the most touching yet faithful pleas to be found in the Book of God, reminding us of the soul-stirring appeals uttered by the Holy Spirit through a later servant, Jeremiah. Not only does it present the appeals of Jehovah for His people to heed His voice and return to Him, but it clearly explains just how they should go about it. The prophet even puts into their mouths the words that, if they came from their hearts, God would delight to hear. They are also given abundant promises of blessing to be poured out on them when they repent and humbly return to Him.

"O Israel, return unto the Lord thy God; for thou hast fallen by thine iniquity" (Hosea 14:1). How bitterly had they proven that "the way of transgressors is hard" (Proverbs 13:15). "Righteousness," we are elsewhere told, "exalteth a nation: but sin is a reproach to any people" (Proverbs 14:34). Had they followed in the paths of uprightness, which their faithful, covenant-keeping God had marked out for them, theirs would have been a very different history. But they refused to listen, and turned away instead. The result was failure and disaster from beginning to end. They had indeed fallen very low. Yet God, who had been so grievously sinned against, still lovingly entreated them to return to Him.

Let us learn from their sad experience both to avoid their sins and to know the abundant grace of our God. The church, as a testimony for an absent Lord, has failed as fully as Israel. But however dark the day, wherever a true heart turns back in repentance to God, He who has been so grievously dishonored will still gladly receive such a person. He waits only for open doors that He may come in and dine in communion, though the hour is late.

If a person thinks, *But I have erred so seriously, I do not know how to approach so holy a God after having dishonored Him to such an extent*; then He Himself will put a prayer into the lips of the returning one, thus assuring each seeking soul of His willingness to hear.

> Take with you words, and turn to the Lord: say unto him, Take away all iniquity, and receive us graciously: so will we render the calves of our lips. Asshur shall not save us; we will not ride upon horses: neither will we say any more to the work of our hands, Ye are our gods: for in thee the fatherless findeth mercy (Hosea 14:2-3).

This prayer, written by God Himself, is worthy of the most careful consideration. Let us take up its clauses one by one, weighing each in the presence of the Lord.

"Take away all iniquity, and receive us graciously," cries the repentant soul. Having been defiled so long that the conscience was almost calloused, the soul, by God's light now sees things as they really are. This produces a hatred of the waywardness that we tolerated so indifferently before. Apathy is replaced by deep conviction. "Take away all iniquity!" is the soul's longing. Sin becomes hateful the moment one gets into the presence of God. Then the need of grace is felt; so the cry comes, "Receive us graciously." What a mercy that we are directed to come to "the God of *all grace*" (1 Peter 5:10)!

There can be no restoration as long as one sin is trifled with and remains unjudged. But the instant a full confession is made and all iniquity is honestly turned from, the Word assures us of instant forgiveness. "If we confess our sins, he is faithful and just to forgive us our sins, and to cleanse us from all unrighteousness" (1 John 1:9). This principle applies to a lost sinner seeking salvation or an erring saint desiring restoration. Sin judged is sin gone; and the soul may enjoy afresh the communion that has been interrupted from the moment evil was allowed to enter the conscience. In the knowledge of this—a knowledge received not by feelings but resting on the testimony of Scripture—praise and worship once more spring up in the heart. "So will we render the calves of our lips."

Only when the life is right and the conscience cleansed from defilement can there be worship in spirit and in truth. Then the happy saint can without hindrance pour forth into the ear of God his grateful praises; and his worship, like incense, will arise from the heart, bowing to Christ as all in all. Israel will enter into this when, restored after their disciplinary wanderings, they rejoice before the One who will dwell in their midst. By this time, God will have purged them from all that has hindered their full acknowledgment of His grace.

"Asshur shall not save us," is the cry of a people who have learned to "cease . . . from man, whose breath is in his nostrils" (Isaiah 2:22). We have seen throughout this book how, in the hour of their distress, they turned not to God against whom they had revolted, but to Assyria, the proud northern power, who was destined to be their ruin. Thus they learned that "vain is the help of man" (Psalm 60:11). They would say then, in the day of Jehovah's might, "Asshur shall not deliver us," but in God alone would they find their Savior. (It is usually God's way to cause the very thing in which His people have dishonored Him to become their discipline—this is how He delivers their hearts from the idols they have followed.)

Nor will they depend on their own armies in that day, mounted like the cavalry of the nation: "We will not ride upon horses" (Hosea 14:3). It is noticeable throughout Israel's history that their strength for warfare consisted not in imitating the manners and customs of the nations, but in relying on God in the spirit of praise. When Judah ("praise") led, they conquered as they counted on the Lord alone for help. When Jehoshaphat met the enemy, he put singers at the head of the army, and a great victory ensued (see 2 Chronicles 20:20-30). They will return to this position when they are humbled before God because of all their failure and sin. "An horse is a vain thing for safety" (Psalm 33:17), though it seems to add wonderfully to human prowess. But it is far better to lean on the arm of Jehovah and remember that the battle is His, not ours.

Idolatry had been Israel's undoing in the past. But in the future they will cry, "Neither will we say any more to the work of our hands, Ye are our gods!" Having learned the futility of serving the many gods who have had dominion over them, they will exalt the Lord alone in that day. This is a lovely picture of a soul who has proven that no power, seen or unseen, except the strength of the mighty God of Jacob can provide deliverance. When everything is laid bare in His presence, and no deceit remains in their spirit, they can add with assurance, "For in thee the fatherless findeth mercy" (Hosea 14:3). Israel had been Jehovah's son, whom He had called out of Egypt. But they had forgotten Him, and scorned His Spirit of grace. So He had to pronounce the Lo-ammi and Lo-ruhamah sentences upon them, as we saw in the beginning of the prophecy. When they return, then they come in on the ground of pure grace and mercy. They come as "the fatherless"; not to claim the rights of a child, but to be the subjects of that lovingkindness which is better than life. How suited to the lips of the remnant of the last days will be the words of this prayer!

The gracious response of the Lord immediately follows: "I will heal their backsliding, I will love them freely; for mine anger is turned away from him" (4). It is as though His great heart of love had been full, near bursting, but their sins had kept Him from expressing all that was there. Now every barrier is removed, and like an irresistible torrent, His kindness flows forth, overleaping and sweeping away every obstruction that a timid faith might yet raise. Loving them freely, He will set them in paths of righteousness, healing their souls and turning them from all their backslidings. Everything of the dark past is forgiven and gone; His wrath has vanished, and His grace knows no bounds.

No longer shall they be like a barren and desolate heath but like a watered garden, tended and kept by God Himself. "I will be as the dew unto Israel: he shall grow as the lily, and cast forth his roots as Lebanon" (5).

In Scripture, dew always pictures the refreshing influences of the Holy Spirit ministering truth in grace to the soul. The manna in the wilderness fell like dew—it was a type of Christ administered in the power of the Holy Ghost. Gideon's signs also pictured God's marvelous dealings in this way. At first, the dew was on the fleece, while the ground was dry. Next, the fleece was dry, but the ground was covered with dew (Judges 6:36-40). Similarly, Israel had been blessed with the Spirit's testimony, while the world lay in ignorance and idolatry. But Israel rejected Messiah at His first coming, and now the chosen nation is dry and desolate, while the Spirit of God is working among the Gentiles. In the millennium He will be poured out on all flesh; then fleece and ground alike will be refreshed with the dew. In Psalm 133:3 "the dew of Hermon" illustrates the same reviving power as in Hosea.

Hosea prophesied that God Himself will be like the dew to His restored people, giving new life and new strength so that His people may evermore rejoice in Him. Under His kindly nurture, they will put on the beauty of the lily and have the strength of the cedar of Lebanon. No fading glory will again be theirs, but a beauty that endures and a strength that can never fail.

Then "his branches shall spread, and his beauty shall be as the olive tree, and his smell as Lebanon" (6). Towering up to heaven like a mighty cedar, Israel's branches will go out in majesty, and their fragrance shall be wafted in the air so that all may know that the Lord has taken them as His own. Nor is it only dignity and fragrance, but there shall be all the loveliness and fruitfulness of the olive tree—the "oil tree," as the word might be rendered. This too speaks of the Holy Spirit, who will permeate the nation as the oil permeates the olive, making it a source of spiritual blessing to the whole earth.

"They that dwell under his shadow shall return; they shall revive as the corn, and grow as the vine: the scent thereof shall be as the wine of Lebanon" (7). Several figures of speech are used to describe the joy of the Lord in His people and their beauty and preciousness in His eyes. Jacob will not only be regathered, but others will find blessing through him, according to the promise to the fathers. Many will "dwell under his shadow," finding rest through the message committed to him. The corn and wine tell of strength and gladness. It shall no longer be said, "Israel is an empty vine; he bringeth forth fruit unto himself" (10:1). But planted again in the land, the vine of the Lord will flourish, and send forth its branches loaded with choice clusters to provide the wine of joy for the whole earth.

Then Ephraim will say, "What have I to do any more with idols?" (14:8) Dwelling in fellowship with God and enjoying His matchless love and grace, the wretched foolishness of the past will be detested. New affection will so possess their hearts that the vain idols at whose altars they once bowed will be hated and forgotten. In holy complacency the Lord looks down and says, "I have heard him, and observed him." In joyous exultation, Israel answers, "I am like a green fir tree." This picture is not of temporary foliage; but like an evergreen, they will be perennially fresh and lovely in His eyes. And since all their goodness is from God, He replies, "From me is thy fruit found." (There is good ground here to question the KJV construction of this dialogue. We might understand Israel as saying, "What have I to do anymore with idols? I have heard Him, and observed Him! I am like a green fir tree." Then Jehovah's answer, "From Me is they fruit found.") Apart from Him, all would be barrenness once more, even as Jesus said, "Without me, ye can do nothing" (John 15:5). But, abiding in the uninterrupted enjoyment of His love, their fruit will never fail nor their freshness ever depart.

This closes Hosea's prophecy. However, the Lord pointedly presses on every reader the importance of weighing everything in His presence. "Who is wise, and he shall understand these things? Prudent, and he shall know them? for the ways of the Lord are right, and the just shall walk in them: but the transgressors shall fall therein" (Hosea 14:9). *The ways of the Lord* has been the theme of the book. Happy will we be if we are, through grace, numbered among the wise and prudent who know and understand God's ways, and the just who walk in them!

May the Lord make His Word effective, for His name's sake! Amen.

JOEL

A PROFILE

JOEL

THE PROPHET OF THE PLAGUE

BY JOHN PHILLIPS

A plague of locusts gave Joel (830-819 B.C.) the illustration he needed to appeal to the conscience of his country. His book is not dated, and opinions vary widely as to when Joel lived and ministered, although it would seem that he was a prophet to Judah rather than to Israel.

Time of Joel's Prophecy

Some contend that Joel prophesied about the same time as Ezekiel, one hundred years or more after Isaiah, and his prophetic utterances are said to relate to the end of the kingdom of Judah. Others claim that his prophecy was given after the exile because no mention is made of Assyria, Syria, or Babylon among the enemies of his people. Probably, however, Joel was the earliest of the writing prophets, coming with his message before any of those nations were a threat to Judah. The enemies he does mention—the Phoenicians, Philistines, Egyptians, and Edomites—belong to the days of Jehoash (2 Chronicles 21:16-17). Scofield says, "In his youth he may have known Elijah, and he certainly was a contemporary of Elisha." What a flood of light that statement casts on the days of Joel!

Joel's prophecy may be divided into four parts:

I. The Present Famine (1:1-20)
II. The Predicted Foes (2:1-11)
III. The Promised Forgiveness (2:12-27)
IV. The Prophetic Focus (2:28–3:21)

The Message of Joel's Prophecy

Locusts are the scourge of many lands, and those who have seen them swarm tell us that their countless legions blot out the sun, cover the ground, and fill the sky whichever way one looks. On the ground they march in regular lines like armies of soldiers, with their leaders in front. Nothing can stop them. They are "the incarnation of hunger," and the devastation they leave in their train is utter and complete.

It would seem that Judah had been invaded by just such a locust swarm, and Joel, seeing them, was caught up by the Spirit and given a message for his people of an invasion to come far worse than a mere locust plague. He saw the enemy coming in like a flood, and the Spirit of God raising up a standard against him. In view of this impending calamity, Joel urged the nation to repent.

Running through Joel's prophecy is a note none can miss. It is "the day of the Lord," one of the most important periods in Bible prophecy. Many of the prophets mention it, for it is that period which closes the present era of man's misrule of earth, ushering in the Lord Jesus as King of kings. The day of the Lord is regarded as a day of terrible judgment, issuing at last in full and permanent blessing.

One of the best-known prophecies of Joel is in 2:28-32 concerning the outpouring of the Holy Spirit. That prediction began to be fulfilled on the day of Pentecost (Acts 2:16-21).

CHAPTER TWO

THE PROPHECY OF JOEL

We know nothing of Joel the son of Pethuel, except what little we can glean from the three chapters forming his message to Israel. Jewish tradition places him in the days of Uzziah, but there is no authoritative proof of this. His name means, "Jehovah is God", and his father's name means "vision" or, "wisdom of God," according to some, or "be ye enlarged" (or "persuaded") according to others.

The immediate circumstances of his testimony seem to be these. The land of Israel had been visited by a terrible plague of locusts, which had devoured every green thing, leaving barrenness and famine in their wake. Joel is inspired by God to impress on the consciences of the nation of Judah (for it is in and to the southern kingdom he prophesied) the fact that this visitation was from the Lord because of the sin of His people.

Following this, Joel is carried by the Spirit to the last days, and he sees in the dire calamity by which they were afflicted a picture of the time of Jacob's trouble that will take place before Messiah receives the kingdom. Thus, the present desolation becomes the text of a solemn prophetic discourse that is far-reaching in character. This duality of meaning emphasizes what has already been noticed in our study of Hosea—that while prophecy is in many parts and may have many applications, it is never limited to local matters, but all has its complete fulfillment in "the day of the Lord" yet to come.

Another important principle is brought to our attention by the manner in which the prophet used the calamity the people were suffering at the time to draw their attention to the condition of their souls. God always wants His children to recognize His hand in all such trials. For the believer, there are no second causes. The Lord has said, "I Jehovah create peace, and create evil." And He asked the question, "Shall there be evil in a city, and the Lord hath not done it?" (Amos 3:6; see also Isaiah 45:7) Evil in both these passages is, of course, calamity—the opposite of a peaceful, quiet condition. If I am called to pass through such experiences, it is because God has seen a need in my soul for just such disciplinary dealings. He has my best interests at heart. My part then is to recognize His purposes and be trained in godliness by the experience. This is the lesson of Hebrews 12, and this same lesson is emphasized in the use Joel makes of Judah's afflictions in this brief but pungent prophecy.

As we turn to consider the teachings of the three stirring chapters of the book itself, may He who alone gives the eye-salve of the Spirit anoint our eyes so that we may see wondrous things in His Word now before us!

JOEL 1: The Locust Plague

The older men of Judah are first addressed and called on to declare if, in all their recollection, or in all the days of which their fathers had told them, there had ever been so grievous an ordeal as that which the land and the people were now groaning under. This is Joel's preamble to impressing on their consciences the serious lessons God would have them to learn (verses 1-3).

"That which the palmerworm hath left hath the locust eaten; and that which the locust hath left hath the cankerworm eaten; and that which the cankerworm hath left hath the caterpillar eaten" (4). Thus the destruction of every green thing had been complete, so that famine and utter ruin stared the people in the face. Most commentators agree that the various forms of insect life spoken of here are most likely not different creatures but probably the various stages of the locust as it advances from the larvae form to maturity. This much-dreaded plague had cut off all the sources of food supply, and left an appalling scene of desolation behind. What was so intensely solemn was the fact that God's voice was in this affliction, but it seemed that the people were so occupied with the measure of discipline that they failed to hear Him who had appointed it.

Nothing is more natural for us than this. Instead of learning godliness we give way to self-pity or hard, stony indifference; we either faint under the discipline of the Lord or despise it. Blessing, however, results only from being trained and deepened in godly maturity. This was what Judah was in danger of missing, as have many others before and since.

The pleasure-loving drunkards, who delighted in their wine, were charged to awake to the realization of their true condition—God's stroke upon them—and to learn the lesson He intended for them. His great army, like a nation of bitter enemies, "strong and without number," had blasted the vine and stripped the fig tree, so that the source of their carnal enjoyment was gone (verses 5-7).

Like a virgin girded with sackcloth, lamenting the untimely death of her betrothed husband, the people of Judah were called to mourn over the sins that had drawn down the judgment of God upon them. His house too was affected; for there judgment must begin. The meat, or meal offering, and the drink offering were cut off, and the priests were left to mourn. When God's people are in a famished condition, there is no real appreciation of Christ; consequently the sacrifices cease to be offered. The meal offering illustrates the manhood of the Lord Jesus. The drink offering portrays His pouring out His soul unto death. But a spiritual famine dulls the perception and sensibilities of those indebted to His one offering for all their blessing; so the gifts of a worshiping people cease (8-9).

The desolate condition of the land is vividly described in verses 10-12. All the fruits of the field were gone, and the trees had withered away, even as joy had departed from the sons of men. This is why such a solemn admonition was given to those whose place it was to minister to the people spiritually: "Gird yourselves, and lament, ye priests: howl, ye ministers of the altar: come, lie all night in sackcloth, ye ministers of my God: for the meat offering and the drink offering is withholden from the house of your God" (13). Insensitivity at such a time! How offensive to God, who wished to see a true appreciation of His dealings with His people.

So Joel warned the elders and all the inhabitants of the land to sanctify a fast, and call a solemn assembly, that they may unitedly cry to the Lord, acknowledging their failure and judging their evil ways (14). The approaching day of the Lord is mentioned as an incentive to this. Not that the day of the Lord (which in its full, prophetic sense, refers to the revelation of Jesus Christ to usher in the kingdom) was really to occur in their time. But since that day will reveal all that has been in accordance with the mind of God, they were called upon to act in the light of that coming day of judgment (15). Similarly Christians are exhorted to live now in view of the day of Christ, when all our works will be examined at His judgment seat. The all-disclosing light of that hour should always be illuminating our pathway so that our steps may be ordered in accord with that day.

Throughout the book of Joel this is the prophet's standpoint. The day of the Lord is coming. It will be the day of *reality*, when all shams and all hypocrisy will be revealed for what they are. Then only what is of God will stand. Therefore the prime importance of ordering their behavior so that it will bear the searching test of Him whose eyes are like flames of fire.

In verses 16-18 Joel again reverts to the desolate condition of the land. The people's hopes had all been blasted. Everything they had worked for lay in withered ruins. But serious as their temporal condition had become, it was nothing compared to the spiritual dearth that prevailed—of which their utter unawareness was the saddest feature.

Joel's spirit is clearly provoked in the closing words of the chapter. He takes his place as one who feels to the full the wretched conditions: "O Lord, to thee will I cry"! This alone can be his resource when "the rivers of waters are dried up, and the fire hath devoured the pastures of the wilderness."

JOEL 2: The Promise of the Outpouring of the Spirit

As we turn to the second chapter, we are ushered at once into the soul-stirring events of the coming day of the Lord. This day will only come when, the church having been caught up to Heaven, God takes up Israel again as a nation and fulfills "all that the prophets have spoken."

In so writing, I do not forget that Peter quoted the last part of this chapter in explaining the wondrous manifestations of the Spirit on the day of Pentecost (Acts 2:16-21). But we will see, when studying this passage, that it applies primarily to a far wider outpouring yet to come. Pentecost was similar to this coming day and was a measure of its fulfillment, therefore Peter could say, "This is that which was spoken by the prophet Joel." But the prophecy was by no means exhausted then, as a careful reading of the whole book of Joel will make plain.

The image of the trumpet, twice used in Joel 2 (verses 1, 15), connects intimately with Numbers 10. There we find the "two trumpets of silver" were used for a double purpose—to blow an alarm, and to summon the whole congregation to the presence of the Lord. The first was to arouse; the second, to instruct. In Joel 2:1-14 the trumpet of alarm is blown to warn the people of the dreadful events about to take place in the day of the Lord. This day is declared to be at hand, and its events are so grave that the plague of locusts under which the people had been suffering was but a feeble picture of what is yet in store for them. Then, in verse 15 to the end of the book, the sounding of the trumpet calls a solemn assembly. Instruction is then given in detail regarding the blessings that will follow the judgments already depicted. In the first part, the day of the Lord is described as "a day of darkness and of gloominess, a day of clouds and of thick darkness, as the morning spread upon the mountains" (2). As the darkest hour precedes the dawn, so before the break of the millennial morn the world in general, and Judah in particular, will pass through the darkest period of tribulation that has ever been known.

For Judah, the chief agency in this ordeal is "a great people and a strong," who are likened to the devouring locusts. This pictures the Assyrian of the last days, the dread northern power, who will overrun the land of Palestine just prior to the glorious appearing of the Sun of Righteousness. Like a devouring fire, the Assyrians will sweep over the land, ravaging without mercy what was like a garden of delight and leaving behind a desolate wilderness (2-3). Like mighty horses running to battle, and as chariots on the mountaintops, they will seem to leap from peak to peak in their unstoppable onslaught. Like devouring flames they will lick up all that is left in their path. Fleeing before them in terror and anguish, "all faces shall gather blackness" in the mad effort to escape the avenging hordes (verses 4-6). The Assyrians' orderly progress, as a disciplined army is strikingly depicted in verses 7-9. Nothing can turn them aside. They enter wherever their prey may hide, and overcome all obstacles as they press on in the fury of their power.

The language of verse 10 is undoubtedly apocalyptic. So tremendous will be the upheavals and overturnings in that day of Jehovah's wrath, that it will be like a terrible earthquake and the trembling of the very heavens. The sun and moon will grow dark, while the stars will seem to be blotted out in the midnight sky. As in the convulsions of the sixth seal in Revelation 6, all that humanity has regarded secure and stable will be overturned. This is a picture of the destruction, not of the material universe, but of the moral, spiritual, and political economies.

Upon this foundation of the coming judgment, God bases an appeal to the conscience of Judah. Jehovah calls on them to turn to Him with all their hearts, bringing forth fruits befitting repentance. He wants reality in heart instead of outward motions, so He says, "Rend your heart, and not your garments" (12), assuring them of His tender compassion and His grace that cannot fail if they sincerely turn to Him. Even though the storm had already begun, who could tell if He would not turn from His wrath, and leave a blessing behind Him? His lovingkindness might yet be toward them, keeping them from further sorrow and preserving His house and its services among them (12-14).

The second trumpet call comes in verse 15. In place of sounding the alarm trumpet, the command is given to "blow the trumpet in Zion, sanctify a fast, call a solemn assembly." God would gather the people before Him that He might instruct them in His ways, and direct their feet in a plain path—if they would only have a heart to do His will. People of all classes are summoned. The priests, the ministers of the Lord, are directed to weep between the porch and the bronze altar, crying to Him before whose house they stand to spare His people and not give His heritage to reproach.

The position of the priests is significant: it illustrates approaching God on the ground that the altar represents—the person and work of the Lord Jesus Christ. Only in His name, and because of His finished work, has the failing saint any claim to draw near. "If any man sin, we have an advocate with the Father, Jesus Christ the righteous" (1 John 2:1). Thus the priests are directed to take their stand on the temple-side of the altar, representing a people who, although in failure, are still the redeemed of the Lord (Joel 2:16-17).

Had there been a responsive heart to God's call to repentance, the avenger would have been turned aside. Jehovah would have arisen in His might as their deliverer to repeal the judgments and bring in blessing and gladness. In the last days, the remnant who are to be preserved for the kingdom will take the place that the priests are here commanded to take. Then all that is promised upon their repentance will be gloriously fulfilled. The northern army will be destroyed, and his boasted power annihilated when the Lord drives him into a barren and desolate land. Every enemy will be overthrown, and the arm of Jehovah made bare (18-20).

It is in view of such an epoch of national repentance that the comforting promises that follow (to the end of the chapter) are given. The land is called on to rejoice because of the great things the Lord will accomplish. Even the lower orders of creation will share in the blessing of the earth's rejuvenation. It will be the glorious inauguration of the liberty of God's children for which the whole creation, groaning and laboring in pain, now waits (Romans 8:19-23). Creation does not share in the present liberty of grace. But the liberty of the glory will be all-embracing. Then "they shall not hurt nor destroy" in all the holy mountain; but the wolf and the lamb will live together, "and a little child shall lead" the strongest and once fiercest of beasts (Isaiah 11:6-9). From the plant kingdom as a whole the curse will be lifted. The pastures of the wilderness will spring into beauty and lush greenness; and the vine and the fig will abundantly yield all types of food-producing plants (Joel 2:22).

The former and latter rains will be given in abundance so that the fertility of the land may be restored and even surpass its ancient fruitfulness. It is a well-known fact that already the God of Israel has given more than a hint of the literal fulfillment of this prophecy. For long centuries the latter rains had been withheld from Palestine, and the land that was once the garden of the East had become largely barren and desolate, scarcely able to sustain its scattered and meager population. But, in our own times, the latter rains have returned in such measure that agriculture is once more in a flourishing condition; vineyards, olive groves, and fig orchards abound. It is as though God were graciously confirming to the world in general, and His ancient people in particular (who are returning to the home of their fathers in some measure) that His eye is always on the land He chose for Himself.

He promised that land to Abraham's seed forever—there His only begotten Son dwelt in His humiliation: there He was crucified and buried, and there He will also descend to assume His great power and reign. Throughout the millennium of Christ's reign (Revelation 20:6) that country will again become the chief garden spot of the whole world, blessed with the rain in its season, and so fertile that "the floors shall be full of wheat, and the vats shall overflow with wine and oil" (Joel 2:23-24).

Then all the past ages of oppression and desolation will be forgotten; for He has said, "I will restore to you the years that the locust hath eaten, the cankerworm, and the caterpillar, and the palmerworm, my great army which I sent among you" (25). How striking the language, "My great army which I sent"! In the judgment described in chapter 1, the people were in danger of seeing only the plague of locusts and forgetting the One who sent it. Here God declares it as *His* army, which He had directed against the land for the discipline of His people. But in the coming day of the Lord, He will abundantly make up for all the loss of the past. Then His people will eat plenty, knowing no lack of any kind; while He who had been their Redeemer from of old will be the object of their praise and adoring gratitude. Abiding in His love, they will never again be put to shame, for He will dwell in their midst and receive the homage of their hearts, never again to be displaced by the idols of the past (26-27).

Then He says:

> And it shall come to pass afterward [that is, after the people of Judah have been restored to their land and the nation as a whole brought into blessing] that I will pour out my spirit upon all

> flesh; and your sons and your daughters shall prophesy, your old men shall dream dreams, your young men shall see visions: And also upon the servants and upon the handmaids in those days will I pour out my Spirit. And I will show wonders in the heavens and in the earth, blood, and fire, and pillars of smoke. The sun shall be turned into darkness and the moon into blood, before the great and the terrible day of the Lord come. And it shall come to pass, that whosoever shall call on the name of the Lord, shall be delivered: for in mount Zion and in Jerusalem shall be deliverance, as the Lord hath said, and in the remnant whom the Lord shall call (28-32).

I have quoted this interesting and important passage in full so that the least-instructed readers may have it all before them, noting carefully its connection. This is no isolated fragment interjected without connection to the balance of the book; on the contrary, it occurs in its exact and proper place: in line with the events of the day of the Lord that the prophet has been unfolding.

Clearly all this can never be fulfilled until the people of Israel are restored to their land. Then God will cause His blessing to go far beyond them, pouring out His Spirit upon "all flesh"; thus bringing the spared nations into the glorious privileges of the millennial kingdom! Old and young will be anointed with the Spirit's unction and will be enlightened so that they may dream dreams, see visions, and prophesy. Nor shall the men alone share in this, but the women also shall enjoy this blessing.

Observe, however that the wonders of verses 30 and 31 will all take place before this day of the Lord is ushered in. Then salvation will be extended to all the Gentiles who had never heard the gospel in this dispensation of grace: "Whosoever shall call on the name of the Lord shall be delivered." why? The answer is, "For in mount Zion and in Jerusalem shall be deliverance"—that is, restored Israel will be a center of blessing for the whole earth. This is not the same thing as the preaching of the gospel of God's grace today. Mount Zion and Jerusalem are not now the depositories of blessing for the Gentiles. Rather the contrary is true. But when the church, the body of Christ, has been caught away to be forever with the

Lord (see 1 Thessalonians 4:14-18), and God has once more taken up the Jews to make them a means of salvation to the unbelieving nations, Joel's prophecy will be fulfilled to the letter.

I think it must be obvious to every careful reader that this is the only unforced and natural explanation of the passage. But this immediately raises the question as to the apostle Peter's use of it on the day of Pentecost (Acts 2:16-21). Are we to entertain the wretched thought that he misapplied it? Or on the other hand, can it be that readers generally have misunderstood his use of it? The latter alternative is, I am persuaded, the correct one.

Note that Peter does not say, "this is the fulfillment" of the prophecy. He simply finds the explanation for the remarkable events of that day in these words of Joel. And he declares, "This is that!" In other words, he did not identify the *events*; he identified the *power*. That which had taken place on Pentecost was the very same thing that Joel said would take place when the day of the Lord had come. That the day spoken of had *not* come, Peter very well knew, and elsewhere plainly declared it (see 2 Peter 3:10). But the same power of the Holy Spirit was operating in that day which will operate when the kingdom is introduced in the future. Therefore, there is here no contradiction and certainly no misapplication. Pentecost was a *sample* of what Joel foretold; and the apostle used the passage illustratively, not as declaring its complete fulfillment at Pentecost. His own declaration in 2 Peter 1:20 should keep any from supposing Peter meant to take the last verses of Joel 2 from their connection and apply them specifically to the ushering in of the Christian dispensation.

Taken in context, Joel's words clearly refer primarily to the bringing in of the kingdom—not the church. But the same power that will operate in the coming day was seen at Pentecost when Peter preached his memorable sermon.

JOEL 3: The Valley of Decision

Still having before his soul the events that will transpire in the day of the Lord, the prophet continued to set forth more detailed information about that long-awaited season of Jehovah's power.

Note that the expression "the day," or, "that day," so often used in connection with the ushering in of the kingdom does not refer to any one day of twenty-four hours. On the contrary, according to 2 Peter 3:10, the day of the Lord covers the entire period from the great tribulation to the passing away of the heavens and earth, thus ushering in the day of God, or the day of eternity.

Four dispensational days are brought before us in Scripture. The present is called "man's day" (1 Corinthians 4:3, literal translation of "man's judgment"). Then the manifestation at the judgment seat of Christ is in "the day of Christ" (Philippians 1:6, 10). (In 2 Thessalonians 2:2 [KJV] "the day of Christ" should be "the day of the Lord," as a glance at any reputable critical version will show.) Then follows "the day of the Lord," which is the entire period during which the once-rejected Lord asserts and makes good His title to the earth. "The day of God" is the eternal state, and is only mentioned in 2 Peter 3:12. It is to the third great "day" that the third chapter of Joel refers and which the opening verses address.

> For, behold, in those days, and in that time, when I shall bring again the captivity of Judah and Jerusalem, I will also gather all nations, and will bring them down into the valley of Jehoshaphat, and will plead with them there for my people and for my heritage Israel, whom they have scattered among the nations, and parted my land (1-2).

The scene depicted by our Lord Himself in Matthew 25:31-46 would seem to connect with this. Joel vividly described the coming of the Son of man when He will sit on the throne of His glory to judge the living nations. It has long since been pointed out by others that this judgment scene is something very different and distinct from the final judgment of the great white throne, as set forth in Revelation 20. There the wicked dead are judged and cast into the lake of fire, the righteous having been raised in glory a thousand years before. On the other hand, the judgment of the sheep and goats, as it may be called, is a tribunal before which appear the nations living on the earth when Christ descends to take the kingdom. It is *pre*-millennial. The great white throne is *post*-millennial. In

Matthew 25 the sheep are rewarded because of their treatment of Christ's brethren, that is, the Jewish remnant. The goats are condemned for their indifference and even cruelty to them. The same discriminating judgment is brought to our attention here by Joel.

The Son of man will place His throne in the valley of Jehoshaphat. To positively locate this valley is an impossibility, since this is the only mention of it in Scripture. A deep ravine just outside Jerusalem now bears this name, separating the holy city from the mount of Olives. But it is likely that the name was given it only in view of this prophecy, not that it was called this when Joel spoke (nor yet for centuries afterward since it is not thus designated before the fourth century of the Christian era). If we understand "Jehoshaphat" as only an untranslated Hebrew expression, all is clear. Then it would read, "The valley of Jehovah's judgment."

There the Lord will judge the nations who have oppressed and scattered His people, selling them into slavery and rejoicing in their degradation. No doubt it is God Himself who has permitted them to persecute Israel in this way for their discipline, but that in no way lessens the guilt of their oppressors. Therefore Tyre and Zidon, with all who have had a share in humiliating the Jews, will be recompensed according to their works (Joel 3:3-8).

Unquestionably, what is especially brought out in Matthew 25 is the treatment of the remnant witnesses fleeing from antichrist's bitter persecution. To minister to them is practically to acknowledge the claims of the true anointed One, while to be indifferent to them is to tacitly consent to the sinful sway of the false prophet. New birth is therefore presumed in the case of those who go into life eternal: their works were the proof.

So we have detailed information in the New Testament account that it was not God's pleasure to reveal through Joel. But the identification of the judgment seems clear, which the call in Joel 3:9-17 makes abundantly plain. The mighty men of the Gentiles will hear an alarm and come up to Immanuel's land. Turning the implements of peace into weapons of war, they will come in great hordes to surround Jerusalem, as predicted in Zechariah 14 and Revelation 19. The whole land will be overrun with them; and all human help for the remnant of Israel, who cling to the Lord, will be gone.

Therefore they cry in the hour of their deepest distress, "Thither cause thy mighty ones to come down, O Lord" (Joel 3:11). Knowing that the hour has struck when the saints will take the kingdom, they turn to God in their affliction, calling for the descent of their once-rejected Messiah and His glorious train. God answers their prayer by sending the warrior on the white horse with all the armies of Heaven, as recorded in Revelation 19. He executes swift and certain judgment on the armed hosts of the nations.

But this is not all. A sessional judgment follows, which all the heathen are commanded to attend. "Let the heathen be wakened, and come up to the valley of Jehoshaphat; for there will I sit to judge all the heathen round about" (Joel 3:12). This is identified with "the harvest of the earth" of Revelation 14:14-16. "Put ye in the sickle, for the harvest is ripe" (Joel 3:13). Nor will the Gentiles alone be judged and the wheat separated from the chaff; the apostate portion of the nation of Israel, who had followed the antichrist, will also be cast as ripe grapes into the great winepress of the wrath of God (Revelation 14:17-20). So we read, "Come, get you down; for the press is full, the vats overflow; for their wickedness is great" (Joel 3:13).

The fourteenth verse is a graphic description of the terrible scene—it's also a verse that has often been utterly misconstrued. "Multitudes, multitudes in the valley of decision [or threshing]: for the day of the Lord is near in the valley of decision." This is the day of the Judge's decisions; not a time when men are being called on to decide for Christ. The valley of Jehoshaphat will be like a great threshingfloor where the divine winnower sits to separate all who will share His kingdom from those who will go away into everlasting punishment. Then every created light will fade away into darkness before the presence of the glory of the crucified One (15)! He who will be revealed as Jehovah of hosts "shall roar out of Zion, and utter His voice from Jerusalem," overturning and shaking to pieces the heavens and the earth. Civil and political frameworks, as well as all religious pretension shall tremble at the sound of His voice. For the Lord alone will be the hope of His people and the strength of Israel in that day (16).

Thus shall the long-awaited kingdom of the Son of man be ushered in, and all Israel will know that Jehovah their God dwells in

Zion, His holy mountain. Then Jerusalem's long period of oppression by the Gentiles will be over; and with her iniquity finished, she will become in truth the holy city, never to be trodden underfoot by strangers again.

The final four verses of Joel 3 apply to that glorious era. Yet for Egypt, the desolation spoken of will not be final, as we know from other Scriptures.

> And it shall come to pass in that day, that the mountains shall drop down new wine, and the hills shall flow with milk, and all the rivers of Judah shall flow with waters, and a fountain shall come forth of the house of the Lord, and shall water the valley of Shittim (18).

It is a scene of plenty and refreshment to which Ezekiel adds fuller details in chapter 47 of his prophecy.

Then Joel goes on to prophesy that Egypt and Edom will be judged for their past treatment of the people of Judah. Edom will be blotted out forever as a nation. The prophet Obadiah declares this. Egypt, on the other hand, will be restored after having been punished for her sins (See Isaiah 19:18-25).

Judah's time of trouble will produce precious fruit, leading to her full restoration and blessing. She "shall dwell forever, and Jerusalem from generation to generation" (Joel 3:20), having been cleansed from all their defilements and made clean in the sight of Him who will dwell in their midst in the city of Zion, His chosen capital. "For I will cleanse their blood that I have not cleansed: for the Lord dwelleth in Zion" (21).

It would hardly be necessary to try to explain this verse somewhat fully were it not that a wretchedly grotesque interpretation has been imposed on it by certain deluded people who too often confuse the simple by using it as their prooftext. The ridiculous notion has been put forth that a certain spared remnant *of this age*, are to have their blood cleansed from all impurities that would result in natural death so that they shall obtain immortality in the flesh! The context makes plain the fact that the words refer to the cleansing of literal Judah from the defilement of the blood of their enemies, which they contracted during the unparalleled horrors of the great tribulation. They will be from then on holiness to the Lord.

Isaiah 4:4 makes this plain, where God speaks of the same glorious time: "When the Lord shall have washed away the filth of the daughters of Zion, and shall have purged the blood of Jerusalem from the midst thereof by the spirit of judgment, and by the spirit of burning." In Lamentations 4:14 the prophets and priests of Judah are described as men who have wandered blindly through the streets, having "polluted themselves with blood, so that men could not touch their garments." Thus, by the part they took in slaying the righteous One, all Israel has become polluted; but in that day the blood of defilement will be cleansed away, and God will be able to dwell among them. Many other passages could be cited, but these are sufficient to show what is really intended.

With this, Joel's burden is concluded. He has carried his hearers and readers on to the full display of Messiah's glory. Beyond that, prophecy, as connected with the earth, does not go. Only in the New Testament do we have unfolded something of those things God has prepared for those who love Him. They will share in His eternal rest after time has run its course and ceased to be.

AMOS

ROMA

A PROFILE

AMOS
THE COUNTRY COUSIN

BY JOHN PHILLIPS

Amos (764-755 B.C.), a native of Judah, was called to preach in and against Israel. He was a herdsman, a backwoods "cowboy" from the barren hill country some six miles southeast of Bethlehem, overlooking the Dead Sea. He was called to preach at a time when both kingdoms were experiencing a period of great power and prosperity. Jeroboam II was on the throne of Israel, and with Syria roundly defeated and Assyria in an era of temporary eclipse, wealth and worldliness went hand in hand. Uzziah was on the throne of David in Jerusalem, and Judah, like Israel, was experiencing imperialist expansion at the expense of the surrounding nations.

The outward prosperity of the kingdoms of Judah and Samaria was deceptive. For within a few years the Assyrians would be besieging Samaria, and Judah would be living in daily terror. In Israel, especially, lawlessness was but thinly veiled, and though the nation gave lip service to Jehovah, immorality and superstition were at the heart of popular religion.

The Message of Amos

The opening of the book shows that Amos saw far beyond the boundaries of his native land. His message embraced past, present, and future and was climaxed by a series of five visions.

I. The Vigilance of the Prophet (1–2)
   Woes Against
   A. Damascus (1:3-5)
   B. Gaza (1:6-8)
   C. Tyre (1:9-10)
   D. Edom (1:11-12)
   E. Ammon (1:13-15)
   F. Moab (2:1-3)
   G. Judah (2:4-5)
   H. Israel (2:6-16)
II. The Voice of the Prophet (3–6)
   A. As to the Present: Privileges Despised (3)
   B. As to the Past: Perversity Described (4)
   C. As to the Prospect: Punishment Declared (5–6)
III. The Visions of the Prophet (7–9)
   A. The Locust (7:1-3)
   B. The Fire (7:4-6)
   C. The Plumb Line (7:7-17)
   D. The Over-ripe Fruit (8:1-14)
   E. The False Altar (9:1-15)

At first, no doubt, Amos would have been welcomed as he poured out his prophecies against the surrounding nations. Even his country manners would have been forgiven. His idiomatic expression "for three transgressions . . . and for four" means that the cup of iniquity was full and more than full. Even when Amos began to denounce Judah, the "Northerners" at Bethel probably listened with glee. But when he turned his attention to Samaria and denounced Israel's sins, it was a different matter.

Before long his preaching aroused the ire of Amaziah, the priest of Bethel (7:10-13), who complained to Jeroboam that Amos was a danger to national security. He also took it upon himself to order Amos out of the country. Amos told this man to his face that, regardless of his humble background and lack of formal education, he could clearly foresee the day when Amaziah's wife would be "an harlot in the city," a victim of the invader's lusts, his daughters put to the sword, his property divided by another, and Amaziah himself dying a captive in a heathen land. It took courage and conviction to be a prophet of the Lord.

The Burden of Amos

The judgments God would bring upon the nation were of a twofold character. There was to be physical disaster. The nation would know famine, drought, blight, locusts, and an earthquake. Those would happen first. If they did not produce the desired result in national repentance then they would be followed by political disaster. The nation would be given over to the horrors of foreign invasion, and it would know the terrors of war and the tragedy of utter defeat.

Although the burden of Amos was one of judgment, yet through his prophecy there runs a note of hope and an oft-repeated exhortation to "seek the Lord." In the three sermons (3–6) and the five visions (7–9) there is an increasing intensity to be noticed. Sins which Amos mentions are greed, injustice, drunkenness, immorality, profanity, and oppression. He shows that the nation, at the very summit of national prosperity, nevertheless was on the brink of disaster.

Amos has a message very much applicable to ourselves. God is patient and speaks again and again to the conscience of a nation. He allows things to go wrong; He brings the nation low. If He is still ignored then He raises up a foreign power to execute His will.

CHAPTER THREE

THE PROPHECY OF AMOS

We have much more information about Amos than is customarily given concerning the minor prophets. He gave us, by the inspiration of God, several autobiographical notes of deep interest, which will be helpful to look at before studying his messages to Israel and the surrounding nations.

His prophecies were given in the reigns of Uzziah king of Judah and Jeroboam II king of Israel. He described himself as a shepherd of Tekoa, a town in the hill country of Judea about twelve miles from Jerusalem. From Tekoa came the "wise woman" sent by Joab to persuade David to permit his murderer son, Absalom, to return to his family, in plain violation of all law, both human and divine (2 Samuel 14:2). Ira the son of Ikkesh, one of David's mighty men, was also born in Tekoa (2 Samuel 23:26). Even after the return from Babylon, the zeal of Tekoa's men is spoken of, though their nobles were reproved in connection with the building of the wall of Jerusalem (Nehemiah 3:5, 27). A desert town, Tekoa was surrounded by solitary expanses, and was a suitable place for men of rural occupation. There Amos pursued his humble calling until set apart by the Lord to the prophetic office.

He wrote that he was neither born into the company of the prophets nor did he choose that calling for himself. But when he was a "herdman and a gatherer of sycomore fruit" (the fruit of the wild fig), the Lord said to him, "Go, prophesy unto my people Israel" (Amos 7:14-15). This was enough for Amos. He was not disobedient to the voice from Heaven; rather, leaving behind the pastures of the wilderness and turning his back on the place of his birth, he declared the word of the Lord way up in the capital of the northern kingdom—much to the disgust and indignation of Jeroboam and his false priest, Amaziah. When ordered to flee to his own land and do his prophesying there, he boldly gave his divine credentials and delivered a message more searching than ever.

We have no record of the length of his ministry or the time or circumstances of his death. But what has been preserved for us is replete with important lessons.

It is always God's way to prepare His servants in secret for the work they will later accomplish in public. Moses in the remote parts of the desert; Gideon on the threshing floor; David with his few sheep out on the hillside; Daniel refusing to be defiled with the king's meat; John the Baptist in the desert; Peter in his fishing boat; Paul in Arabia; and Amos following the flock and herding the cattle in the wilderness of Tekoa—all alike attest to the truth of this fact. Only the one who has learned of God in the school of obscurity will be likely to shine in the blaze of publicity.

Amos had no thought of becoming or being recognized as a prophet like men today select "the ministry" as a profession. Doubtless he would have been content to pursue his humble vocation as a small farmer, or possibly a mere farmer's hand or assistant, to the end of his life, if such had been the mind of God for him. But as he followed the flock, his soul was communing with Jehovah. As he gathered the wild figs of the wilderness, his heart was meditating on the great issues of the soul's relationship to God and the importance of walking in His ways. As he tended the herds, he was learning wondrous lessons of a faithful Creator's love and care. So, when the time was right for him, the Lord kindled the already prepared fuel into a flame. The humble herdsman became a mighty, Spirit-energized prophet of God, not only to his own people, but to all Israel and the nations around.

We read of no doubts or hesitation, no bargaining or questioning as to temporal support; just as there was no fleshly impatience or desire to attract attention as a prophet or speaker. Throughout his prophecy, we have the record of a simple, humble man of God, who could wait or run as his Lord saw fit.

In all this, how much there is for our souls today! Many self-made ministers have inner lives that are in sad contrast to their ministry. Many too insist on taking the place belonging to a servant of God, when they have never spent any time in His school, learning His ways, as did Amos. Their words therefore are empty and disappointing, as might be expected when coming from men who have not been sent by the Lord. It was blessedly different with Amos. The more we learn of the messenger, the more we are prepared to listen to his message.

Those hidden years had not been wasted. Not only were they years in which he listened to the voice of God speaking to his own soul, but in them he was acquiring experience, and insight into men and things that would be invaluable to him later on. Again and again in his public messages he used illustrations that showed how closely and thoughtfully he had observed the many things, animate and inanimate, surrounding him in his early life. The following passages make this abundantly plain: 2:13; 3:12; 4:9; 5:8; 6:12; 7:1-2. We will notice others as we proceed.

The theme of the book of Amos is emphatically one of judgment on Israel and Judah and the nations surrounding them.

In the first two chapters we have eight separate burdens, addressed respectively to Damascus, Gaza, Tyrus, Edom, Ammon, Moab, Judah, and Israel. The first five are dealt with in chapter 1, and the last three are covered in chapter 2.

The second part of the prophecy is comprised of chapters 3–6, giving the word of the Lord to Israel (the ten-tribed kingdom of the north).

The third and last division takes in chapters 7–9, in which we have a series of five visions and a considerable parenthesis (7:10-17) devoted to the personal history of the prophet, which we have already noted. The visions close with the declaration of millennial blessing and restoration, as seen in both the preceding books, Hosea and Joel, and generally throughout the Minor Prophets. For, though judgment is the theme, yet its chief purpose is to prepare the way for glory. The Lord will not stop until He has established righteousness and blessing in all the earth.

AMOS 1 and 2: The Indictment of the Nations

Amos did not hide what some might call his humble origins. He boldly began his prophecy with, "The words of Amos, who was among the herdmen of Tekoa, which he saw concerning Israel in the days of

Uzziah king of Judah, and in the days of Jeroboam the son of Joash king of Israel, two years before the earthquake" (1). Here the prophet's name, his humble calling, the place he lived, and the date of his prophecy are all plainly set forth.

The earthquake referred to would doubtless mark an epoch for more than one generation, but we have no record of it. In Jewish traditional lore it is said to have occurred when Uzziah impiously presumed to take the office of the Lord's priest. Josephus connects these two incidents, but there is no proof of this.

From verse 2 we can gather that the nations addressed are considered in their connection with Jerusalem and mount Zion. There Jehovah had set His name. And from there He would roar in His indignation and utter His voice in judgment so that the pastures of the shepherds would mourn and the top of Carmel wither.

Notice that each separate prediction begins with the same solemn formula, except for the change of the name: "For three transgressions of Damascus, and for four, I will not turn away the punishment thereof; because . . ." Jewish expositors generally understand this structure to say, "Three transgressions have I forgiven them, but the fourth I will visit in judgment." It at least implies that, in His long-suffering, God had waited again and again, looking for some evidence of repentance before finally dealing in wrath, but there was none. In three transgressions they had filled up the cup of their wickedness. In the fourth it had overflowed and declared that all further testing was useless. They were corrupt and abominable in His sight. Judgment therefore must take its course.

The crowning sin of each people is especially seen in the terrible combined indictment and sentence that proceeded from the seer's inspired lips.

Damascus had "threshed Gilead with threshing instruments of iron." Ruthlessly persecuting the exposed borders of Israel across the Jordan, they showed no mercy to age or sex but swept over the land, cutting down all equally and treating them like grain under the flail. For this they would be judged without mercy by the moral governor of the universe, whose eyes saw all their ways (3-5).

Gaza, the ancient Philistine capital, had made God's people their prey, taking them captive and selling or giving them to Edom. (How graphic a picture of false religion delivering people to the power of the flesh!) In this way they helped a cruel unbrotherly foe to destroy and enslave his close relative. But as they had sought the destruction of the erring people of the Lord, so God's fire and hand would be against Philistia until it was totally destroyed (6-8).

Tyrus, the merchant city by the sea, once in "brotherly covenant" with Israel, in the days of Solomon and Hiram (see 1 Kings 5:12), had forgotten the promises it had made. They too sided with Edom, delivering to them the captives they had taken. Therefore, the fire would devour the seemingly impregnable wall of Tyre and blot out her palaces (9-10).

Edom, always the most bitter enemy of the seed of Jacob, had been unrelenting in his fury and "did pursue his brother with the sword, and did cast off all pity." In return, the Lord would forget to pity Edom in the day of His righteous wrath, repaying him for the indignities heaped on Israel (11-12). The prophecy of Obadiah connects closely with this passage.

Ammon's fiendish display of hatred against Israel had called down the divine retribution on his own guilty head. By the most cruel methods he had tried to blot out the hope of the chosen nation in order to enlarge his own border. For this, he would be exposed to all the fury of Jehovah's tempest in the violent winds of His wrath (13-15).

Moab, on the other hand, is not charged with cruelty to Israel, but with executing judgment on Edom when guilty of the gravest crimes himself. Therefore their ruler would be destroyed and all their princes slain (2:1-3).

So far the prophetic messages have been directed against the people surrounding the land of Israel. History is the witness of their fulfillment. Gaza, Tyre, Edom, Ammon, and Moab are now only *names*. Their glory has long since disappeared. Damascus still exists, but her people have gone into captivity and the Moslems dwell in her palaces. Historical records have proven the predictions of the herdsman-prophet to be the word of Jehovah.

But Amos did not only speak against the heathen. He also had to proclaim the coming of the long-delayed judgment against Judah and Israel because of their unholy ways.

Judah, privileged above all others, had despised the law of the Lord and refused to obey His commandments. The lies of their false teachers had caused them to err. They preferred these prophets over the Heaven-sent messengers of the God of their fathers. Sadly, the fathers had turned away from their Rock, and the children had walked in their ways. Because of this, Jerusalem's palaces, like those of the nations, would be burned with fire; the place where Jehovah had set His name would be given up to His enemies (4-5).

The indictment of Israel is the longest of all. The proud northern kingdom is charged with covetousness, licentiousness, and idolatry. Yet they were utterly unconcerned about the damage they caused. They sold the righteous for silver and the needy for a pair of shoes. The most commonplace article of commerce was more valuable in their greedy eyes than the cause of the poor. Though they lived in the most vile uncleanness, they still called themselves by the holy name of the Lord. In this way they profaned the Lord's name in the sight of the heathen. Idolatry inflamed them, and they drank "the wine of the condemned in the house of their god." They lay down by every altar on the pledged garments of the needy. The law had forbidden keeping the pledged garments of the poor overnight; they not only scorned the law, but openly devoted those garments to the worship of their idols. The judges also, contrary to all law, used the fines of those they condemned to buy wine for their idolatrous festivals. This was "the wine of the condemned" (6-8).

Yet the Lord, as He poignantly reminded them, had expelled the Amorites before them. He had brought Israel out of Egypt and had led them forty years through the wilderness. He had raised up prophets among their sons and Nazarites, devoted to Himself, among their young men. But they led astray the consecrated ones by wine, and refused to listen to the warnings of the prophets (9-12). It is a sad and pitiful picture, but how often has it been duplicated since! Those who receive the greatest privileges are often the greatest offenders.

Finally, their iniquities were full. The last sheaf had been loaded on the cart, and the mercy of the Lord had come to an end. Therefore no one would stand "in that day"—the day of the Lord's anger (13-16).

How serious are the charges recorded here! These words of old are searching too. Oh, that we who today are called by the name of the Lord may consider them well!

AMOS 3: The Chastisement of the Chosen Nation

With this chapter, the second division of the prophecy begins, going on to the end of chapter 6. This section presents the word of the Lord to Israel—a last somber rebuke before He carried out the predicted judgment we just studied.

Amos did not address merely the ten tribes under the name "children of Israel" but "the whole family which [the Lord] brought up from the land of Egypt" (Amos 3:1). Though divided into two kingdoms at that time, they were here viewed as one nation. Their special privileges made them far more responsible than their ignorant Gentile neighbors. "You only," God said, "have I known of all the families of the earth: therefore I will punish you for all your iniquities" (2). This is a divine principle we should never lose sight of—responsibility flows from relationship. Because Jehovah had separated Israel from the nations and covenanted with them Himself, they were expected to yield that obedience which their favored position demanded. If they did not yield, they would have to be the special objects of His discipline.

The same is true concerning the assembly of God in this dispensation, both collectively and individually. We are exhorted to walk worthy of our exalted calling (see 1 Thessalonians 2:12). If we do not, we incur our Father's discipline. Punishment does not prove that God is against us; on the contrary, it is His love for us that leads Him so to act (see Hebrews 12:5-6). The world may continue in its sin and know little of such sovereign care, but it must be different with the people who are called by the name of the Lord.

Amos 3:3 lets us into the secret of true fellowship. Two can walk together only when they are united. It is not a question of agreeing on all details, but of having common ground for communion. God cannot walk with those who oppose Him in the intimate, happy sense that is contemplated here. Neither can saints walk together if one seeks to honor God and the other has lapsed into loose thoughts and evil ways.

Beginning with verse 4, Amos declared the reason for his message—results spring from adequate causes. The trumpet was to be blown so that the people might tremble, for God was about to bring evil on them. "Shall there be evil in a city, and the Lord hath not done it?" is His challenge (6). This verse has disturbed some who are over-zealous for the reputation of the Lord of hosts. But evil is, of course, *calamity*—not sin. We saw this in the first chapter of Joel; God uses calamity as His rod of discipline. Amos was to warn the careless inhabitants of the cities of Israel of this fact.

He had good cause to prophesy. God had revealed His secrets to him; therefore he needed to boldly proclaim them. "The Lord God hath spoken, who can but prophesy?" (8) This is high ground indeed; but it is the only proper ground for one who seeks to communicate divine truth. If God has not spoken, then one man's guess is as good as another's; one philosopher's speculations are as worthy of consideration as anyone else's. But if God Himself has spoken, as He has in His Word, that settles everything for the one who fears Him. His servant has nothing to do but proclaim what has been revealed, rejecting "oppositions of science falsely so called," and all vain "imaginations" (1 Timothy 6:20; 2 Corinthians 10:5).

This is the value of Scripture; and Satan would subtly seek to rob us of this certainty at the present time. God has revealed His will in His Word. "The Lord God will do nothing, but he revealeth his secret unto his servants the prophets" (Amos 3:7). Therefore the man of faith accepts the prophetic writings as a final court of appeal; for indeed the Lord Jesus Himself has set His seal on them. And we are told that "holy men of God spake as they were moved by the Holy Ghost" (2 Peter 1:21). Faith triumphs here; mere reason stumbles in the dark, vainly trying to peer into the future, to explain the past, or to understand the present.

It has often been alleged by opponents of the Bible's inspiration that unless we are prepared to believe that the writers of the various books were infallible, it is futile to talk of the inerrancy of Scripture. And this in face of the solemn declaration of the Lord Jesus that "the Scripture *cannot be broken*" (John 10:35, emphasis added). The question of human infallibility is not relevant at all. When God speaks, one needs only to be obedient—not infallible—in proclaiming what He has made known. So it was with Amos and his fellow servants of the prophetic band. An amanuensis need not have exact knowledge of the events concerning which he writes at the dictation of another. He hears the word and transcribes accordingly. Knowing this, we can understand the Old Testament writers "searching what, or what manner of time the Spirit of Christ which was in them did signify [or point out], when it testified beforehand the sufferings of Christ, and the glory that should follow" (1 Peter 1:11). Only unbelief causes any difficulty here.

Amos's prophetic message is given in verses 9 to 15. He foretold Israel's dispersion, but he also disclosed that a remnant would be saved.

In the palaces of Philistia and Egypt it would be declared that, because of their sins, the Lord God would no longer be a defense to His people. The nations that had once been witnesses of His power would now witness His righteousness. When His people did not walk with Him, He could only give them up to discipline.

However, as the shepherd "taketh out of the mouth of the lion two legs, or a piece of an ear; so shall the children of Israel be taken out that dwell in Samaria in the corner of a bed, and in Damascus in a couch" (12). The shepherd who lost one of the flock would have to be responsible for it, unless he could bring proof that it was attacked by beasts. Therefore, he would be anxious to recover a portion, even if it was only the tip of an ear. Likewise God would preserve a portion of Israel, though a very small remnant, from being devoured by the wild beasts of the Gentile empires. Israel had to be judged because of their idolatrous practices, of which the altar at Bethel, set up by Jeroboam the son of Nebat, was a standing memorial. Its fall would involve the destruction of those who gloried in their power and reveled in luxury, unconcerned about the fallen state of Israel (see also 6:1-6).

AMOS 4: Yet Have Ye Not Returned

In Amos 4 Israel is reminded of the various means through which God had been speaking to them to try and draw them back to Himself. Sadly, they had pursued their ways of sin, heedless of warning or punishment. They despised the discipline of the Lord.

In verses 1-3, the great women of Israel are most likely addressed, for in place of "kine [cows] of Bashan," the feminine form is used in the original. Hedonistic, insolent, and self-indulgent, these haughty women oppressed the poor and crushed the needy to serve their own carnal desires. Indifferent to the sorrow their ill-gotten pleasures inflicted on others, they feasted and rejoiced—forgetting that the holy One of Israel was looking on. He swore by His holiness to repay their sins, taking them away in the height of their foolishness, as the angler hooks the greedy fish that is insensible to the danger lurking in the bait so temptingly displayed.

Verses 4 and 5 have been interpreted in a variety of ways. Some commentators understand them as a call to repentance. In this case they consider "a sacrifice of thanksgiving with leaven," to be in accordance with Leviticus 7:13, where leavened bread accompanied the sacrifice of thanksgiving as the offerer's acknowledgment of his own personal unworthiness. But a thankoffering was only appropriate when the people were right before God. To call them to the heretical altar of Bethel to bring a thank offering when they needed a *sin offering* would surely be contrary to the mind of God.

I understand the passage to be ironic, similar to Elijah's taunts of the priests of Baal. In fact, it would seem as though the prophet were saying, "Bring a sacrifice of leaven as a thank offering, for it is so like you, you children of Israel!" The leaven here is not meant to accompany a sacrifice or a presentation of firstfruits; but the leaven *is* the offering they are ironically called to bring. The whole passage is a sad commentary on the pitiful condition of Israel, whose whole system of worship was completely sinful, while they prided themselves on their pomp and ritual.

Does not He who sees the pretentiousness of a guiltier Christendom regard it with even greater abhorrence? Where the conscience is alive it will surely lead to abandoning so glaring a sin.

That God had no intention of accepting a sacrifice offered at Bethel or Gilgal is clear from Amos 5:5. Everything that revolved around these centers of apostasy was detestable to the One who had set His name in Jerusalem. Though even there it had also been profaned.

Because of their oppression and idolatry, He had sent a terrible famine on them, giving them "cleanness of teeth in all [their] cities, and want of bread in all [their] places." But there had been no evidence of repentance, so the Lord had to say, "Yet have ye not returned unto me" (4:6). The rain too He had withheld, and that in such a way that had their conscience been tender, they would have questioned why rain was given to one city while being withheld from another. Again, however, we read the sad refrain, "Yet have ye not returned unto me, saith the Lord" (verses 7-8). He had also afflicted them with blight and mildew so that their scanty crops were ruined before they were full grown. And if the orchards, vineyards, and gardens seemed to flourish, the palmerworm (the locust in its most voracious form) was sent to destroy them. Still there had been no awakening—their conscience remained dormant. "Yet have ye not returned unto me, saith the Lord" (9).

Then He afflicted them with pestilence, "after the manner of Egypt." The putrid carcasses of their young sons slain in battle, together with their horses, polluted the air so that the people breathed in disease and death. But no one seemed to discern who was afflicting them, so again God said, "Yet have ye not returned unto me" (10).

A great catastrophe, possibly an earthquake, with an accompanying fire, had added to their woes. He had overthrown some of them like He had destroyed Sodom and Gomorrah; the survivors were like burning sticks plucked out of the embers. "Yet have ye not returned unto me, saith the Lord" (11). Failing to discern His hand in all that had happened to them, they wanted only to escape their trouble. This is always the way of those oblivious to divine grace. Shutting their eyes to the most obvious evidence of God's work, they pursue their heedless way until the pit closes over them.

I experienced the California earthquake of April 18, 1906, and was an eyewitness of its horrors. One of the more disturbing things I noticed was the persistent efforts of the preachers of all denominations to quiet the fears of the populace by assuring them that God had no part in the calamitous events that had taken place. "Natural causes" were the explanation for everything! Those without Christ were only too ready to believe this. In this way their partially awakened consciences were lulled to sleep and their ears were closed against the voice of God, who through Amos said, "*I* have overthrown some of you!" I had the opportunity to explain to many, from verses 11 and 12 of this chapter, this truth. I trust that for some this bore the fruit of repentance and salvation. That will be revealed on that final day.

Because of Israel's utter indifference, only one thing remained: they must meet God in judgment, the God whose warnings and discipline they had despised. "Therefore...prepare to meet thy God, O Israel" (12).

Though they did not know Him, He was the One who formed the

mountains and created the winds. He discloses to man his secret thoughts. He made the morning darkness and walked on the earth's high places. This was Jehovah, the mighty God of hosts (13).

They would have to meet Him—but how? And you too, my reader, if still unsaved, think how you will stand in that great day of God's wrath!

For the believer living carelessly, this warning also has an application. Taking his own way, he may despise the chastisement of the Lord, and fail to listen to His reproving voice. But he cannot continue this way for long. Sooner or later God must be met. Keep short accounts then with Him who knows the secrets of all hearts!

AMOS 5: A Lamentation for Israel

Sad and solemn are the dirgelike refrains of the prophet's lament over the fallen nation he loved so well. They had crumbled in their allegiance and fidelity to God, and their works merited no blessing whatever. If God would lift them up, He would have to do it in *pure grace;* otherwise, nothing but judgment could be their portion.

In the same way, everything God has committed to humanity has failed, including the testimony entrusted to the church. But God has infinite resources in Himself, always ready to be displayed when the objects of His grace fail. This can encourage everyone who sighs and hurts over the divisions and utter breakdown of what should have been a beautiful testimony to Christ and the glory of God in these last days. Still, despair need not overwhelm the soul. God may yet hear the cries of His people. If there is brokenness and repentance, He "is able to do exceeding abundantly above all we ask or think" (Ephesians 3:20).

The virgin of Israel had fallen so low that she could never rise again—that is, as far as her own will was concerned. Nor were any of her leaders able to raise her up. But God still pleaded with her, crying in the ears of any who might heed, "Seek ye me, and ye shall live"! No one could deliver her, except the One she had deserted. To look to Bethel, Gilgal, or Beersheba—where the high places that told of idolatrous self-will were set up—would be all in vain (which was declared ironically in Amos 4:4). The fact that a certain sacredness was associated with each of those places would not prevent their going into captivity. Bethel was no longer the house of God, nor did Gilgal now speak of reproach rolled away. Rather, Bethel had become a stronghold of demons, and Gilgal was itself a reproach.

Something that, at one time, may have been associated with the work of God, all too easily becomes corrupted when pride and self-will are at work. We may have to refuse it, in faithfulness to the Lord, despite its former blessedness and its past acknowledgment of God. Scripture must always be the guide—not human rules and authority. "That which was from the beginning" is the original ground—and only that!

So Israel was exhorted to seek the Lord and live, "lest he break out like fire in the house of Joseph, and devour it, and there be none to quench it in Bethel" (Amos 5:6). Sadly, the warning went unheeded; so, in just a few years, the threatened judgment was carried out, and the "house of Joseph" was dispossessed of their land—never to be regathered until the day of the coming glory.

The shepherd of Tekoa soared to the loftiest heights of inspired poetry in verses 7-9. The stars in their courses had, no doubt, often been his contemplation as he watched his flocks on the hillside at night. The book of Job too had evidently been studied, for verse 8 is closely linked with Job 9:9 and 38:31.

> Ye who turn judgment to wormwood, and leave off righteousness in the earth, Seek him that maketh the seven stars and Orion, and turneth the shadow of death into the morning, and maketh the day dark with night: that calleth for the waters of the sea, and poureth them out upon the face of the earth: The Lord is his name: That strengtheneth the spoiled against the strong, so that the spoiled shall come against the fortress (7-9).

The Hebrews generally understood the seven stars or the Pleiades to refer to the brilliant star-groups that display the majesty and glory of their Creator. The prophet called the wayward of the house of Israel to contemplate Him who created and still guides the heavenly bodies; who causes the sun to rise in its glory, dispelling the darkness; whose hand controls the planetary movements that bring the night again; and who gives rain to the thirsty ground. With *Him* men must deal, whether they want to or not. His eyes had seen all the unholy ways of the people who were called by His name.

Willfully rejecting light, they hated the person who rebuked them, and despised the one who spoke the truth (10). They have many successors. It is very common to find those living carelessly or sinfully, filled with indignation against anyone who faithfully disapproves of their unholy life. Easygoing, people-pleasing preachers and teachers are popular, while faithful, God-fearing leaders are ignored or despised. But those who would stand for God must expect opposition from the unspiritual and worldly-minded.

Knowing that he would be hated for rebuking them, Amos nevertheless proclaims his solemn message without excuse or hesitation. He impressed on their consciences the sins that were about to draw down judgment on their guilty nation. They oppressed the poor, thought only of their own comfort, afflicted the just, took bribes, dealt unjustly with the needy in the place of justice—the gate. They were so overbearing and insolent that it seemed prudent to refrain from exposing their wickedness, so evil were the times (11-13). But God's faithful servant glossed over nothing, used no flattering words. He exposed their hypocrisy and then urged them to "seek good, and not evil," so that they might live and that the Lord of hosts might be with them. If the word was heeded, God could still possibly be gracious to the remnant of Joseph (14-15).

Men like Amos are never popular with the crowd. But it is far better to have God's approval than people's. Like Paul, Amos spoke "not as pleasing men, but God, which trieth our hearts" (1 Thessalonians 2:4). Yet he did not berate or verbally abuse them; he simply recounted their guilt and issued a tender, loving call to repentance.

If this call went unheeded, then weeping would replace their empty songs—which it did very soon. All their joys were overshadowed, and even in the vineyards of gladness the lament of the desolate was heard (Amos 5:16-17).

It is remarkable how low people can fall and yet how religiously and piously they can talk. As wretched as Israel's condition was, there were still some who desired the day of the Lord in the hope of being delivered from their troubles, which were the fruit of their own sin. Amos pronounced a woe on such people. What profit would there be if a man fled from a lion and was met by a bear? Seeking to escape this second danger, he would flee to his house. But as he leaned against the wall, a poisonous snake, concealed in some corner or drapery, would strike him with its venomed fangs. There could be no escape from judgment. The day of the Lord will be the day of unveiling. Therefore, for the wicked it will be a day of darkness and not of light; "even very dark, and no brightness in it" (18-20).

Along with this pretended desire for the day of the Lord was the falseness of the feasts and solemn assemblies. Outwardly, there seemed to have been some pretense to honor Jehovah in the reign of Jeroboam II, but God was actually dishonored by the unholy practices the people indulged in. Therefore He hated the feast days, and would not accept their offerings. He looked for righteousness to roll on as a mighty stream in the land, not for outward forms and ceremonies (21-24). But their present hypocritical course had been characteristic from their beginning. Even in the days of the wilderness they had set up the tabernacle of their false gods beside the sanctuary of Jehovah. They had offered sacrifices and offerings to them throughout those unforgettable forty years. "Therefore will I cause you to go into captivity beyond Damascus, saith the Lord, whose name is The God of hosts" (27).

This is intensely important and worthy of our most serious consideration. The Lord declared that the Assyrian captivity was the result of the Israelite's sinful idolatry "in the wilderness" (25). More than seven hundred years had passed since that first apostasy; but it had never been really judged, so they must be judged for it! How this passage rebukes those who refuse to face the fact that unjudged evil is always at work, leavening the whole lump! Again we see the same lesson that we noted at length in our study of Hosea 7:4-7. Oh, for hearts to bow to the truth presented in Scripture, and thus to be kept from the defilement of unjudged sin!

AMOS 6: At Ease in Zion

The house of Joseph was not alone in provoking the Lord. As noted before, the name *Israel* refers not just to the ten tribes, but also to the whole nation. Therefore this division of Amos's prophecy concludes with a stirring warning to those who are indifferent in Zion, and to those who trusted in the mountain of Samaria (1). In the southern kingdom, the danger threatening their northern kin seemed distant. They took comfort in the fact that Samaria would, as they supposed, withstand a siege long enough to give them plenty of opportunity to prepare if the enemies drew near. So they took their ease, and were not concerned about obeying God's call to repentance, nor did they grieve over the sorrows of their northern brothers.

The phrase "at ease in Zion" speaks to the condition of many professed Christians today, who pay no attention to God's special message for the present and who show no concern for walking in the power of the truth. But if God's people are indifferent to what is important in God's eyes, they should not expect His help when difficulties arise.

In verse 2 we read that Philistine cities, once splendid and magnificent, had been destroyed. The ruins of Calneh, Hamath, and Gath were somber reminders of past glory. How was Israel any better than these kingdoms? They put off the day of judgment, while violence and corruption abounded within their borders. Stretched out on beds of ivory and carved couches, they feasted without fear on the choicest from the flocks and herds. They sang and played their musical instruments, drank wine, and delighted in expensive lotions. But God finished His indictment by declaring, "They are not grieved for the affliction of Joseph" (verses 2-6).

Does this not speak to every saint of God today? Are we not in grave danger of living to please ourselves, rejoicing in our possessions, and forgetting the demise of Joseph—that is, forgetting the sad state of the church, indifferent to the discord made by self-will that dishonors the Lord, the church's glorified Head? Surely, true love of God will result in the soul's disturbance over the present state of that which is so precious in His sight. Such concern will lead to searching the Scriptures and evaluating everything in their light. Those who grieve "for the affliction of Joseph" will seek to walk in "the old paths" in which the people of God have walked, even if one has to walk alone (Jeremiah 6:16). Moreover, there will need to be a clear display of that "love to all the saints" which should characterize everyone who enters in any degree into the truth that "there is one body, and one Spirit" (Ephesians 4:4).

Because of this lack of concern for the distress of Joseph, the Lord could not work on their behalf. Rather He would "abhor the excellency of Jacob" and deliver even the city of David to the Gentile oppressor (Amos 6:7-8).

When the destruction would finally come, the terror of Jehovah's wrath would close every mouth; even as they buried the dead, the name of the Lord said in prayer would be unsuited to their defiled lips (9-10). It is sad indeed to be under God's rod of judgment, and still be utterly unable to approach the One who appointed it. This is the hardening power of the deceitfulness of sin!

Verses 11-14 look toward the Babylonian captivity, which followed the Assyrian invasion of the north more than a century later. When the Babylonians came in like a torrent, flooding the land, it was by direct command of the Lord. They were *His* rod, because of Judah's having turned "judgment into gall, and the fruit of righteousness into [poisonous] hemlock." The holy One would have to take sides against His own, because they turned His truth into a lie and walked in uncleanness. So is it still. "The righteous Lord loveth righteousness" (Psalm 11:7) and will not join His name with what is contrary to it.

With this message, the second division of the prophecy of Amos comes to a close.

AMOS 7: Teaching by Symbols

The last section of the book of Amos contains a series of five visions, symbolically proclaiming divine judgment. In Amos 7:1-9 three of these visions are described, while the balance of the chapter gives a most interesting and instructive bit of autobiography.

In the first vision, the prophet was shown a plague of locusts (not merely grasshoppers) "in the beginning of the shooting up of the latter growth...after the king's mowings." In Palestine two crops a year were easily harvested. Under favorable conditions, "the latter growth after the king's mowings," would have referred to the second crop, which would be depended on to supply most of the food for the winter. But the prophet saw devouring locusts destroying every tender shoot, leading to the heartfelt prayer on the part of Amos, "O Lord God, forgive, I beseech thee: by whom shall Jacob arise? for he is small." The Lord responded to his intercession, and replied, "It shall not be."

Undoubtedly, the locusts symbolized a desolating scourge—like an army sweeping away everything before it, leaving no remnant. As in Moses' day, the Lord's anger was provoked, and He would have destroyed the nation; but the intercession of the mediator intervened. God loves to be implored. He delights in answering the cry of those who bear His needy people on their heart.

In the second vision (verses 4-6), Amos saw a devouring fire of such intensity that it licked up in its fury the waters of the great deep "and did eat up a part." Again this represents threatened judgment of the fiercest character, yet it is not complete destruction. Once more the cry came from the heart of the man of God, "O Lord God, cease, I beseech thee: by whom shall Jacob arise? for he is small." And again, in grace, God answered, "This also shall not be, saith the Lord God."

It was the horror of overwhelming wrath without discrimination, falling on all alike, that appalled the prophet. Therefore, in the next vision he was assured that each person would be dealt with according to his own iniquity.

The Lord stood on a wall, to test its correctness by the plumb line in His hand and cried, "Amos, what seest thou?" The answer was given, "A plumbline." The Lord replied,

> Behold, I will set a plumbline in the midst of my people Israel: I will not again pass by them any more: And the high places of Isaac shall be desolate, and the sanctuaries of Israel shall be laid waste; and I will rise against the house of Jeroboam with the sword (8-9).

This was an image easily understood. If a wall is not perpendicular, it is clear immediately, to the annoyance of the builder. God's unerring Word is such a plumb line. It tests every soul unmistakably, revealing every departure from it and calling down judgment on the violator of it. Throughout the whole land of Israel, that Word was despised—the people took their own ways and did not seek the Lord's counsel. No one then had any right to complain when they were judged according to their ways. Every high place in the land was a silent testimony to the disobedience of the nation. Desolation would fall on them all in the day when the sword would be drawn against the house of Jeroboam (referring to Jeroboam II, the monarch in whose reign Amos uttered his prophecies).

When Amaziah, the apostate priest of the high place at Bethel, heard these words, he angrily denounced Amos as a traitor to the king. As head of the idolatrous ritualistic system, established and supported by Israel's wayward kings, he would try to get the grim preacher of truth out of the way, because his trade would be endangered by Amos's words. So he sent a message to Jeroboam:

> Amos hath conspired against thee in the midst of the house of Israel: the land is not able to bear all his words. For thus Amos saith, Jeroboam shall die by the sword, and Israel shall surely be led away captive out of their own land (10-11).

Amos had declared unpalatable truth indeed. But Amaziah seemed to have reported Amos's words incorrectly, either intentionally or his own guilty conscience led him to misunderstand them. We have no record of Amos declaring that Jeroboam would die by the sword (which was not the case, see 2 Kings 14:23-29). Amos said that the sword would be drawn against his *house*; which was fulfilled in the violent death of his son Zechariah (see 2 Kings 15:10).

We read of no reply to Amaziah's charges on the part of the king. That energetic monarch may have considered the shepherd-prophet and his predictions as beneath his attention, or he may have feared to touch one who was evidently sent of God. So the enraged prelate was left to deal with the intrusive preacher himself. He told Amos that he is trespassing in a parish that belonged to someone else! "O thou seer," he said, "go, flee thee away into the land of Judah, and there eat bread, and prophesy there: But prophesy not again any more at Bethel: for it is the king's [sanctuary], and it is the king's court [or palace]" (12-13).

Many man-made priests and preachers echo Amaziah, telling Spirit-sent men of God that they must not fish in the waters *they* claim nor touch any of *their* flock. Looking on God's people as their own possession, they cannot endure the free servant who comes with the plain word of the Lord, not seeking financial or other gain but simply declaring the whole counsel of God.

Being a hireling himself, Amaziah insinuated that Amos was the same when he urged him to go to Judah and "there eat bread." He could not conceive of someone proclaiming God's word with no thought of personal profit. His own greedy heart considered the office of high priest as a good way to make a living, and he took it for granted that Amos was as much a professional man as he was.

Then he commandeered the right to be the supreme minister and spiritual adviser of the king and people at Bethel. Today we would call Bethel a cathedral city, and Amaziah was its ecclesiastical head. Away with this unlicensed interloper from the south!

Modestly and faithfully, Amos answered the proud and indignant priest, "I was no prophet, neither was I a prophet's son." He was neither a professional seer nor did he obtain his appointment through human hands or descent. "But I was an herdman, and a gatherer of sycomore fruit [the wild fig of Palestine]: And the Lord took me as I followed the flock, and the Lord said unto me, Go, prophesy unto my people Israel" (14-15). Here were credentials that were as inexplicable to Amaziah as they have been to thousands of others since. Amos entered his ministry by the direct call of God. Like the New Testament apostle, his calling came "not of men, neither by man" (Galatians 1:1), but by divine appointment. In neither Testament do we ever read of one man empowering another to speak the word of the Lord. An Elijah may, at the command of God, anoint an Elisha, or a Paul may choose a Silas; but God alone gives the gift and accredits the servant.

But Amaziah was to hear more. As he impiously attempted to control divinely-given ministry, he would next hear his own doom pronounced.

> Now therefore hear thou the word of the Lord: Thou sayest, Prophesy not against Israel, and drop not thy word against the house of Isaac. Therefore thus saith the Lord; Thy wife shall be a harlot in the city, and thy sons and thy daughters shall fall by the sword, and thy land shall be divided by line; and thou shalt die in a polluted land: and Israel shall surely go into captivity forth of his land (16-17).

These are clear words, and though we have no further record, we cannot doubt that they were fulfilled to the letter. We read of no reply on Amaziah's part. His conscience was on the prophet's side; and that may have sealed his lips. How every word must have come back to him when, stripped of all his honors, he lifted his tear-dimmed eyes heavenward in the Assyrians' land!

AMOS 8: A Famine of the Word

Amos 8:1-3 contains the fourth vision and its interpretation. Notice that, with the exception of the final object lesson, all would be familiar pictures to someone acquainted with agricultural life. Locusts are the dreaded plague of the Eastern farmer. Often too Amos may have helped combat a brush or forest fire that threatened to destroy crops and herds. The use of the plumb line would be quite familiar to him, as stone walls were used almost exclusively both in dwellings and other enclosures. And the subject of this fourth vision would be as common as the rest.

The Lord showed him a basket of summer fruit, that is, overripe fruit which could no longer be preserved. In reply to God's question, "Amos, what seest thou?" the prophet answered, "A basket of summer fruit." Then God explained the simple symbol. Israel had become like rotting fruit. The end was near—the time of being cast away. No longer would grace be extended to those who had rejected it so repeatedly. The temple songs would change to woeful cries of anguish and despair, while the dead bodies of those who hated God's message would fill the cities and be discarded in silence.

Accompanying this declaration that the end had come is a somber summation of the sins of the people. They swallowed up the needy in their covetousness, making the poor of the land languish (4). This is reminiscent of James 5:1-6, where we read, "Ye have heaped treasure together in [not *for*] the last days." This same covetous spirit made the appointed feasts and the sabbaths a burden. Outwardly the people observed them, but inwardly they longed for the close of the day so they could buy and sell and make money (Amos 8:5-6). For this the Lord swore, "Surely I will never forget any of their works." All were under His holy eye. All were noted in His book. All would be confronted at His judgment seat!

If the eye of an unsaved sinner rests on this page, let me impress on you the seriousness of this statement. You may forget your sins, but God has declared that He will always remember them. And if He remembers, you must be banished from His presence forever. But everyone who now confesses his guilt, trusting the One who died to save, God says to them, "Their sins and iniquities will I remember no more" (Jeremiah 31:34; Hebrews 10:17). Are your sins remembered or forgotten, dear reader?

For Israel's sins the land had to tremble, and its people would be swept away as by the overflowing Nile. The sun would go down at noon, and the earth would be darkened during the day. This is a poetic image for utter desolation; the result of their grasping selfishness, their heartless misconduct toward the poor, and God's displeasure with their ways. Their mourning would be bitter in that day, when repentance would come too late to avert the threatened calamity, which would be like mourning for an only son, and the end be a day of woe (Amos 8:8-10).

But there would be more: a famine was to come upon the very ones who would "swallow up the needy," and buy the poor "for a pair of shoes." It would not be a famine of bread or a thirst for water, but of hearing the words of the Lord, which they had rejected. From sea to sea, as a people forsaken, they would wander, seeking everywhere for the once-despised word of the Lord. But it would be too late; they "shall not find it" (11-12).

Undoubtedly, this prophecy was partially fulfilled when Israel was carried off to Assyria. But a larger fulfillment awaits them in the days of the antichrist. And Israel and Judah will not pass through that famine alone. Guiltier Christendom, so richly blessed with the Holy Scriptures, will have utterly turned from the truth to fables. The day will come when the grieved Spirit of God will have left the earth; and when the very Scriptures of truth will be taken from those who have esteemed them so lightly.

Then "shall the fair virgins and young men faint for thirst," because the water of life, which they refused, shall be withdrawn. They will be left to die in despair and be given up to strong delusions, so that they might believe a lie. All who disobeyed the truth and took pleasure in unrighteousness will be judged. The famine will result, not in their turning to God, but in turning even more toward their idols, only to find, as in Elijah's day, that no one is there to hear or care. So will they fall, never to rise again (13-14).

AMOS 9: Not a Grain Lost

This final chapter divides into two parts. Verses 1-10 give the last of the five visions and Jehovah's recital of the afflictions awaiting Israel in their exile. But He assures them that not a grain of His wheat would be lost. Then, in verses 11-15, as is customary with the prophets, Amos looked ahead to Israel's restoration to glory and blessing in the last days. Then their tribulations will be forever past, and the nation will be saved in the recovered remnant.

This time the vision concerns the house of God. The Lord was seen standing on or by the altar. He commanded that the capitals of its columns be struck so that the posts would shake. The fleeing priests and people were devoted to a destruction from which there could be no escape (1). He declared that though they dig into *sheol,* the world of spirits, or attempt to climb to the heavens, His hand would find them. They might hide themselves on the top of lofty Carmel or in the depths of the sea, but they would not escape the judgment their sins deserved. Even when they were in captivity among their enemies, God would send a sword after them and set His eyes on them for evil and not for good (2-4).

This was the vision. Amos used it as a text in the following verses. He described the power of the God they had scorned, and called on nature as a witness to His greatness and wisdom. At His touch the land melts and the people in it mourn. He spreads the clouds over the heavens and pours the rain upon the earth. Jehovah is His name (5-6). Who, then, could oppose such a God, or who could expect to prosper if they despised Him? Israel's special privileges would not help now. They were no more deserving than anyone else. They were in no way superior to the Ethiopians. The same One who brought Israel out of the land of Egypt had brought the Philistines from Caphtor, and the Syrians from Kir. In His eyes, Israel was now only a sinful kingdom, even worse than their neighbors. So He would obliterate them from off the face of the earth.

Nevertheless He remembered His promise to the fathers, and His word concerning the coming Seed; so He spared a remnant. He "will not utterly destroy the house of Jacob" (7-8). He will sift them among all nations like wheat is sifted in a sieve, but the smallest grain would not fall to the ground. Only the sinners of His people would die by the sword, those who said, "The evil shall not overtake nor prevent us" (9-10). The Lord Jesus used this same image when He addressed the self-confident Peter. He would go into Satan's sieve, not for destruction, but so the chaff could be separated from the wheat (see Luke 22:31).

This too will be the result of Israel's sifting among the nations. "They are not all Israel, who are of Israel," said the apostle Paul (Romans 9:6). That is, not everyone who is descended from Jacob is a child of faith. Only those who bow to the Word of the Lord and believe His testimony concerning Christ are the Israel of God. These will be the wheat that will be preserved for the coming kingdom.

In that day, David's tabernacle, long fallen, will be raised again. Then restored Israel will possess the land of Edom, and all the saved nations will acknowledge their rule (Amos 9:11-12). Notice that this Scripture was quoted by James in Acts 15 to justify the call of the Gentiles, though there is probably more in his use of it than that. It harmonizes perfectly with the thought of grace going out to the nations. It also shows that, after God's present work of gathering a people for Himself from among the Gentiles is completed, the Lord will turn His hand once more to Israel. He will raise up the tabernacle of David, fulfilling all the promises made through the prophets (Acts 15:16-17).

In that glorious restoration period, Palestine will once more be cultivated and made to blossom as the rose. The remnant of Israel will be settled in their own inheritance. The ruined cities will be rebuilt and inhabited. Vineyards and gardens will flourish, and God Himself will plant His chosen people in the land given to their fathers and confirmed by His oath. "And they shall no more be pulled up out of their land" (Amos 9:15); they will dwell there under the beneficent rule of the Lord Jesus Christ. The words "saith the Lord thy God" abruptly close the book of Amos. God has spoken, and He will perform His word for His own name's sake.

OBADIAH

A PROFILE
OBADIAH
THE PROPHET OF EDOM'S DOOM

BY JOHN PHILLIPS

The prophecy of Obadiah is a classic warning against anti-Semitism. The nation that curses and persecutes the Jew will inevitably reap what it sows. The nation that harbors and protects the Jew will surely enjoy the blessing of God (Genesis 12:2-3).

The Date of Obadiah

There is wide disagreement as to the date of Obadiah. Some would place him as the earliest of the prophets, whereas others place him in the days of Jeremiah. Although there are a number of people in the Old Testament with the name of Obadiah, none of them can be positively identified as the prophet of that name. The dating of Obadiah hinges on the interpretation of verses 11-14. It is thought by some that the reference here is to events in the days of Jehoram (2 Chronicles 21:16-17), whereas others see in the reference events in the days of Ahaz (2 Chronicles 28:17). Others link the passage with Jeremiah 49:14-16 and make the two prophets contemporaries. It is not necessary to assume that either prophet quoted the other, although there is a close similarity between these two passages. Jude and 2 Peter give us an example of God inspiring two men with a like message.

The Structure of Obadiah

This short prophecy is in two parts, one part dealing with Edom and the other with Israel. This is instructive when we remember that Jacob and Esau, from whom these two nations sprang, were twins. There was little love lost between the twin brothers from the very first, and with the passing of time the gap between their descendants widened into bitter national hostility.

I. The Doom of Edom Predicted (1-16)
    A. The Doom Declared (1-2)
        1. The Ambassador's Mission (1)
        2. The Ambassador's Message (2)
    B. The Doom Described (3-9)
        1. Edom's Territory Subdued (3-4)
        2. Edom's Treasures Stolen (5-6)
        3. Edom's Treaties Subverted (7)
        4. Edom's Troops Slaughtered (8-9)
    C. The Doom Deserved (10-14)
        Edom had:
        1. Encouraged Judah's Foes (10-11)
        2. Enjoyed Judah's Fall (12-13)
        3. Enslaved Judah's Fugitives (14)
    D. The Doom Dawns (15-16)
        1. The Fixed "Day of the Lord" (15a)
        2. The Fearful "Day of the Lord" (15b-16)
II. The Deliverance of Israel Predicted (17-21)
    A. The Character of It (17a)
    B. The Completeness of It (17b-20)
    C. The Climax of It (21)

The Fierce Hatred of the Edomites

When the children of Israel were on their way to Canaan after their exodus from Egypt, the Edomites refused them passage through their territory. In later years the Edomites were thrashed again and again by kings of Judah but were never completely subdued. When at last Nebuchadnezzar sacked Jerusalem, the joy of the Edomites knew no bounds, and they did all they could to befriend and assist the Babylonians. As the wall of Jerusalem was assaulted, the Edomites screamed with delight, "Rase it, rase it, even to the foundation" (Psalm 137:7). Their exultation was brief, however, for within four years Edom itself was invaded by Nebuchadnezzar and completely overthrown. That event was clearly foreseen by Obadiah (assuming he was a contemporary of Jeremiah) and stated in a most emphatic way. Long centuries afterward we find Edomite hostility to the things and people of God still in evidence, for Herod the Great, who massacred the babes of Bethlehem in his efforts to slay the infant Christ, was an Idumean and a descendant of the Edomites.

The False Security of the Israelites

The Edomites dwelt in mount Seir, a mountainous region reaching from south of the Dead Sea to the Gulf of Akabah. (The territory is now included in the Hashemite Kingdom of Jordan.) Bozra was its ancient capital. In Obadiah's day the capital was Sela (Petra), the rock city which, although desolate now, still remains one of the wonders of the world. The Edomites had good grounds for thinking their city impregnable. They failed, however, to reckon on God.

The Day of the Lord

Edomite territory comes back into focus in the last days, though as far as the Edomites or Idumeans are concerned as a race or nationality, the last remnants were wiped out in A.D. 70 helping to defend Jerusalem against the Romans. No one today can trace his ancestry back to the Edomites. Thus it will be the residents in the old Edomite territory whom Christ will judge (Isaiah 63:1-6). It appears that in a coming day the nation occupying Edomite territory will assist the armies of antichrist against the Jews, just as the Edomites once assisted Nebuchadnezzar. The ultimate triumph, however, is for Israel.

CHAPTER FOUR

THE PROPHECY OF OBADIAH

In only one chapter, God has embodied that part of the prophet Obadiah's ministry which would best admonish and edify us. Brief as it is, its twenty-one verses are brimming with needed instruction, and each saint of the Lord would be wise to take it to heart.

Who Obadiah was, where he was born, of what tribe and family in Israel, his occupation, and the exact time in which he lived—all these are matters God has not been pleased to reveal. There was an Obadiah in the court of King Ahab, who cared for the persecuted prophets of the Lord (see 1 Kings 18:1-4), but he is most likely not the writer of this little book now before us. Other Obadiahs are briefly mentioned in 1 and 2 Chronicles; but whether any of them is identical with this prophet, we have no means of determining—nor is it at all important that we should know. It is the message, not the bearer of it, with which God wants to engage us.

The Doom of Edom and the Deliverance of Jacob

The first sixteen verses are concerned with the sin and doom of Edom. The last five verses set forth the deliverance coming to the house of Jacob when the house of Esau will have fallen to rise no more.

Many important lessons spring from the history of the two sons of Isaac and their respective houses. Before either child was born, God chose Jacob, saying, "The elder shall serve the younger" (Genesis 25:23). This was electing grace, and wondrous grace, surely! For who would be more unworthy than cowardly Jacob, and who, from a worldly standpoint, would be more admired than the apparently brave and magnanimous Esau? But God *chose* Jacob, making clear His purpose of grace.

Let the reader see clearly what is being shown here. God was not selecting Jacob for Heaven and condemning Esau to Hell. Theologians have so imagined, but Scripture does not speak this way. God chose Jacob to inherit the blessing of Abraham and to be the conservator of the promise. In so doing, He made Esau subject to his brother. This is the fulfillment of a principle often noticed in the book of Genesis—the setting aside of the elder and the giving of the birthright to the younger. Similarly God sets aside the first man to make the Second Man first: For "that was not first which is spiritual, but that which is natural; and afterward that which is spiritual. The first man is of the earth, earthy: the second man is the Lord from heaven" (1 Corinthians 15:46-47). This mystery is demonstrated in the cases of Cain and Abel, Ishmael and Isaac, Esau and Jacob, Reuben and Joseph, Manasseh and Ephraim.

Consistent with this principle, Esau and the race that bears his name are represented in Scripture as types of the flesh; Jacob, as the type of the new man learning to overcome by discipline. When in the last book of the Old Testament God summed up, as it were, concerning the two families, He declared, "I loved Jacob, And I hated Esau" (Malachi 1:2-3).

In reading the prophecy of Obadiah, we may trace a typological as well as a natural interpretation. What is said of Edom coalesces with the condemnation and final doom of the flesh—that hateful thing which ever flaunts itself, even in the breast of the believer, against all that is of God. It shall at last be utterly destroyed and become as though it had never existed. The future triumph of the house of Jacob, in the day of the glory of the kingdom, signifies the final blessing when the flesh is overcome forever and the person of God's design alone remains.

From the Lord a report had come concerning Edom, resulting in an ambassador being sent among the nations to raise up their armies against the mount of Esau. Though once all-powerful, Edom was to be made small among them and greatly despised.

Edom had always been the enemy of Israel, even as the flesh

wars continually against the Spirit. When calamity came on the house of Jacob, Edom had rejoiced. But now on him unsparing judgment was to fall. This judgment, no doubt, will go on to the time of the end, for it is just before God's kingdom is established that Edom's power is to be utterly broken. There will be a people of his lineage dwelling in Idumea in the day of the last great coalition against Israel, but they will be overthrown. And when the rest of the world is brought into blessing under Messiah's rule, Edom's descendants will be blotted out from under heaven.

As with the flesh, so with Edom—his pride was insufferable. Dwelling in his Idumean heights and rocky fortresses, he considered himself invulnerable against all attack. But Jehovah declared, "The pride of thine heart hath deceived thee . . . Though thou exalt thyself as the eagle, and though thou set thy nest among the stars, thence will I bring thee down" (Obadiah 3-4). No power can help when the Lord's set time for His destruction has come. Edom had fallen into the condemnation of the devil; exalting himself and seeking his own glory. On the part of the creature this is rebellion against the Creator, and cannot go unpunished.

Nor would Edom's desolation come as though thieves had broken in to steal, for thieves, when they have enough would leave something behind. In the day that Esau's hidden things would be searched out, however, there would be no gleanings left. His destruction would be complete (5-6). Deceived by their own allies and betrayed by those in whom they had trusted, the wise would be destroyed out of the mount of Esau, and the mighty men of Teman would be dismayed. None would be spared, but every one cut off by slaughter (7-9).

His violence against his brother, Jacob, had well merited such stern dealing. When Israel came out of Egypt, no family ties served to dispose the king of Edom's heart to be kind to the Canaan-bound pilgrims. Rather they were forced to circumvent his land, adding much to the weariness of their journey (Numbers 20:14-21). From that day on, the seed of Esau had continually been the inveterate enemies of Jehovah's favored people.

When the hour of Jacob's calamity struck, Edom stood complacently to one side, delighting in the disgrace to which his brother was subjected. The desolation of Jerusalem caused him not grief but joy. He joined with the Babylonians in casting lots for a division of the spoil (10-11). All this Jehovah's eye had seen, and it was an offense to Him. It was the very opposite of that love which rejoices not in iniquity, but rejoices with the truth. God said:

> Thou shouldest not have looked on the day of thy brother in the day that he became a stranger; neither shouldest thou have rejoiced over the children of Judah in the day of their destruction; neither shouldest thou have spoken proudly in the day of distress. Thou shouldest not have entered into the gate of my people in the day of their calamity; yea, thou shouldest not have looked on their affliction in the day of their calamity, nor have laid hands on their substance in the day of their calamity; Neither shouldest thou have stood in the crossway, to cut off those of his that did escape; neither shouldest thou have delivered up those of his that did remain in the day of distress (12-14).

Because of having acted so contrary to every brotherly instinct, Edom would reap as he had sown. Judgment would soon overtake him, until of Edom it could be said, "They shall be as though they had not been" (15-16). When other nations, such as Egypt, Assyria, and even Sodom and Gomorrah, are restored and brought into blessing in the millennial kingdom, Edom shall have fallen to rise no more.

What a fitting picture this gives us of the carnal mind and its final destruction! Ever the enemy of the new life imparted to the children of God (because it is not subject to His law, since in its very nature it cannot be), rejoicing in irreverence and lifting up its haughty head in defiance of all that is holy, how much sorrow and secret anguish has the carnal mind cost every conscientious saint! But soon it will be cast down to rise no more; soon the bodies of our humiliation will be made like the body of Christ's glory. And then the flesh and sin will have vanished forevermore.

There are those who idly dream of a present destruction of the carnal mind—a shortcut to Canaan across the land of Edom—but it is all a delusion. Esau's doom will come when Christ appears to reign; likewise, the end of the flesh in the believer will come at the redemption of our bodies when we are made like Him.

Coinciding with the fall of Edom will be the salvation of Israel, when "upon mount Zion shall be deliverance, and there shall be holiness" (or, "it shall be holy"). Then Jacob will come into his rightful inheritance, and devour the house of Esau as fire devours the stubble until "there shall not be any remaining of the house of Esau; for the Lord hath spoken it" (17-18). In that day the lands of all their former enemies, who had been for so long like thorns in their sides, will become Israel's possession, "and the kingdom shall be the Lord's" (19-21).

So may the believer look on with joyful confidence to the hour when the flesh and all that now disturbs and distresses us shall be overthrown forever, and Christ alone will be exalted. "Even so, come, Lord Jesus."

JONAH

A PROFILE

JONAH

THE UNWILLING PROPHET

BY JOHN PHILLIPS

The Lord Jesus believed that Jonah (784-772 B.C.) was a literal person and that Jonah's experience in the belly of the great fish was authentic history, for Jesus referred to the incident as an illustration of His own death, burial, and resurrection (Matthew 12:40). As Jonah was a sign to the Ninevites, so was the Son of man a sign to His generation (Luke 11:30). The Lord referred to Jonah in the same context as the queen of Sheba and Solomon, thus placing him on the same level of validity.

Time of Jonah's Prophecy

Jonah lived in the Northern Kingdom of Israel and prophesied of the prosperity Israel enjoyed in the days of Jeroboam II (2 Kings 14:25). He must have lived, therefore, about that time or perhaps a little earlier. His name means "dove," and certainly his ministry to Nineveh was Spirit-anointed, resulting in one of the greatest religious revivals in history. His home was at Gath-hepher, not far from Nazareth, the well-known Galilean town where the Lord Jesus in later years spent the greater part of His life. Jonah is the only prophet to whom the Lord directly likened Himself.

Jonah's prophecy follows the chapter divisions of the Bible.

I. Jonah's Disobedience (1)
II. Jonah's Distress (2)
III. Jonah's Discovery (3)
IV. Jonah's Displeasure (4)

History of Jonah's Life

Jonah was a Hebrew prophet commissioned to preach to a Gentile audience in Nineveh, one of the most important cities of Assyria. Probably Jonah knew well enough that Assyria would one day be used of God to punish the sins of his own people, so nothing would have pleased him more, as an ardent patriot, than the overthrow of Nineveh. The news "Yet forty days, and Nineveh shall be overthrown" (3:4), must have sounded like music to his ears. Far from wanting to see Nineveh repent and escape the wrath of God, he longed to see the sentence executed (4:2). It seems that Jonah deliberately fled to Tarshish so that the forty-day hourglass of divine patience would run out and wrath would overflow.

Jonah's experiences in the fish's belly were so terrible that he called that awful prison house in which his disobedience landed him "the belly of hell" (2:2). Like the Lord Jesus on the cross, Jonah's thoughts in his hours of anguish turned to the Psalms. He quoted from many of them in his passionate outburst of prayer (Psalm 42:7; 31:22; 69:1; 3:8).

Jonah discovered that his efforts to thwart the divine will were futile, and all his agonizing experiences in vain. Delivered from the sea monster, he found himself again facing the mandate of God, for the "forty days" would begin from the hour his feet trod the streets of Nineveh, not before.

His eight word message rang like the knell of doom through Nineveh, bringing immediate fruit as the city repented in sackcloth and ashes, much to Jonah's disgust. In grace, God reasoned with His petulant prophet, seeking to show him the sinfulness of his resentment. That the Lord's remonstrance was successful is seen in the fact that Jonah wrote the book which bears his name, keeping back nothing of his own sorry part in the narrative. The book of Jonah is a great Old Testament revelation of the grace of God, which reaches to even "lost sinners of the Gentiles."

CHAPTER FIVE

THE HISTORY OF JONAH

Among the Minor Prophets, Jonah is the only one which, in the ordinary sense of the word, does not contain any prophecy at all—except his announcement of the threatened destruction of Nineveh within forty days, which was not fulfilled. Yet the book is distinctly prophetic, and Jonah is twice referred to by our Lord Jesus Christ as a prophet. No spiritually-minded person can read the book of Jonah without discerning the fact that Jonah's whole history, or at least that part of it here recorded for our instruction, is in itself a prophecy. It sets forth the course of Israel, of whom Jonah was a type or picture, and likewise foreshadows the wondrous mystery of the Lord's death and resurrection.

However, this truly sublime and heart-searching book has often been the butt of the worldly-wise rationalist's ridicule and the puzzle of the unspiritual religionist, both of whom have never learned the importance of bowing to the authority of the Word of God. There was a time when it was fashionable for men of science, themselves unconverted, to sneer at "Jonah's whale," not believing that a whale could devour a man because of the creature's anatomical structure. But even if the Bible had declared the "prepared" fish to be a whale—which rightly read, it does not—still, the sperm whale that in early ages frequented the Mediterranean could have fully met the requirements of the case. Thus once more, rationalism is shown to be *irrational*, and the Scriptures are confirmed in every way to be trustworthy.

No thoughtful and conscientious child of God could think of questioning the inspiration of a book upon which the Lord Jesus Himself has set His seal. Indeed, it is significant that the authenticity of

Deuteronomy, the last part of Isaiah, and the books of Daniel and Jonah have often been disputed by critics. Yet these four portions of the Word of God have been validated in a most remarkable way by the One who could not lie. He who knew all things quoted Deuteronomy as the very word of God when meeting Satan in the wilderness. When He read from the scroll in the synagogue of Nazareth, He found in the words of Isaiah the message of the Holy Ghost. In like manner He warned of the "abomination of desolation" spoken of "by Daniel the *prophet,*" and declared unhesitatingly that Jonah was a sign to the Ninevites after having been in the belly of the great fish. How serious is the blasphemy of those who, in the face of all this, sit in judgment on these portions of the God-breathed Scriptures and profess to be wiser than the Omniscient Himself!

Just when Jonah lived we have no means of knowing for certain. We learn that in the reign of Jeroboam II of Israel, a prophecy of Jonah's was fulfilled. But whether it was made during Jeroboam's lifetime or not, we are not informed. We are simply told that "he restored the coast of Israel from the entering of Hamath unto the sea of the plain, according to the word of the Lord God of Israel, which he spake by the hand of his servant Jonah, the son of Amittai, the prophet, which was of Gath-hepher" (2 Kings 14:25). Though this would seem to indicate that Jonah lived and prophesied at that time, it does not necessarily prove it. He might have uttered his prophecy at an earlier date, only to be fulfilled later. Either way, since God has not been pleased to state definitely the time of his birth and death, we can leave it as a matter of small significance.

The fact, however, that he was born in Gath-hepher *is* important, because it refutes the self-confident words of the Jewish scholars, "Search and look, for out of Galilee ariseth no prophet" (John 7:52). Gath-hepher was in Galilee. This is only one example of how easy it is to win a dispute by mere assumption, when contending with those ignorant of Scripture. Truly, it is essential to "prove all things," and hold fast only to what is good and proven in God's Word.

Without question the great theme of this book is divine sovereignty. The frequently repeated expressions, "The Lord prepared" and "God prepared," show this clearly. Throughout the book of Jonah we will see that however man may plan, and whatever he may attempt, it is God who is over all and working all things in such a way as to bring glory to His own name.

With these few introductory thoughts, we turn directly to the record itself.

JONAH 1: The Unwelcome Message

"Now the word of the Lord came unto Jonah the son of Amittai, saying, Arise, go to Nineveh, that great city, and cry against it; for their wickedness is come up before me" (1-2). This was a most unexpected and unwelcome mission for an Israelite to be sent on. Like the nation for whom he stood, Jonah was called to be the bearer of a message from God to the Gentiles. Israel had been separated from the nations—not to dwell in a cold, formal exclusiveness, in utter indifference to the fate of the people around them. Instead Israel was to be a light in a dark world, making known the mind of God and revealing His character to those who were sitting in the shadow of death. In Jonah's history we see Israel's failure in this respect, the disasters they encountered because of that failure, and the foreshadowing of the day when, restored and brought again into blessing, they will once more be entrusted with a commission from the Most High. We need not doubt that Jonah was really restored in soul at the end of his experience whatever the unhappy state portrayed at the conclusion of his book. Why? Because evidently he himself narrated his account for the benefit of our learning; and it is related in the manner of a recovered and chastened man. He simply let us know something of his own pride and self-will and the way the Lord humbled him and brought him in touch with Himself once more.

It seems clear enough that pride and bigotry were at the bottom of all his stubbornness and disobedience. He knew that God was longsuffering and delighted in mercy. Jonah told us that in the end. He therefore feared for his prophetic reputation; and his thoughts were so far from those of the Lord that he could not endure grace being shown to a Gentile power. He knew that Jehovah would have spared Sodom and Gomorrah had there been found in them only ten righteous people. If Jehovah would have done that then, how could Jonah depend on God now to pour out His wrath on Nineveh if its wicked inhabitants bowed to the warning and fell before God in repentance?

What a picture we have of the deceitfulness of the human heart—even in a saint of God! And how often do we need to reproach ourselves for allowing the same evil inclinations to act in us! How much easier it is to insist on the judgment of a brother, for instance, if he has hurt or injured *me*, than if he has hurt others, or sinned against God only! My own reputation must be maintained at all cost, and I must be cleared of all blame, whatever it may mean to others! Have we not seen whole congregations of God's people thrown into sorrow and confusion in order that one self-willed person might have his way and be justified in it? This same miserable pride of heart is strikingly portrayed for our thoughtful consideration in the book of Jonah.

Rather than go to these Gentiles, and risk his reputation,

> Jonah rose up to flee unto Tarshish from the presence of the Lord, and went down to Joppa; and he found a ship going to Tarshish: so he paid the fare thereof, and went down into it, to go with them unto Tarshish from the presence of the Lord (3).

To leave the path of obedience is invariably to leave the presence of the Lord, at least as far as the experience of one's own soul is concerned. In reality, it was impossible for Jonah to go where the eye of God was not on him. In his own consciousness of communion and enjoyment, however, the moment Jonah made up his mind to act in disobedience, he lost the sense of the Lord's presence in his soul.

As he fled, notice what a lot of *going down* there was! He went *down* to Joppa. He went *down* into the ship. He went *down* into the sides of the ship. And in the next chapter he confessed, "I went *down* to the bottoms of the mountains" (2:6)—*down* until he could go no deeper, unless he had sunk into the pit of woe. But that could not be; for whatever his failure, he was still a child of God and the Lord was about to restore him in a marvelous manner.

Oh, that we all might lay this to heart! The path of the one who acts in self-will is always a downward one, no matter what the profession may be. One may boast of acting for God and talk of having His approval. But if self is served instead of Christ, the feet will soon slide, and the steps will be down, down, down—until humbled and repentant, the soul turns back to God, and is ready to confess the wrong of its behavior.

From the next few verses we learn that God loved His poor, failing servant too well to permit him to prosper as he took his foolish and sinful course. "The Lord sent out a great wind into the sea, and there was a mighty tempest in the sea, so that the ship was like to be broken" (4). God had begun to act. Let man try as he will, he will have to learn that all his power is as nothing when he contends with the Almighty.

All on the ship were at once alarmed—all except the miserable man for whose sin the storm had come. He was sound asleep, having gone down into the side of the ship, unaware of the anxiety and distress he had brought on so many others who had no share in his evil way. What a picture of a person who has taken the first wrong step and, though discipline has begun, is sleeping on in self-complacency, utterly unconscious of the fact that the hand of the Lord has been stretched out against him! This shows how the deceitfulness of sin can harden us, as the apostle warned (see Hebrews 3:13).

Awakened at last by the shipmaster, who had exhausted every pagan device known to him to appease the imagined wrath of his gods, Jonah was put to shame before them all. The earnest question, "What meanest thou, O sleeper?" followed by the rousing command, "Arise, call upon thy God, if so be that God will think upon us that we perish not," made him realize the terrible circumstances they were in. But it still did not open his lips in confession. So the sailors cast lots, and God condescended to use this means to point out the guilty man. "The lot is cast into the lap; but the whole disposing thereof is of the Lord" (Proverbs 16:33).

"The lot fell upon Jonah." Even then it was only in reply to the questions of the frightened men that "he said unto them, I am an Hebrew; and I fear the Lord, the God of heaven, which hath made the sea and the dry land." Though his confession seemed calm, he knew that his case was desperate. Undoubtedly, his spirit was agitated, but there is no evidence as yet that his conscience was disturbed. Like a man who has risked all on a false expectation and now finds that he must lose, Jonah determined to lose like a man, as people say, philosophically reminding himself that it could not be helped.

The terrors of his pagan shipmates, when they realized the true state of affairs, probably went home to his conscience. "Then were the men exceedingly afraid, and said unto him, Why hast thou done this? For the men knew that he fled from the presence of the Lord, because he had told them." Even *natural* consciences will be alarmed at what a backslidden child of God takes in stride. This deadness of spirit is the awful effect of trifling with God and grieving His Holy Spirit.

In desperation, seeing that all their efforts were useless, the mariners asked Jonah what they should do to stop the storm. He told them to throw him into the sea, admitting that he knew the tempest was sent for his sake. His conscience was evidently waking up now, but to what extent it is hard to say. The men hesitated to carry out his word; but when nothing they did could bring the ship to land, they gave up and prepared to do as he directed them. Crying to the Lord to not count Jonah's death against them, they threw Jonah into the sea. Notice that they respected the sovereignty of God, which Jonah had virtually denied ("Thou, O Lord, hast done as it hath pleased thee"). Immediately the waters became calm, and "the men feared the Lord exceedingly, and offered a sacrifice unto the Lord, and made vows." Dark and ignorant though their spirits were, their hearts responded to the mercy of the God who had granted them so remarkable a deliverance.

As for His unworthy servant, there was mercy for him too—though in a way that would arrest his attention and glorify God. "Now the Lord had prepared a great fish to swallow up Jonah. And Jonah was in the belly of the fish three days and three nights" (17). Dispensationally, it is Israel who, because of their failure as God's witnesses, has been cast into the sea of the Gentiles. But despite all their hardships, they have been marvelously preserved by the Lord and are yet to bear His testimony to the whole world.

JONAH 2: Out of the Depths

When the scribes and Pharisees hypocritically requested a sign that they might know for certain of the Lord's messiahship, He significantly replied:

> An evil and adulterous generation seeketh after a sign; and there shall no sign be given to it, but the sign of the prophet Jonas: For as Jonas was three days and three nights in the [belly of the great fish]; so shall the Son of man be three days and three nights in the heart of the earth. The men of Nineveh shall rise in judgment with this generation, and shall condemn it: because they repented at the preaching of Jonas; and, behold, a greater than Jonas is here (Matthew 12:39-41).

In these solemn words Jesus did two important things for us. He authenticated the story of Jonah, and He unfolded a marvelous type that we might otherwise overlook. The prophet's entombment in the great fish and his subsequent deliverance were intended as a sign to the Ninevites, and a type of the death and resurrection of the Lord Jesus Christ. It is true that Jonah found his suffering in the path of disobedience, while in Christ we contemplate with adoration the ever-faithful One who suffered to accomplish all His Father's will. But this is only proof that God causes even the wrath of man to praise Him, and what would not do so He restrains (Psalm 76:10). To the Ninevites, Jonah was a man who had passed through death and resurrection. In this he portrays the glorious mystery of the gospel. He who is now set forth as the object of faith, is the One who was delivered for our offenses and raised again for our justification. Jesus went into death but could not be held by it. In a fuller sense than Jonah ever knew, He could say, "The waters compassed me about, even to the soul." But God has raised Him from the dead, thereby testifying to His satisfaction in the work of His Son. This is the only sign now set before us. All who trust in the risen Savior are forever delivered from wrath and judgment—that judgment so rightfully ours.

Also in Jonah's experience we find a picture of Israel, the unfaithful witness-bearer, refusing the thought of grace going out to the Gentiles. The Jews' present condition relates to this second chapter, as the apostle Paul indicated when he wrote of the Jews,

> [They] both killed the Lord Jesus, and their own prophets, and have persecuted us; and they please not God, and are contrary to all men: Forbidding us to speak to the Gentiles that they might be saved, to fill up their sins alway: for the wrath is come upon them to the uttermost (1 Thessalonians 2:15-16).

By and by their deliverance will come, when they are ready to confess that salvation is of the Lord, all undeserved by them. In that day they will become the messengers of the same boundless grace to heathen millions, once hated and despised.

As vital as is Jonah's being a type of Christ and Israel, we must not lose sight of God's dealing with the prophet's own soul; for this has a moral lesson of the deepest importance for us as well. In his affliction Jonah cried to the very God from whom he had been attempting to hide. Divine life, like water, seeks its proper level or sphere. Whatever his failings, Jonah was a child of God still, and he turned instinctively to the One he had been grieving. We are a long way on the road to recovery when we are *ready to admit* God's righteousness in disciplining us, and when we *recognize* that we are under the hand of God. Having already acknowledged to the mariners that such was the case, he now cried to Him who heard him even "out of the belly of hell" (Jonah 2:2).

The floods hemmed him in, even pressing in on his soul. The weeds wrapped around his head. All God's waves and billows crashed over him. Nevertheless he affirmed that he would look again toward Jehovah's holy temple (verses 1-5). How blessed it is when the soul does not faint beneath the Lord's discipline, nor despise it, but looks up to God and counts on His grace, despite the guilt pressing in on the conscience.

Jonah went down to the bottom of the mountains, but was able in the anticipation of faith to say, "Yet hast thou brought up my life from corruption, O Lord my God." His soul would have fainted within him, but he remembered the Lord and was assured that his prayers would be heard (6-7). He was in the place in which the future remnant of Israel shall be—in their experience, when the blindness of the present condition has passed away. Right now they are far away; yet, as in Solomon's prayer, they are looking toward the temple of Jehovah, though in ruins, as in the day Daniel opened his windows toward Jerusalem.

Jonah exclaimed, "They that observe lying vanities forsake their own mercy" (8). He had forsaken his own mercy when he tried to flee from God's presence. He knew then the condition of the heathen by his own experience. Now, however, he was confident that he would wander no more; though, as we well know, his confidence was still misplaced. His heart was no more to be trusted after he had been in the belly of the fish than before. When he cried, "I will sacrifice unto thee with the voice of thanksgiving," and when he added, "I will pay that that I have vowed," there is still no response on the part of God. Jonah was not yet at the end of himself. As in the conversion of a sinner, so it is with the restoration of a saint: he must get to the end of himself before the Lord will undertake his case. The sinner must learn that he is without strength, and the erring saint must learn that in himself he is no better or stronger than other men, before God can manifest His grace.

So it is here, after prayers, pledges, and vows have availed nothing, that the crisis is reached. At last Jonah simply admits, "Salvation is of the Lord." Then, and not until then, "the Lord spake unto the fish, and it vomited out Jonah upon the dry land" (8-10). Jonah had thus, figuratively speaking, passed through death and resurrection. He was now ready to go to the great and godless city of the Ninevites and declare the word of God to them.

He hadn't yet fully conquered his rebellious self, which will become obvious later on. But he was in God's school, and he would have a patient and gracious Teacher.

JONAH 3: Death and Resurrection

It is very important, in studying the Old Testament types, to distinguish between a person's individual and official roles. In other words, one may be a type of the Lord Jesus, if looked at officially; but, if that person is viewed morally, he may be a marked failure. This is strikingly illustrated in the case of David. As the anointed of the Lord, he is pre-eminently a type of the true King, the Anointed of Jehovah, yet to be set upon the holy hill of Zion. However, there was much in his life that was altogether opposed to the holiness and perfection of Him who was truly the Man after God's own heart.

In Jonah's story the same principle applies. His history is, as we have seen, sad and sorrowful in the extreme. But grace delights to take up people like Jonah: so we find the divine expositor Himself declaring that His own death and resurrection were set forth in symbol in the experience that the prophet from Galilee passed through. It is in his role as the one who tasted death but triumphed over it that Jonah becomes the bearer of Jehovah's message to the Ninevites.

All of Jonah's disobedience had not changed God's mind about sending him to preach to a pagan people. The servant might fail, but he is a servant still. Abraham and Job provide additional examples of this. Abraham was supposed to intercede for Abimelech because the patriarch was also a prophet, even though he had just lied about his relationship with Sara (Genesis 20). Job, no doubt after he was restored in soul, had to pray for his friends—though he had justified himself rather than God through his trials (Job 42:8-10).

There is a serious lesson here for those entrusted with the gospel or a special ministry to the people of God. The Lord will judge them not merely as saints but as servants. Failure does not relieve them from their responsibility to serve but demands all the more self-examination so that they may be in a right state of soul to minister in holy things. In so writing, I have no thought of sanctioning clerical pretensions or treating Christ's servants like a special class who are supposed to be above the frailties common to humanity—and even to saints! I only emphasize what Scripture frequently insists on: that he who serves should do so because he was called by God to his particular ministry. When so called, they have a most serious responsibility to walk in a manner worthy of that calling. A "one-man" ministry is rightly rejected by many as unscriptural. An "any-man" ministry is equally wrong. He who runs unsent has failed even in his very start.

Jonah had been called by God to his mission. He was now given the command the second time to "Arise, go unto Nineveh, that great city, and preach unto it the preaching that I bid thee" (Jonah 3:1). This time he apparently does not hesitate, for we read, "So Jonah arose, and went unto Nineveh, according to the word of the Lord."

His present obedience is as conspicuous as his former disobedience. However, we know from the next chapter that he had not yet truly understood how far he had departed from God. It is a serious thing to realize that people may be outwardly correct in their demeanor and zealous in the Lord's work after a failure, while in reality they are not yet restored in soul. The root of the problem is unreached. Certain *acts* may be confessed, and the confession may be real and genuine, as far as it goes. But the *state of the soul* that led to these acts has not been faced in the presence of God. This was Jonah's great lack here, and it was a vital one. But God has His own way of exposing to His servant the true state of His soul. And He has His own way of restoring that soul.

"Yet forty days, and Nineveh shall be overthrown," was Jonah's message to that hedonistic city. The result was just as he had feared. He had gladly accepted that his personal "salvation is of the Lord." But when the people of Nineveh accepted that same offer of salvation Jonah was filled with anger to see God's mercy extended to the repentant city. So perverse is the human heart, even though it be the heart of a saint! In a few graphic sentences the story of the great awakening is told.

> So the people of Nineveh believed God, and proclaimed a fast, and put on sackcloth, from the greatest of them even to the least of them. For word came unto the king of Nineveh, and he arose from his throne, and he laid his robe from him, and covered him with sackcloth, and sat in ashes. And he caused it to be proclaimed and published through Nineveh by the decree of the king and his nobles, saying, Let neither man nor beast, herd nor flock, taste any thing: let them not feed, nor drink water: But let man and beast be covered with sackcloth, and cry mightily unto God: yea, let them turn every one from his evil way, and from the violence that is in their hands. Who can tell if God will turn and repent, and turn away from his fierce anger, that we perish not? (5-9)

Could all the annals of revival history furnish a scene to parallel this? From the greatest to the least, all cried out to God. Notice that it is not to the Lord—that is, Jehovah—that they directed their prayers. Here, as in all Old Testament Scripture, *Elohim* (God) and *Jehovah* are used with scrupulous exactness. Uninstructed people may stumble at the use of the two names because they fail to see that *Jehovah* is the covenant name that links God with His people in known relationship, while *Elohim* speaks rather of sovereignty and creatorship. So the sailors of chapter 1 rightly used the broader title or name until, instructed by the erring prophet, they called to Jehovah not to hold them accountable for Jonah's blood. So too these Ninevites addressed their petitions to Elohim. As a result, we are told that "God saw their works, that they turned from their evil way; and God repented of the evil, that he had said he would do unto them; and he did it not" (10).

Would anyone find a difficulty here? Let that person know that the God who judges is always ready to repent and manifest His grace on the least evidence of a heart humbled and broken by its sin.

His is love, 'tis love unbounded,
Without measure, without end.
Human thought is here confounded,
His too vast to comprehend.

Sadly, Jonah's soul was in no condition to enter into and enjoy such love and grace! His was the spirit of the elder son in the parable of the prodigal son, as the next chapter makes clear.

JONAH 4: The Repentance of Nineveh

The Holy Spirit has declared that "the carnal mind is...not subject to the law of God, neither indeed can be" (Romans 8:7). It is a humbling truth, but experience and Scripture corroborate it. Not that only the carnal mind in an unconverted person is so hopelessly evil—the carnal mind is as unreliable and vile in the greatest saint as in the worst sinner. Indeed, we understand its incurable destructiveness when we see it at work in one whom we consider a good example of a Christian.

No child of God dare trust the flesh. It will betray him into unholy thoughts and ways every time it is permitted to have control. I say *permitted* purposely, for no Christian needs to be governed by its power. Rightly viewed, the flesh is a foreign thing that should not have place for even a moment. Believers are called to refuse the flesh's influence. In place of yielding ourselves to it as if it had authority over us we are told to make no provision for the flesh to fulfill its lusts. We are to reckon ourselves dead to it and to yield ourselves to God as alive from the dead. If we do not do this, defeat is certain—the triumph of the flesh is assured. But if we walk in the Spirit, we shall not fulfill the lust of the flesh.

Now in Jonah we see a saint under the power of the flesh. No doubt, finally he was enabled to judge his failure, but God still commanded him to record his sins so they would serve as a warning for generations to come. The flesh, most certainly, led to his fleeing from the presence of the Lord. This same power also controlled him when he sat down outside the city, after delivering his message, to see what the Lord would do. Instead of his heart being filled with joy because of the repentance of the Ninevites, he was filled with anxiety about his own reputation.

Probably few of us realize what a strong place self has in our affections, until something arises that touches our own personal dignity. It is then that we show our true spirit. There is more of Jonah's disposition in us than we like to admit even to ourselves. Yet to admit failure is one of the first steps to deliverance from it.

When all Heaven was rejoicing at the repentance of not just one sinner but a vast multitude, we are told that "it displeased Jonah exceedingly, and he was very angry" (Jonah 4:1). His state of mind was most wretched, yet he was completely unconscious of it. Puffed up with a sense of his own importance, the salvation or sorrow of so many of his fellow creatures was nothing compared to his own reputation. Yet so utterly unaware was he of the wretched state of his soul that he could turn to God and express his shameful failure as though he had not failed at all—or even as though the failure, if there were any, was on the part of the Lord Himself.

> He prayed unto the Lord, and said, I pray thee, O Lord, was not this my saying, when I was yet in my country? Therefore I fled

> before unto Tarshish: for I knew that thou art a gracious God, and merciful, slow to anger, and of great kindness, and repentest thee of the evil. Therefore now, O Lord, take, I beseech thee, my life from me; for it is better for me to die than to live (2-3).

It's almost unbelievable that a servant of God could be in such a dreadful state of soul! However, Jonah's condition was nothing but an aggravated form of that insidious disease—pride—that so readily finds a congenial place for growth in the heart of any saint out of communion with God.

The Lord's gentle response might well have broken Jonah down, had he not been so thoroughly self-occupied. "Then said the Lord, Doest thou well to be angry?" There is no reproach, just the serious question that ought to have awakened him at once to his soul's true condition.

How often the Lord would ask us a similar question when we cherish unholy thoughts or feelings or walk in our own paths and neglect His ways! "Doest thou well" to be pleasing yourself and dishonoring Him? Surely not! But it is amazing how slow we can be to admit how poorly we are doing when we have become hardened by the deceitfulness of sin.

Jonah did not respond to God in words. Rather, acting in self-will and wounded pride, he went outside the city, built a shelter, sat under its shadow, and waited to see what would become of Nineveh and of his prophetic reputation.

In grace, God prepared a gourd that, growing rapidly, soon overshadowed the petulant prophet and sheltered him from the fierce rays of the almost tropical sun. Because it ministered to his comfort, Jonah was quite glad to have the gourd. This is the first time we see Jonah joyful and it is the last as well. His gladness was as truly inspired by selfishness as was his sorrow.

But God next prepared some things that would blast that joy. A worm was sent to destroy the gourd; then a powerful east wind was sent by Him who has His way in the whirlwind and in the storm. The sickening heat made Jonah faint; and in his wretchedness he wished once more that he might escape his trials by dying, saying "It is better for me to die than to live."

Again God gently asked, "Doest thou well to be angry for the gourd?" Gloomily the offended prophet answered, "I do well to be angry, even unto death." His was the callousness that comes from allowing sin to go unjudged until all capacity to discern between right and wrong seems gone.

Jehovah's reply revealed His grace, which evidently accomplished its purpose, for Jonah had no word of self-vindication to offer. He permitted God to have the last word and closed his record abruptly, as though what followed were of too sacred and private a nature for him to publish abroad. The Lord said,

> Thou hast had pity on the gourd, for the which thou hast not laboured, neither madest it grow; which came up in a night, and perished in a night: And should not I spare Nineveh, that great city, wherein are more than sixscore thousand persons that cannot discern between their right hand and their left hand; and also much cattle? (10-11)

The question is unanswerable. Jonah grieved for the loss of the gourd because it had ministered to his comfort. Jehovah yearned over the sinners of Nineveh because He loved them. How opposite were Master and servant! But we must leave the history where God leaves it. The rest we shall know at the judgment seat of Christ. In the meantime, may we seek the grace to daily judge ourselves for anything that, if left to develop, would lead us as far from God as Jonah wandered!

MICAH

A PROFILE

MICAH

A TALE OF TWO CITIES

BY JOHN PHILLIPS

Micah (736-700 B.C.) was a younger contemporary of Isaiah and, although his chief ministry was to Jerusalem, he was also commissioned to speak for God to Samaria. His ministry was during the reigns of Jotham, Ahaz, and Hezekiah of Judah, so he lived to see the evils he pronounced on Samaria in the north actually come to pass. No doubt his messages helped bring about the great spiritual awakening in the south during the days of Hezekiah (see Jeremiah 26:18). It must have been a great consolation to Isaiah to have his witness supported by such an able contemporary as Micah. Every spiritual man rejoices to see younger men taking up the burden of the things of God. Isaiah, we know, was a scholar who probably ministered to the upper classes in Jerusalem, for he had important contacts with King Hezekiah. Micah, on the other hand, was a man of the fields and probably had more to say to the rank and file of the nation.

Micah's home was in Moresheth-Gath near the Philistine border. He looked out over rich, fertile fields and could see the towns and fortresses that dotted the plain. He lived in an exciting hour. Samaria was about to fall and the dreaded Assyrian war machine roll on to the borders of Judah. Judah's sins were as scarlet as those of Israel—so how could she expect to escape? Not far from his home Micah may well have seen the embassies hurrying from Jerusalem to Egypt and returning with empty promises of Egyptian aid. It was all so pointless—there was only one place from which help could come.

Themes of Micah

The prophecy divides into three parts. Micah commands attention by use of the word *hear* or *listen* (1:2; 3:1; 6:1).

I. The Prophecy of Retribution (1-3)
   A. The Calamity of It (1)
   B. The Cause of It (2-3)
      1. The Sins of the People (2:1-13)
      2. The Sins of the Princes (3:1-4)
      3. The Sins of the Prophets (3:5-10)
      4. The Sins of the Priests (3:11-12)
II. The Promise of Restoration (4-5)
   A. The Restoration Depicted (4:1-8)
   B. The Restoration Delayed (4:9-5:6)
      1. The Times of Judah's Misery (4:9-13)
      2. The Times of Judah's Messiah (5:1-6)
   C. The Restoration Described (5:7-15)
III. The Plea for Repentance (6-7)
   A. The Standards of the Nation (6:1-8)
   B. The Sins of the Nation (6:9- 16)
   C. The Sorrows of the Nation (7:1-6)
   D. The Savior of the Nation (7:7-20)

Message of Micah

No class was exempt from the corruption of his day, so no class was exempt from Micah's message. There were many false hireling prophets who plied their trade for gain, giving themselves over to spiritism and consulting demons to gain a knowledge of the future. Micah fearlessly denounced those men. He spoke out also with great boldness against the people, bluntly naming their sins. Royalty did not escape his lash as, turning on the princes, he accused them of violence, oppression, and corruption. They were merciless in their treatment of the poor, and cruel in their greed for gold. Finally, Micah denounced the priests, accusing them of unblushing graft.

Despite all the corruption in the moral, religious, and national life of the people, the prevailing attitude was one of complacency. God was in the midst of His people; therefore they could come to no harm. Micah plainly told them otherwise. Like so many of the Old Testament prophets, he prophesied not only in the context of his day but also in the context of the day of the Lord. He saw far into the future, speaking of "the last days" (4:1) and vividly describing the great restoration that is future even to us. Both comings of the Messiah are foretold, and Micah closes his prophecy with a passionate plea for repentance.

Micah liked to play on words, employing as puns the names of Gath, Aphrah, Saphir, Zaanan, and Beth-ezel, various towns he mentioned. Indeed he concluded his prophecy with a pun on his own name, Micah, which means "Who is like Jehovah?" He concluded with the challenge, "Who is a God like unto thee?" (7:18) The more we get to know of this great and living God, the more we will appreciate the parting thrust of Micah.

CHAPTER SIX

THE PROPHECY OF MICAH

Micah's prophecy, while simple in structure and clear in general, contains a number of seemingly involved and obscure passages. In taking up its study, one feels more than ever the need of divine illumination to understand correctly the many enigmatic sayings in the prophecy.

The theme of the book is plain, however. It is the wretched state of all Israel because of their sin, coupled with the wonderful deliverance to be brought by God—whose "goings forth have been from of old, from everlasting," yet who was to come out of Bethlehem Ephratah to procure salvation for His people (Micah 5:2). So, though the first chapter begins with the solemn arraignment for the "transgression of Jacob" and "for the sins of the house of Israel," the book concludes with the precious assurance that He whom they have offended will cast all their sins into the depths of the sea (7:19).

In all this we are on familiar ground. Only in the details is there some difficulty, and those involve no essential truths or fundamentals of the faith.

Micah is called "the Morasthite," that is, a man of Moreshah. He called this city, Moresheth-gath in 1:14; then in verse 15, he called it Mareshah. All three names designated a town lying to the southwest of Jerusalem, in the land of Judah.

Micah was cited by the elders of Jerusalem in the days of Jeremiah, a hundred years later, as an example of one who prophesied against Israel, but was not persecuted by the godly king Hezekiah (Jeremiah 26:16-19).

His prophecy might have been delivered all at once, since there are no clear breaks in its continuity. It seems more likely, however, that it consists of three discourses and a prayer—each of the former beginning with a summons to hear. In that case the first division would embrace chapters 1–2; the second, chapters 3–5; and the third, chapter 6; while chapter 7 would be the fourth and last section.

Coming a little later than Isaiah, Micah was his contemporary for the greater part of his ministry. In verse 1 we find that his message is directed to all Israel, not merely Judah, where the prophet himself lived.

MICAH 1: The Summons to Hear and Heed

"Hear, all ye people; hearken, O earth [or land], and all that therein is: and let the Lord God be witness against you, the Lord from his holy temple" (2). In spirit, the people were called back to the days of Leviticus 1:1, when the voice of Jehovah was heard from the sanctuary, setting forth the holiness that was appropriate in those among whom He dwelt. Here, He spoke again from the sanctuary; but this time His purpose was to convict His people of having violated His Word in every point, thus forfeiting all rights to the blessings of the covenant entered into at Sinai and confirmed in the plains of Moab. They were summoned to let Adonai Jehovah (the divine title rendered here "the Lord God") be witness against them. To do so would justify God and condemn themselves, which, for a failed people, paradoxically was the path of blessing.

It is a great thing to bow to the whole Word of God, even when it judges me and condemns my ways. To do so leads me to something better. But to excuse myself at the expense of God's truth is a process that hardens the conscience.

In Micah 1:3-4, the Lord is represented as coming out of His place to investigate Israel's condition. The language used is highly figurative; its beauty must be acknowledged by all. Like volcanic fires bursting forth and rending the earth, so is the awakening of Jehovah to judge His people.

The transgression of Jacob and the sins of the house of Israel were the reason for this display of power and wrath. Samaria, with her mixture of idolatrous rites and Israelite worship, was "the transgression of Jacob." Jerusalem, in its treachery and apostasy, was the sin of Judah. Therefore Samaria was to become a desolation, as a vineyard given over to destruction. All the carved images and idols of every kind were to be beaten to pieces, and her "hires" (Lesser translates, "her wages of sin") burned in the fire. Nothing would survive the day of Jehovah's fury (5-7).

Verse 8 seems to be language put into the mouth of the devastated nation; or it may be the prophet's own picture of his bitter sorrow at the fate about to befall Samaria. It is an instance of the peculiar character of this book.

Nothing could now delay the avenging hand, for "her wound is incurable"! It is solemn indeed when God must pronounce this message on the condition of those who bear His name. Like a spreading pestilence, "it is come unto Judah; [and hath reached] unto the gate of my people, even to Jerusalem" (9). The whole body was affected; the whole head, sick (see Isaiah 1:5-6).

How tragic that the Philistine enemies of Israel should hear of so wretched a condition prevailing among those who were called "The redeemed of the Lord!" That's why Micah protested, "Declare ye it not at Gath, weep ye not at all." But "in the house of Aphrah roll thyself in the dust" (Micah 1:10). The prophet played on the city name *Aphrah,* which means "the dust." There should fallen Israel return and roll themselves in the dust because of their sins.

To city after city, desolation and woe were assured. *Saphir,* "the fair," would be given up to shame. *Zaanan,* "the place of flocks" would have no one entering or leaving her gates. "The mourning of Beth-ezel" or, *Beth-haezel,* "the house at hand" would "receive of you his standing." Here again the prophet played on the name. Bethezel was evidently what we would call a halfway house or lodging; however, Micah prophesied that it would no longer be a resting place for travelers on their way to the city of the great King.

The dweller in *Maroth,* "bitterness," would find only the bitter, and would weep for the good that would not be coming. To Jerusalem's gate, evil would sweep down like a flood. What is so solemn about this is that it is "from the Lord"—He is the One who is judging His people because of their sin (12).

Verse 13 is difficult to interpret. For some reason, Lachish is declared to be "the beginning of the sin to the daughter of Zion." Hence her people would flee before the advancing enemy.

The two following verses are also not clear enough to give an authoritative explanation. They seem to imply an unsuccessful effort to form a Philistine alliance for protection from their common enemies. But *Achzib* ("the lie") would deceive the kings of Israel. Typically, the passage may point us to the coming day when the lie of antichrist will be believed; when apostate Israel will turn to him in vain for protection from the onslaught of the last Assyrian. The Assyrian, however, shall prove to be the very rod of Jehovah's anger.

Unhappy Israel, fallen so low that her conscience no longer troubled her, may well have made herself bald and mourned in anguish for her delicate children, who were destroyed by the sins of the fathers. "They are gone into captivity from thee" (16).

The whole chapter is a dirge of unappeasable sorrow because the nation had forsaken the One who would have blessed them so richly had they but walked in His ways. May there be in us a different spirit! Otherwise we too must learn in bitterness of soul the folly of forsaking the living God.

MICAH 2: Is the Spirit of the Lord Straitened?

It is God's will that those whom He has taken into covenant relationship with Himself should be overcomers. If we do not overcome, the fault is in us—not in Him. He has abundant resources for the believer to draw on. But if we are ruled by unbelief and disobedience, spiritual paralysis will inevitably result.

This had often been proven in Israel's case, and never more so than when Micah was sent to them with Jehovah's message. Their state of soul at that time was wretchedly low. Consequently, their ability to perceive divine things was so dulled that they had lost the power to distinguish what was of God and what was of man.

This inability to discern spiritual things always occurs when people do not walk in obedience to revealed truth. They lose the power to distinguish truth from error, and may, under the deadening influence of the deceitfulness of sin, do the most outrageous things. All the while they calmly announce that their efforts were for the glory of God, and they are deeply grieved if their pretensions are not believed and bowed to.

In this second chapter of Micah the prevailing unrighteousness (as described in verses 1 and 2) is given by God as the reason why He devised evil against the whole family of Israel. They had ignored His righteous laws in their dealings with each other, so He would treat them as they had treated their fellow Israelites. He told them He would bring disaster on them from which their pride could never save them. They would fall on difficult days (3). Lamentations and mourning would replace their careless songs. Their fields would be divided among strangers. None of them could "cast a cord by lot in the congregation of the Lord" (4-5)—that is, no one of Israel would be left who had authority to divide the land and measure it off, placing the landmarks according to the covenantal inheritance.

So unpalatable was this that they cried, "Prophesy ye not"! Like many today, they would silence the messenger and forget the message. But God said, "They shall prophesy." His servants would not be rejected with impunity. On the other hand, the Word given and rejected, the Lord said, "They shall not prophesy to these, that reproach may not overtake them" (the proper translation of Micah 2:6, according to eminent scholars).

The judgment was now decreed, and must surely fall. Nevertheless, God asked the questions, "O thou that art named the house of Jacob, is the spirit of the Lord straitened? are these his doings? do not my words do good to him that walketh uprightly?" The Lord would surely have recognized any repentance and shown Himself strong on their behalf in spite of the impending judgment.

This is full of comfort and encouragement for any who in these last days of the church's history on earth have an ear to hear what God has said in His Word. Nothing can avert the approaching judgment of haughty Christendom, nor raise the fallen assembly of God. But wherever there is individual faithfulness, or wherever a few humbly seek to heed the Word of God, there will be blessing.

God's Word will always "do good to him that walketh uprightly." Spiritual things "are spiritually discerned," and therefore only the upright and godly soul will find profit and blessing in the Scriptures. But where effort is made to discern the Scriptures, that Word will be found sufficient for all the needs of the pilgrim path. There will never be a circumstance so trying or a crisis so serious that the man of God will be left unequipped to do good works if he feeds on the Word of truth. Scripture, with the Holy Spirit's enlightenment, is all that is required in every emergency.

If, however, the professed people of God be "risen up as an enemy" and refuse to heed His Word (as in verses 8-9), then comes the call for separation from what is unclean and unholy, "Arise ye, and depart; for this is not your rest: because it is polluted" (10). To continue in fellowship with what is opposed to God will result in desolation. We are called to "buy the truth, and sell it not" (Proverbs 23:23).

With Israel, any false prophet was more acceptable than a God-sent messenger (Micah 2: 11). An evil man "speaking lies in hypocrisy" (1 Timothy 4:2) and "turning the grace of our God into lasciviousness" (Jude 4) would have been a prophet well-suited to them in their fallen condition.

They dismissed the Shepherd of Israel and would not follow His ways. So they were dismissed by Him. Nevertheless the Lord's anger would not burn forever; Micah's message closes with a precious promise of future restoration and blessing (2:12- 13). God will Himself assemble the lost sheep of Jacob, gathering the remnant of Israel and placing them in His fold. If walls rise before them to bar their return to the land of their rest, He will send His *breaker* (literally, "wall breaker") to open a way for His redeemed. So He will lead them in triumph back to Immanuel's land, as it is written, "Their king shall pass before them, and the Lord on the head of them."

What a happy ending there will be when all Israel's discipline is accomplished and they ask the way to Zion!

MICAH 3: Princes and Priests Apostate

The second division of the book begins with a summons to the heads and princes of Israel to hear the prophet's rebuke. No longer are the common people addressed, but Micah now turns to the princes, or judges, in verse 1-4, and the prophets in verses 5-8. These two are then grouped with the priests in verse 9-12.

It is a frightening thing when the leaders of God's people cause them to err; when those who should have been a bulwark for the truth turn away from it, "speaking perverse things, to draw away disciples after them" (Acts 20:30).

They who should have known justice, who were raised by God to rule the nation in righteousness, were the very ones who were leading the people astray. This has often been the case in the history of the church. Therefore we need to test all that is taught or practiced by the only infallible rule—the unerring Word of God. If Christians are content to be styled "the laity" and leave their spiritual interests in the hands of their guides, they have themselves to blame if they are led in wrong paths. Each of us is responsible to grow in godliness, and to discern the things that take us in the opposite direction.

It too frequently happens that leaders become pretentious and arrogant. They regard themselves as "the clergy," whose special task is to find sustenance in "the ministry." But they forget that to minister is to *serve,* not to lord their position over others and treat them as possessions. No pride is worse than spiritual pride. No pretension is more abhorrent than ecclesiastical pretension. Sadly, though, there is never a lack of vain, self-confident men, who are ready to grasp high-sounding titles and powers, if the people love to have it so. And it is pathetic indeed to realize that, generally, the people themselves are responsible for this kind of thing. They are too ready to accept the assertions of some gifted, uninspired man, rather than search the Word for themselves for the direction of their life.

In Micah's time, the people were indifferent; the princes lived recklessly, despising the "lower classes" and flourishing in their presumption and avarice. In place of caring for the flock of God, with a strong sense of accountability, they viewed God's people as their lawful prey and "flay[ed] their skin from off them" (2-3).

I am reminded of the grim jest of Pope Leo X who, it is said, made the remark to his companion princes of the church, "What a profitable thing this myth about Jesus Christ has been to us!" And all because the Bible had been kept from the people, and they were willing to have it that way.

The hour of judgment is coming, though, when all these contemptible leaders must answer to the great Shepherd of the sheep for their unholy ways. "Then shall they cry unto the Lord, but he will not hear them: he will even hide his face from them at that time, as they have behaved themselves ill in their doings" (4).

In the next section Micah addressed "the prophets that make my people err." The princes ruled by sheer power because of the awe in which they were held. The prophets, however, perverted the very words of the Lord, burdening the people until they were too discouraged to search out and follow the path of life.

Prince and prophet had been blended into one splendid hierarchy in Christendom for centuries; but in our day they have been largely divorced. We can more easily distinguish between those whose power rests on clerical claims and those who lead astray because of professed spiritual insight—which they think entitles them to be heard as exponents of the truth when they really pervert and set aside the Word of God.

However their systems may differ, false teachers have one characteristic mark: They "serve not our Lord Jesus Christ, but their own belly; and by good words and fair speeches deceive the hearts of the simple" (Romans 16:18). This was what marked the false prophets in Micah's day—and in all days before and since. "Who, when they have something to bite with their teeth, cry Peace; but who prepare war against him who putteth nothing in their mouths"—such is Lesser's graphic translation of a verse that in the King James version is a little ambiguous (Micah 3:5).

The true prophet of the Lord is not concerned about financial or other reward. He depends on God who has sent him, and is consequently free to speak His Word, "not as pleasing men, but God, which trieth our hearts" (1 Thessalonians 2:4). Every false religious system is marked by greed, and its advocates act on the thought that "the gift of God may be purchased with money" (Acts 8:20). It is the error of Balaam and is especially characteristic of the last days.

In perverting the truth for personal profit, false teachers obscure God's guidance by words without knowledge. As they have hidden the light from others however, so they themselves shall go into the night at last. Micah 3:6-7 is intensely solemn, and should cause teachers of error to tremble.

> Therefore night shall be unto you, that ye shall not have a vision; and it shall be dark unto you, that ye shall not divine; and the sun shall go down over the prophets, and the day shall be dark over them. Then shall the seers be ashamed, and the diviners confounded: yea, they shall all cover their lips; for there is no answer of God.

How unspeakably awful it will be when those who have posed as the very oracles of divine truth shall awaken to the reality that they are lost and ruined forever. And though they cry out in the anguish of their despair, there will be no answer from God!

How different this was from the experience of Micah, Jehovah's true servant! In simple confidence, he could say, "Truly I am full of power by the spirit of the Lord, and of judgment, and of might, to declare unto Jacob his transgression, and to Israel his sin" (8). Not fearing the responses of others, he could faithfully proclaim the mind of God revealed to him by the Holy Spirit. He was the servant not of men, but of Jehovah of hosts. His ministry was lived in the energy of faith, the mighty power of God.

The last section, verses 9-12, sums up God's condemnation before He tells of future blessing in chapter 4.

Despising discernment, and perverting all justice, the rulers built up Zion with blood. Yet, they had the audacity to declare that the Lord was in their midst and approved of their actions. "The heads thereof judge for reward, and the priests thereof teach for hire, and the prophets thereof divine for money: yet will they lean upon the Lord, and say, Is not the Lord among us? none evil can come upon us" (11). So they made God the minister of their unrighteousness and used His holy name as their answer to any who sought to reach their consciences.

Saints of God are called to follow righteousness. If we overlook this, it is utter arrogance to talk of having the Lord's presence and to declare ourselves in line with His Word. Verse 11 can be considered in light of Jeremiah 6:13, where the condition a few years later is not improved but deteriorated, which is always the case when evil is left unjudged.

Because of this hardened condition, Zion was to be plowed as a field and Jerusalem destroyed; the mountain of Jehovah's house being treated as the idolatrous high places. If righteousness is not preserved by His saints, God will annihilate their pretensions. He who is holy and true will not tolerate iniquity.

MICAH 4: The First Dominion

It is refreshing indeed, before resuming the sad story of failure and sin, to briefly turn our eyes to the happy scenes in the first half of Micah 4.

The three opening verses are an almost exact duplicate of Isaiah 2:2-4. Do we have here a case of plagiarism? No. For this is not merely the literature of men—it is the inspired Word of God. Jesus said, "The testimony of two men is true" (John 8:17). In these duplicate passages, God has affirmed the promise of millennial blessing through both Micah and Isaiah so that all may know that neither prophet wrote from his own ideas, but was moved by the Holy Ghost. We need not be disconcerted that He chose to use the same language on each occasion.

In the last days, the time to which all prophecy points, "the mountain of the house of the Lord shall be established in the top of the mountains" (Micah 4: 1). The future millennial temple will not stand on mount Moriah but on a magnificent plateau. It will be lifted up above all the surrounding hills after the land has gone through some remarkable topographical changes caused by a great earthquake. This quake will occur when the feet of the Lord Jesus stand again on the mount of Olives (see Ezekiel 40:2; 48:8-12; Zechariah 14:4).

There, in commanding position, shall the house of the God of the whole earth be located. And there shall the nations come up regularly to worship and to learn the ways of Jehovah. From this sanctuary the law will go forth, and the word of the Lord from Jerusalem, the metropolis of the world in the age to come.

At last all earthly governments will end as the times of the Gentiles draw to a close. From then on our once rejected Lord Jesus will show "who is the blessed and only Potentate, the King of kings, and Lord of lords." He will administer unerring justice and bring in everlasting righteousness. No more will nation lift up sword against nation; but all warlike instruments will be destroyed, and the implements of peaceful agricultural pursuits will take their place.

In that day of universal blessing there will be no curse of poverty to contend with, no troublesome property disputes to settle, no struggle to acquire or conflicts to control what can never be properly governed. But in contentment and comfort "they shall sit every man under his vine and under his fig tree; and none shall make them afraid." What men have vainly strived to attain through socialist and communist propaganda and all other equally impracticable economic systems will have been attained. And it will be maintained for a thousand years by the personal presence of the One who has the right to reign (1-4). The statement of the fourth verse is not found in Isaiah, but there the call to walk in the ways of the Lord occurs immediately after what is here found in Micah 4:3. Micah presents a more complete picture and then gives the remnant's answer to the exhortation of Isaiah 2:5 in the lovely words, "For all people will walk every one in the name of his god, and [or but] we will walk in the name of the Lord our God for ever and ever." Faith lays hold of the promise, and the believer walks now by the glory that is coming.

However, the nation to whom "the first dominion" is yet to be given must, before that day of triumph, be scattered among all nations because of their sins. The Lord Himself will regather them before the kingdom is set up in power. So the prophet goes on to tell how Jehovah will assemble the lame and afflicted remnant and bring them back by omnipotent power to the land of their fathers. The nation itself, which will continue in unbelief and accept the false Christ when he arrives, will never be restored. But a repentant remnant will be found in the last days who will become the nucleus of a new nation in the land. "The Lord shall reign over them in mount Zion from henceforth, even forever." Then the first dominion will indeed be Israel's, when Jerusalem will be the joy of the whole earth (6-8).

Much has to happen before the glorious vision will be fulfilled, however. The daughter of Zion, like a woman in labor, would first pass through her hours of bitter anguish. She would be exiled to

Babylon and there made the sport of unfeeling Gentiles who were blind to her beauty and ignorant of her wondrous destiny. Her enemies will magnify themselves against her until the time of God's favor comes. Then the Lord Himself will appear to act the part of her kinsman-redeemer, delivering her from her bondage and bringing her into everlasting blessing. In that day their enemies' wealth shall be devoted to Him and their substance will gladly be dedicated to the Lord's use (9-13).

MICAH 5: The Smitten Judge

The promises we have been considering will all be made good by the Messiah, of whose rejection at His first coming we now read. In the Hebrew arrangement of the text, the first verse from chapter 5 is the last verse of chapter 4. This separates the picture of the afflicted Judge of Israel from the One born in Bethlehem, whose origins are from eternity. It is easy to detect rabbinical opposition to the New Testament narratives in this, slight as the difference might seem to the careless reader.

Accepting the Hebrew arrangement, it would seem as though the judge in question was simply one of the many rulers of Israel who would be treated shamefully by the northern foe. But the light of the New Testament makes it clear that the smitten One is none other than He who could say, "I gave my back to the smiters, and my cheeks to them that plucked off the hair: I hid not my face from shame and spitting" (Isaiah 50:6). He came to his own, but His own people received him not. In the high priest's house they "did spit in his face, and buffeted him; and others smote him with the palms of their hands, Saying, Prophesy unto us, thou Christ, Who is he that smote thee?" Likewise, in the Roman praetorium the rough soldiers spat "upon him, and took the reed, and smote him on the head" (Matthew 26:67-68; 27:30).

But of Jesus Christ it had been declared by the prophet, "Thou, Bethlehem Ephratah, though thou be little among the thousands of Judah, yet out of thee shall he come forth unto me that is to be ruler in Israel; whose goings forth have been from of old, from everlasting [or, the days of eternity]" (Micah 5:2). In plain language, seven centuries before God incarnate appeared on earth, the place of His birth was distinctly designated. This honor would be given to David's city. This is the passage to which the scribes turned when they explained to Herod where Christ was to be born. They held prophetic truth in their hands as they searched the Scriptures; but the truth did not hold them, nor did they permit the Scriptures to search their hearts.

This lesson is important for us all. Mere familiarity with the written Word of God will only make us the guiltier if we do not allow it to control all our ways. To read the Book; to study its various lines of truth; to be able to speak intelligently of the great doctrinal principles of Scripture—yet not to have received that Word in an honest heart and be transformed and guided by it, is dreadful indeed.

One has said, referring to the not uncommon practice of Bible-marking, "It is a small thing how you mark your Bible, but it is of all importance that it mark you."

To Bethlehem, then, came the eternal One, "God was manifest in the flesh" (I Timothy 3:16). Over His manger-bed angels hung, adoring their God and ours. A few shepherds and, later, some wise men from distant lands came to worship; but the rest of Israel and the nations went on in their indifferent, careless way. God the Son had become the Son of man; but man, in the main, was unconcerned. "He [was] despised and rejected of men" (Isaiah 53:3), and the Judge of Israel was slapped in the face! The Messiah was cut off, and He had nothing.

For this, judgment fell on the city that wickedly judged Him, and Jerusalem has for centuries been oppressed by the Gentiles. And she shall continue to be until the times of the nations are completed—"until the time that she which travaileth hath brought forth: then the remnant of his brethren shall return unto the children of Israel" (Micah 5:3). Dispersed among all peoples, scattered into every country, suffering under every sky, Israel endures the awful curse invoked by her own elders: "His blood be on us, and on our children" (Matthew 27:25).

A Son was born to her and a Child given before she ever labored for His birth. Her pains, however, are yet to come. In the great tribulation, under the antichrist, her labor will be endured in anguish.

Then she will truly be delivered, seeing in the Crucified her own Son and her Savior! Compare Revelation 12: 1-5 and Isaiah 66:7-9, "Before she travailed, she brought forth; before her pain came, she was delivered of a man child." Therefore Israel's pains are still in the future, and she shall be in excruciating labor before she recognizes and acknowledges her Messiah.

Then many sons will be hers when "the remnant of his *brethren* shall return unto the children of Israel" (Micah 5:3, emphasis added). Jesus called the remnant "my brethren" in Matthew 25:40. So the word of the elder prophet will be fulfilled, "As soon as Zion travailed, she brought forth her children" (Isaiah 66:8). At that time Jesus will be revealed as the long-waited-for Shepherd of Israel, who "shall stand and feed [or shepherd] in the strength of the Lord." He shall give abiding rest to His regathered flock. And His majesty and glory will be made known throughout the world, "for now shall he be great unto the ends of the earth" (Micah 5:4). This prophecy connects the rejection of Christ, when He came in humble grace, with His acceptance and worldwide acknowledgment when He comes the second time, in power and dignity to become His exalted Person.

But the hour of His appearance will be the hour of Israel's deepest sorrow. Jerusalem will be surrounded with armies. The antichrist will reign with blasphemous pretensions in the city. The legions of the revived Roman empire will have entered into a league with him both offensively and defensively. From the south a fierce horde will pour into the land. From the north the dreaded power known as, "the Assyrian," of whom Sennacherib was only a type, will march down in exultant triumph, spreading desolation on every side. Only "then shall the Lord go forth, and fight against those nations, as when he fought in the day of battle" (Zechariah 14:3)—Christ is "this man [who] shall be the peace" (Micah 5:5). He who has made peace with God for guilty men by the blood of His cross; He who, seated as man on Jehovah's throne, *is* our peace; He shall be the peace in that day. And in Him weary, distracted Israel will find their rest.

The arrogant Assyrian will be overthrown, and God's chosen people will be delivered from his cruel power (5-6). Then, freed from all their enemies, "the remnant of Jacob shall be in the midst of many people as a dew from the Lord, as the showers upon the grass," bringing refreshment and blessing to all nations at the Lord's bidding and waiting for none (7).

The lion of Judah's tribe will rise in His might, subjecting all enemies to His power. So shall Israel become the head, and never again the tail (8-9). Everything that has exalted itself against the Lord will be put down. Evil of every kind will be rooted out, and righteousness will be triumphant to the ends of the earth (10-15). This is the conclusion all the prophets looked forward to; so it becomes a fitting conclusion to the second section of this book.

MICAH 6: The Lord's Controversy

We now enter the third division of the prophecy of Micah. The prophet no longer looks to the future, neither its joy nor its sorrow, but he directs the people's attention to *their ways* and impresses on their conscience a deeply significant moral truth. In other words, this final message is the practical application of what has gone before. And it uses shame to get the point across, similar to the major part of the prophecy of Jeremiah and much of Hosea.

The mountains and the hills (a frequent simile for the chief cities and their surrounding villages) are called on to hear the searching words of "the Lord's controversy." We are told, "The Lord hath a controversy with his people, and he will plead with Israel" (1-2).

God always has a controversy with those who walk in disobedience. There can be no fellowship or communion while His Word is not obeyed. He desires truth in the innermost parts; nothing else will satisfy the One who is holy and true. The moment the conscience is reached and the heart bows before Him in true self-judgment, controversy ceases and communion is re-established.

Let the reader note: I do not write of union, but of something that flows from it and should always be maintained with it—communion. Union implies being participants of the common life of all God's children. "He that sanctifieth and they who are sanctified are all of one" (Hebrews 2:11). All who are sanctified are eternally united to Him from whom they derive their new life. This link can never be broken. If it could be, the life graciously given would be something we could lose, not something eternal.

Communion, on the other hand, is the normal state of one who has been made a child of God. It is the practical evidence of living in abiding fellowship with the Father and the Son. For the saints of Micah's day, communion was, according to the revelation then made, enjoyment of Jehovah's favor. Israel had forfeited this by disobedience, and it could only be regained by self-judgment. The principle endures. Only when I unsparingly condemn what I know to be contrary to the Word of the Lord in my own life, will I enjoy communion with God.

To reawaken Israel to the desire for communion with Him, the Lord took them back over their early days, reminding them of His patient grace with them from the day He first brought them out of Egyptian bondage (Micah 6:3-5). He had led them like a flock through the wilderness, permitting no one to curse them. And in His holy discipline, He dealt with them Himself when they sinned so that they "may know the righteousness of the Lord."

All His correction had blessing as its ultimate goal. It is appropriate then that the humbled should ask, "Wherewith shall I come before the Lord, and bow myself before the high God?" Did He demand sacrifices and offering? Was it these that Israel lacked? Would the Lord be pleased with thousands of rams and myriad of rivers of oil? If a man were to place on the altar his dearest and best, his firstborn, would that be payment enough for the sin of the soul? Were these the ways to restore the interrupted communion (6-7)?

No! It was righteousness that was lacking. So righteousness then must be maintained. "He hath showed thee, O man, what is good; and what doth the Lord require of thee, but to do justly, and to love mercy, and to walk humbly with thy God?" (8) Only when the people would bow before Him, confess the sin of the past, and seek strength to walk as He prescribed here, could there be that happy sense of the Lord's favor which lifts the soul above all circumstances and enables it to rejoice in God Himself.

This communion is the Lord's desire: "The Lord's voice crieth unto the city, and the man of wisdom shall see thy name: hear ye the rod, and who hath appointed it" (9). This is the beginning of blessing. When the soul bows before God and acknowledges the rightness of His discipline, then restoring grace can come. As long as he kicks against the goads, the discipline must continue. But when he heeds the rod and confesses his need of it, he has reached the point where restoration begins.

The next three verses itemize the sins the people needed to address: covetousness, extortion, corrupt business practices, violence, deceit. All these evil things were evidence of their wrong state of soul (10-12). God must deal with them in wrath if they show no sign of repentance; they would be made desolate because of their sins. Their lives would be unsatisfying while they resisted God and opposed His holiness. They might sow, but they would not reap; in fact, all their work would be for nothing. The work of their hands would fail to meet the needs of their bodies until, like the prodigal, they came to their senses and admitted their guilt (14-15; see also Deuteronomy 28:38- 40; Haggai 1:6).

The chapter closes with the sad fact that Jehovah's law was despised, while "the statutes of Omri are kept, and all the works of the house of Ahab, and ye walk in their counsels; that I should make thee a desolation, and the inhabitants thereof a hissing; therefore ye shall bear the reproach of my people" (Micah 6:16). Earnestly and tenderly the Lord had pleaded and set His case before them, but the words fell on deaf ears and calloused consciences. The people seemed bent on their own destruction. These things were written for our admonition. May we have ears to hear and hearts to understand!

MICAH 7: Future Repentance and Blessing

This last chapter, which forms the fourth division, is closely allied to the book of Lamentations. It is the prayer of the repentant remnant in the days of the great tribulation, the time of Jacob's trouble. The prophet here sets forth the proper language of those who no longer walk in pride but, humbled because of their sin, acknowledge the justice of the divine hand that struck them. There are no excuses, nor do they look for other reasons. They accept all as what they deserved, yet they look up in faith to the God of their fathers, whose unfailing grace they count on for restoration.

The three preceding discourses, or divisions, were all designed to lead to this desired end, so that this chapter could display the future result of the discipline which at the time seemed to have no effect. It was the Word of the living God though, and could not return to Him void but must accomplish that for which it was sent.

In the six opening verses we have a graphic portrayal of the conditions in the fearful days of the antichrist. To the remnant, it will look like every good person has been destroyed: "there is none upright among men." Treachery and deceit will be so prevalent that one will not dare to trust his most intimate friend. Even the wife held close to her husband's heart may betray him to the unholy inquisition of that fearful time. For those will be the days of vengeance that our Lord described in Matthew 24:9-31, when the abomination of desolation shall stand in the holy place. Also in Matthew 10:21-36, Jesus quoted this very passage from Micah when referring to the final events before the appearing of the Son of man.

Such appalling times have been known already in many places, as in the dark days of Roman Catholicism's power. But for Israel, in a special sense, darker days are yet to come.

The confidence of the remnant and their submission to the will of God are beautifully delineated in Micah 7:7-10. Acknowledging the rightness of God's judgment, they still look to Him in faith, crying, "I will wait for the God of my salvation"; and they are assured that He will hear. The enemy may seem to triumph; but though fallen, Israel will rise, and the Lord will be their light when the darkness has become the deepest. In humility they will say, "I will bear the indignation of the Lord, because I have sinned against him." This shows how truly their afflictions have resulted in the peaceable fruits of righteousness. Because of that they can count on God for deliverance and wait in patience until He pleads their cause and executes judgment for them, and they will glorify Him for His righteousness. Then Israel's enemies, who taunted her in her desolate condition, will admit that she is indeed the chosen of the Lord.

"In that day" earthly prosperity will return to Jerusalem, and her walls will be rebuilt. Her children will be brought back from Assyria and all the places they have been carried captive. Though the land shall first be desolated by the armies of the nations, because of Israel's sins, the old ruins will be rebuilt. The flock of Jehovah's heritage will be gathered from their hiding places and shepherded in the choice pastures of Bashan and Gilead, "as in the days of old" (1 1-14).

As the Lord had long ago brought them in triumph out of Egypt, so He will then show amazing things when He accomplishes the salvation of His chosen in the last days. The Gentiles, who have despised and hated the Jews, will be astonished when the remnant are reestablished in the land of their fathers and the first dominion has returned to Jacob (15- 17). It will be a marvelous display of the Lord's grace, and lovingkindness.

No wonder the book closes with so precious an expression of adoring gratitude:

> Who is a God like unto thee, that pardoneth iniquity, and passeth by the transgression of the remnant of his heritage? he retaineth not his anger forever, because he delighteth in mercy. He will turn again, he will have compassion upon us; he will subdue our iniquities; and thou wilt cast all their sins into the depths of the sea. Thou wilt perform the truth to Jacob, and the mercy to Abraham, which thou hast sworn unto our fathers from the days of old (18-20).

This will be God's happy ending for Israel. Established in Christ's kingdom, they will experience the blessedness of forgiven sin. And they will trace all that blessing back to the stricken Judge, who came in grace to save but was despised and rejected by the very people who held in their hands the Scripture of truth, foretelling the actual things which they in their unbelief fulfilled.

In the hour of their deepest anguish, they will turn back to the same sacred books and learn from them that the Nazarene was the long-expected One whose origins have been of old, from everlasting. At last convinced of their terrible sin, the remnant will bow in bitterness of soul before God, confessing the guilt of their fathers and judging their own past unbelief. Then grace will act on their behalf, and they will be restored to their land and their God. Every renewed heart will cry out with worshipful praise, "Who is a God like unto thee, that pardoneth iniquity?" Into the sea of His forgetfulness He will cast all their sins, justifying them freely by His grace through the same wondrous redemption that is now the ground of blessing for every Jew and Gentile who trusts in the name of Jesus.

Micah's prophecy reaches the end to which all the prophets pointed—when the oath of Jehovah to Abraham, Isaac, and Jacob will be performed. Their seed will be established in their ancient heritage, never again to be uprooted. They will enjoy all the blessing of the new covenant, confirmed by the precious blood of Christ.

NAHUM

A PROFILE

NAHUM
THE PROPHET OF NINEVEH'S DOOM

BY JOHN PHILLIPS

There was not a cloud in the sky when Nahum wrote (648-620 B.C.). Mighty Nineveh, capital of Assyria and mistress of the world, was at the peak of its prosperity and power. The dates of Nahum's prophecy can be fixed with fair certainty. His book was written after 663 B.C., for that was the year when No-Ammon (Thebes, the famous Egyptian city) fell. This city had fallen to Assyrian arms, and Nahum used its fall as a parable of the impending fall of Nineveh (3:8). It was written before 612 B.C. for that was when Nineveh itself fell, and this fall was the subject of Nahum's prophecy.

Strength of Nineveh

The city of Nineveh seemed impregnable. Standing on the left bank of the Tigris, its walls towered one hundred feet into the air and were further strengthened by more than twelve hundred mighty towers. The walls were wide enough for three chariots to drive abreast on them, and they enclosed 1,800 acres. The city could maintain its own food supply in case of a siege, and the sides not protected by the Tigris were surrounded by a moat. Nothing seemed more unlikely than the fate Nahum announced against Nineveh.

Doom of Nineveh

Nineveh's doom was declared and described in the book of Nahum, for it was a deserved destruction.

I. Nineveh's Doom Declared (1)
  A. The Lord's Patience (1:1-3a)
  B. The Lord's Power (1:3b-5)
  C. The Lord's Presence (1:6-8)
  D. The Lord's Purpose (1:9-14)
  E. The Lord's Protection (1:15)
II. Nineveh's Doom Described (2)
  A. The Siege of Nineveh (2:1-8)
  B. The Sack of Nineveh (2:9-13)
III. Nineveh's Doom Deserved (3)
  A. The City's Fierceness (3:1-3)
  B. The City's Filthiness (3:4-7)
  C. The City's Fury (3:8-10)
  D. The City's Fear (3:11-13)
  E. The City's Fall (3:14-19)

The history of the Assyrian Empire had been long and bloody. The Assyrians were notoriously warlike, bloodthirsty, and cruel, and had long been a scourge to surrounding nations. Israel had been uprooted by them, and Judah had been threatened, invaded, and cowed. The brief repentance of the Ninevites under the preaching of Jonah more than a century before had long been forgotten. Nothing but judgment remained. Having abused the mercy of God, Nineveh must now taste His wrath.

Nahum foretold for Nineveh utter desolation, and this was something new. Normally empires fell, but cities survived. Babylon, for example, the seat of the Babylonian Empire, passed in turn to the Persians and the Greeks, but not so Nineveh. God reserved for it "an utter end" (1:8). At the time Alexander the Great was pushing his conquests eastward, he marched over its site not knowing that the capital of a world empire was buried beneath his feet. The city of Nineveh passed so completely into oblivion that for centuries the place where it had once stood was not known.

Nahum's language is fierce and his vision is focused strictly and sharply on one greatly longed-for event: the fall of Nineveh. For a hundred years and more the Hebrews had longed for the downfall of Assyria. As Sir George Adam Smith puts it, "Nahum's book is one great *At Last*! Nahum has eyes for nothing else. To him, God is a God of vengeance. His arsenal is vast. He has storms and hurricanes and thunderbolts and earthquakes and volcanoes to command. When finally He rises up in judgment His foes must go down before Him like standing corn before a scythe. Nor all the vaunted strength of Nineveh, nor all its military might shall stand before the outpoured wrath of God."

Nahum foretold, in chapter 1, the destruction of Nineveh and the subsequent peace of Judah, and he based his warnings on the revealed character of God. In chapter 2 Nahum gave a graphic portrayal of the siege and sack of the city. In chapter 3 he set out the reasons why such a complete overthrow was inevitable and righteous.

The swollen waters of the Tigris inundated a part of the city, making possible the invasion of this otherwise impregnable fortress by the Medes and Babylonians. Nahum foretold this in 2:6. The city was then given over to fire as described in 3:13-15. The fate of Nineveh had hung over the city for centuries and was long delayed, but over its ruins might well be written the words, "The mills of God grind slowly, yet they grind exceeding small." When God finally settles accounts, He settles them in full.

CHAPTER SEVEN

THE PROPHECY OF NAHUM

"Search and look," said the prejudiced Pharisees, when dismissing the claims of the Lord Jesus, "for out of Galilee ariseth no prophet" (John 7:52). We have already seen in Jonah's case, however, that their assertion had no support from the Scriptures, which they so coolly used against others. Jonah was unquestionably out of Galilee, and there are the best of reasons for believing the same of Nahum. He is called the Elkoshite—that is, a man from Elkosh or, as it is sometimes written, Elkesi.

It is well known that there was an Assyrian village on the banks of the Tigris by this name. But Jerome, the church father, stated positively that when he retreated to Palestine from the turmoil of an unfriendly world, he was shown the site of Elkosh in Galilee where Nahum was reported to have been born.

The prophecy of Nahum bears every evidence of having been delivered prior to the death of Sennacherib and therefore at least a century before the destruction of Nineveh—the main subject of his message. Nahum was most likely a contemporary of Isaiah's, uttering his poetic prediction during the reign of Hezekiah. Nahum then was undoubtedly a Galilean who came from his northern home to speak God's words of comfort to the trembling people of the south, whose hearts were in fear because of the Assyrian invasion of Judah.

The book seems to divide readily into two parts. Chapter 1 presents the eternal One as the rock and refuge of those who confide in Him, whatever the danger that threatens them. Locally, it was the army of Sennacherib that seemed about to overwhelm them. But

God was above all, as was soon made clear. Chapters 2 and 3 give the destruction of Nineveh, the Assyrian capital. The description of the siege and destruction of the guilty city is a masterpiece of dramatic poetry.

It is of interest to note that both the Galilean prophets dealt largely with Nineveh in their ministries. Jonah was used to bring about the repentance of the generation of his day, about one hundred and fifty years before Nahum declared the city's final overthrow because its iniquities had reached Heaven. In that destruction it is easy to see a picture of the future end of the impious Assyrian of the last days, the antichrist.

Nahum means "consolation"; and consoling indeed are the precious words of cheer he was inspired to deliver in this first chapter.

NAHUM 1: Faith's Refuge

Vengeance belongs to God. To the Thessalonian saints Paul wrote, "It is a righteous thing with God to recompense tribulation to them that trouble you" (2 Thessalonians 1:6). He is always watching over His people; and while He permits many things for their discipline, He will never overlook an indignity done to His redeemed. "He reserveth wrath for his enemies" (Nahum 1:2). The enemies of His people are His enemies. Faith rests on this, and thus we are spared much worry and anxiety. Our natural response would be fear and apprehension, but the response of faith is calm and quiet. Flesh sees the Assyrian armies; faith looks up to the God of battles. For a good example of this, read 2 Kings 18–19, which describes the actual scenes to which the first part of Nahum's prophecy refers.

Nahum 1:3 offers precious comfort for the afflicted soul, as well as a solemn warning for those who harden themselves against the Lord's discipline. Slow to wrath and mighty in power, the Lord still cannot ignore iniquity. He will not acquit, or hold guiltless, the wicked. Long ago, God had declared to Moses that He was "merciful and gracious, longsuffering, and abundant in goodness and truth, Keeping mercy for thousands, forgiving iniquity and transgression and sin, and that will by no means clear the guilty" (Exodus 34:6-7). As full of love as He is—God is love itself—He is also light;

therefore sin must be judged. This is where the cross comes in. But even for men who have found forgiveness in Christ, God will not tolerate unjudged evil. If we won't judge ourselves, we must be judged by Him. For "when we are judged, we are chastened of the Lord, that we should not be condemned with the world" (1 Corinthians 11:32). Exodus 34:7 is for the sinner's warning, while Nahum 1:3 is for the saint's comfort. Yet the principle is the same; for whether in the case of people in general, or of His children in particular, God's holy eye overlooks nothing until all is judged. But if the whirlwind and the storm seem about to overwhelm, and the sky is black with clouds, the believer can have peace in knowing that the Lord has His way in all that seems frightening and, at times, arbitrary. The stormy wind merely fulfills His word, and "the clouds are the dust of his feet."

Look up then, when you are tried and distressed, for God is just above those heavy clouds of sorrow. As the dust in the distance announces the traveler's approach before he is seen, so the clouds proclaim the nearness of the One who knows all your pain and comes in love to dry your tears. At His word your stormy seas are rebuked and your rivers of sorrow are subdued, just as He dried up the Red Sea and rolled back the waters of the Jordan. All creation must acknowledge His power and all elements yield to His authority. No one can stand before His indignation nor survive the day of His wrath. Yet He is good, a fortress in the day of trouble, "and he knoweth them that trust in him" (4-7).

What comfort words like these would be to Hezekiah and his people, besieged in Jerusalem, terrorized and taunted by the arrogant Assyrian who polluted the air with his blasphemies against Jehovah!

Little did Rabshakeh and Sennacherib know who they would really be fighting against. Little could they realize that Jerusalem would flourish long after Nineveh had become a heap of ruins. In accord with Isaiah 10:5-19, Nahum foretold in 1:8-10 the very manner in which the imperial city by the Tigris was to be destroyed. Secular history gives its testimony in the record of Ctesias that while a drunken feast was going on, the floodgates of the city were swept away by a sudden rise of the river, and the palace foundations were washed away. The Babylonian army, which had been besieging Nineveh for some time, entered by the breach, and burned the city while the inebriated inhabitants vainly tried to escape (see 3:11).

This would be proud Nineveh's deserved end. Meantime an evil counselor had come from Nineveh, scheming wickedness against the Lord (1:11). This is God's description of haughty Sennacherib, who may well be viewed as a type of the last great Assyrian, so often contemplated in the prophecies.

But all his boasting was in vain—he had invaded Judah only by Jehovah's permission. The Lord needed to discipline Judah for her sins, and He got the desired effect: Hezekiah and his princes were humbled before Him. Now God would act on their behalf. Though He had afflicted them, He would do so no more. The Assyrian hosts were blasted by the breath of His mouth, and Sennacherib himself was murdered a short time afterward by the hands of his own sons (14; see also Isaiah 37:36-38).

Freed from the Assyrian danger, Judah could keep her feasts in peace, rejoicing in the prophets God sent to encourage her. His messengers are spoken of in Isaiah 52:7 in almost the same language. Delivered and exultant, the people were called upon to perform their vows, for the army that had recently terrorized them would never return to their land.

Who can fail to see in all this a wonderful picture of the millennial blessing? Then the last coalition against Israel will be overthrown, and the Lord Jesus Himself will descend with "beautiful feet" upon the mountains to proclaim a peace that will never be disturbed.

NAHUM 2: The Destruction of Nineveh

It is important, in reading the prophets, to distinguish between what relates primarily to events long since fulfilled, and what addresses solely the future. Fulfilled prophecy is confirming proof of Scripture's divine inspiration. That which tells of what is to come is "a light shining in a dark place," enabling devout readers to put a proper value on that which they see around them.

On the other hand, all of prophecy is a connected whole; it must be read in view of what it all points to—the coming day of the Lord.

For many peoples and nations, however, that day has already come. Their course has been run; their abundant evils have been judged; and their civilizations have passed out of existence.

The glory of Nineveh has been nothing more than a memory for more than two and a half millennia. Nahum predicted this outcome at least a century before his words had their awful fulfillment in the Babylonian conquest. Nineveh's fall is given in detail in Nahum 2 and 3, a portion of Scripture (and of literature in general) unsurpassed for graphic delineation and poetic fervor.

"He that dasheth in pieces,"—the leader of the Chaldean hosts—is seen, in vision, coming up against Nineveh, who was proudly resting in her glory on the banks of the Tigris. Founded by Nimrod, as was her rival Babylon, Nineveh exemplified the world in its grandeur and independence of God; while Babylon modeled the religious world, the home of superstition and traditional ritual. The former would have to fall before the rising power of the latter, just as, centuries later, paganism had to succumb to an unholy, pseudo-Christianity that seemed to meet the need of humanity's hopeless depravity. Yet a certain question must occur to the thoughtful student: Which was worse—the world without God or the world with a perverted idea of God, wrapped in the darkness of medieval superstition and ignorance of the Scriptures of truth?

Nineveh could attempt to defend herself as best she may, but no power could avert her richly deserved judgment (Nahum 2:1). She had been the instrument used to punish Israel; but with the punishment over, Israel's ungodly enemies would not escape their own judgment. This principle is taught in 1 Peter 4:17-18—judgment begins at the house of God. What, then, about those who do not acknowledge Him? If He will not overlook His own people's sins, how solemn the day when the wicked have to answer for all their lawlessness! If God permits the powers of evil to mar the branches of the vine He planted Himself, who shall prevent the wild trees from being destroyed (Nahum 2:2)?

The appalling final assault on Nineveh is vividly described in verses 3-4. Since this passage has often been applied inappropriately, I quote it in full so that its true meaning will be clear in its context.

> The shield of his mighty men is made red, the valiant men are in scarlet: the chariots shall be with flaming torches in the day of his preparation, and the fir trees shall be terribly shaken. The chariots shall rage in the streets, they shall jostle one against another in the broad ways: they shall seem like torches, they shall run like the lightnings.

These verses strikingly portray the wild disorder that must have prevailed when the Babylonian army and their Median allies poured into the doomed city. Yet what strange and strained interpretations are often forced on so clear a passage! If it wasn't such a common view, who could believe that rational people would attempt to see here references to railroads, electric cars, and automobiles! Many sermons have been preached and books written, however, that declare such mechanical devices fulfill this portion of Nahum's prophecy. This is an instance of the careless way people sometimes read Scripture. Clearly, "the day of his preparation" was the day of Nineveh's destruction; and the "chariots with flaming torches," running "like the lightnings," were the war machines of the victorious Babylonians.

The king of Nineveh vainly tried to rally his warriors against the terrific onslaught. But drunk, as a result of their unholy feasts, the fighting men stumbled as they hurried to the wall, only to find it was too late to attempt a defense (5). The rise of the river opened the already weakened sluice gates, and the floods crumbled the foundations of the palace, drowning any hope of resistance (6).

Diodorus Siculus described the end of the siege in the following language:

> There was an old prophecy that Nineveh should not be taken till the river became an enemy to the city. And in the third year of the siege, the river being swollen with continual rains, overflowed every part of the city and broke down the wall for twenty furlongs; then the king, thinking that the oracle was fulfilled, and the river become an enemy to the city, built a large funeral pile in the palace, and collecting together all his wealth and his concubines and eunuchs, burnt himself and the palace

with them all; and the enemy entered at the breach that the waters had made and took the city.

Nineveh's pride was abased with violence; her people led away captive. She had arrogantly thought she would be established forever, but her end had come because she exalted herself against the Lord (7).

Verses 8-13 are too plain to require comment. In unmistakable language, they describe the desolation following the overthrow of what had been the world's most glorious city. So exactly were the words fulfilled that for ages the very site of Nineveh was lost. It wasn't until the nineteenth century that Layard and Rawlinson's excavations brought to light the ruins of a metropolis so vast that no one could doubt any longer Jonah's and Nahum's testimonies to its splendor and magnificence, and its destruction when in the very zenith of its glory.

It may be good to clarify that the lion of verses 11-12 is the king, and the lions and lionesses are his household who perished with him in his burning palace.

NAHUM 3: Beyond Healing

We have been reading of Nineveh's doom, and the last chapter continues the story, telling us that that doom was without remedy. But this last chapter does more. Its first four verses give us Jehovah's terrible indictment and show us why unsparing judgment had to fall upon Nineveh.

A city of blood, full of lies and robbery—such is the divine description. All Nineveh's glory was stained by the iniquity of its people (1). Cruel warfare and bloodthirsty carnage were its haughty inhabitants' delight. The sight of armies rushing together in battle was their joy. Nineveh seems to have been inbred with the spirit of its founder, Nimrod the Cushite, "a mighty hunter before the Lord" (Genesis 10:8-9)—taking pleasure in the wanton chase of nations for prey.

It is no wonder then that other nations would celebrate the Assyrians' fall beneath the power of their enemies (Nahum 3:2-3).

Immorality abounded; the filth of the flesh and spirit—prostitution and sorcery—were openly carried on and linked with the worship of their demon-gods (4). So Jehovah's face was against them, and He determined to make them an object lesson and a warning to all who would follow their deadly ways (5-6).

It was only a little before that their great king Sargon reputedly destroyed No Amon (called in the KJV "populous No") and carried her people into captivity. But Nineveh was equally guilty and must herself become a prey. In that day the surrounding nations would take up a taunt against her, crying, "Nineveh is laid waste: who will bemoan her?" (7) Her course had left her friendless and alone in the day of the Lord's anger. Imperious and vindictive, she sought only her own glorification and in no sense the welfare of the subject cities and provinces. So she had to learn that "righteousness [alone] exalteth a nation: but sin is a reproach to any people" (Proverbs 14:34). No human power can endure that persistently practices and encourages corruption and violence. The Most High rules in human kingdoms whether they acknowledge Him or not; and He puts down one people and exalts another at His own pleasure, taking into account all of their ways (Nahum 3:7-10).

The eleventh verse seems again to refer to the last drunken orgy to which, history tells us, the whole city was given up on the night of its awful fall.

Unable in any way to resist the invading hordes, Nineveh's very strongholds poured forth their inebriated hosts for destruction like a fig tree casting her first ripe figs into the eater's mouth when shaken (12). Thus her ruin was complete in the day when the fire devoured her palaces (13-15).

Destroyed like green leaves devoured by locusts, Nineveh's splendor reached its end. Verse 17 describes the Assyrians themselves as locusts that had been made numb by cold, unable to pursue their prey. And when they are warmed by the sun, they "flee away, and their place is not known where they are."

This was how Saracus, grandson of the famous Esar-haddon, Assyria's last king, would perish, together with all his nobles and his people (18). For the God he did not know nor cared to know, had solemnly declared, "There is no healing of thy bruise; thy wound is grievous: all that hear the bruit [or report] of thee shall clap the hands over thee: for upon whom hath not thy wickedness passed continually?" (19)

Nineveh has fallen to rise no more. Her mighty men have passed off the scene, together with all their guilt and sins, never again to be numbered among the living until that day

> When the sun is old, and the stars are cold,
> And the leaves of the judgment-book unfold.

But in the crisis of the last days a fierce and unholy power will occupy the land once dominated by Nineveh on the Tigris. It will have the traits and bitter hatred of God and His people that characterized Assyria. And, appearing in Asshur's spirit and power, it will be emphatically designated "*The* Assyrian" or "the king of the north," whose final doom is prefigured in Nineveh's fall of old.

Thus this prophecy of Nahum has for us a double value. It lets us know how completely God's prophetic Word has been fulfilled in the past, which assures our hearts of its literal fulfillment in the future. May we "eat the book" until our whole being is pervaded with its truth so that we may walk as strangers and pilgrims through a scene over which the Most High has written the awful word *TEKEL* (Daniel 5:27).

HABAKKUK

A PROFILE

HABAKKUK
THE PROPHET WITH A PROBLEM

BY JOHN PHILLIPS

Habakkuk (619-610 B.C.) has been called "the doubting Thomas of the Old Testament." He seems more concerned with solving a problem than with delivering a message. We can learn a valuable lesson from Habakkuk, for this man, when faced with a seemingly unsolvable problem, took it to God, instead of abandoning his faith as some would do. He was a contemporary of Jeremiah and clearly saw the handwriting on the wall for Judah. The rising power of the Chaldeans (the Babylonians) filled his vision, and herein lay his problem. That the Judeans were wicked was an obvious fact, but still they were the people of God. Habakkuk could see that God must punish sin, and that Judah could not possibly escape the chastening hand of God. But when he looked at the Babylonians, the people God would use to chastise Judah, he could see that they were worse than the Jews. How could God punish a nation by a less righteous nation? War is God's scourge, and with it He whips the rebellious nations. Habakkuk's problem is perennial and is as pertinent today as it was then. How Habakkuk took his doubts and difficulties to God and how he found his answer is the theme of the book.

Structure of Habakkuk

Habakkuk had a burden, a vision, and a prayer. In his short book we observe faith sighing, faith seeing, and faith singing.

- I. The Prophet Is Troubled (1)
  - A. By the Crimes of Judah (1:1-4)
  - B. By the Coming of Judgment (1:5-17)
    1. The Invincibility of the Chaldeans (1:5-11)
    2. The Iniquity of the Chaldeans (1:12-17)
- II. The Prophet Is Taught (2)
  God is righteous. This applies:
  - A. Individually (2:1-4)
  - B. Internationally (2:5-20)
    1. The Rapaciousness of the Chaldeans (2:5-8)
    2. The Relentlessness of the Chaldeans (2:9-11)
    3. The Ruthlessness of the Chaldeans (2:12-14)
    4. The Repulsiveness of the Chaldeans (2:15-18)
    5. The Religion of the Chaldeans (2:19-20)
- III. The Prophet Is Triumphant (3)
  - A. Faith Surrenders (3:1)
  - B. Faith Sees (3:2-16)
  - C. Faith Soars (3:17-19)

Lesson of Habakkuk

The key verse of Habakkuk is 2:4b: "The just shall live by his faith." This great statement is repeated three times in the New Testament (Romans 1:17; Galatians 3:11; Hebrews 10:38). Habakkuk, like so many of us, wanted to understand everything, but God showed him this could never be. Instead he must trust—trust God in the dark—for God is not going to give all the answers in this life.

When Habakkuk learned this simple lesson he soon discovered that God could be trusted. The world has the saying, "Seeing is believing," but faith replies, "Believing is seeing." God showed Habakkuk that if the Babylonians were going to be used to punish Judah, He in turn was going to visit the sins of the Babylonians upon their own heads in due time. But more, not only would the Babylonians be overthrown but ultimately God's loving purposes for His people would be fully realized. The book that opened with a sob closes with a song.

There has probably never been a darker hour in this world's history than the one in which we live. When our hearts begin to fail us with fear, looking on those things that are coming upon the earth, it is time to turn back to this little-known book of Habakkuk and again read his message. He tells us that "God is still on the throne" and that all appearances notwithstanding, His wise and loving purposes cannot be thwarted.

Deep in unfathomable mines
Of never failing skill,
He treasures up his bright designs
And works his sovereign will.
(William Cowper)

CHAPTER EIGHT

THE PROPHECY OF HABAKKUK

One of the shortest books of Scripture—the prophecy of Habakkuk—contains important truth that no reverent student of God's Word can afford to overlook. Brief as Habakkuk is, it is directly referred to and quoted from a number of times in the New Testament.

Paul, the great apostle to the Gentiles was particularly partial to it. He found in Habakkuk the inspired authority for the fundamental doctrine of justification by faith, as well as the certainty of judgment on all who reject the Holy Spirit's testimony about the Lord Jesus Christ. Compare Paul's word in Acts 13:40-41 with Habakkuk 1:5; and Romans 1:17, Galatians 3:11, and Hebrews 10:38 with Habakkuk 2:4. There also seems to be a close connection between Habakkuk 3:17-18 and Philippians 4. We will look more closely at these passages further on in our study.

Very little is known about Habakkuk personally. Like John the Baptist, he is "the voice of One," but he himself is hidden. The turmoil of his spirit, however, is vividly portrayed in his compelling and soul-stirring prophetic poem. Jewish tradition asserts that he was from the tribe of Simeon, and he is commonly supposed to have been Jeremiah's contemporary during the latter part of "the weeping prophet's" ministry. Habakkuk's book seems to corroborate this, since it was written in view of the Chaldean (Babylonian) invasion. We have no record of his birth or death. He is said to have remained in the land when most of the people were carried away by the triumphant armies of Nebuchadnezzar.

The literary form of the book is a dialogue, and the structure is very simple. Habakkuk, overwhelmed by the prevalence of evil, unburdened his heart to Jehovah, who in grace answered His servant's cry. The divisions are easily found. Chapter 1, verses 1-4 give the prophet's complaint. Verses 5-11 are the Lord's answer. Then in verses 12-17, we have Habakkuk's protest to the Lord's answer. Verse 1 of chapter 2 stands by itself, since there is no immediate reply to the cry that ended chapter 1. In 2:2-4 the Lord went far beyond the prophet's thoughts and predicted the final blessing through the Messiah. In the meantime "the just shall live by his faith." The actual response to Habakkuk's challenge at the end of chapter 1 is given in 2:5-8. The balance of the chapter records prophetic rebukes. Having been made to understand the Lord's plans, His servant delivers His word to four classes of people who do not walk in His ways. A woe is pronounced on each of them: the covetous, verses 9-11; the unrighteous, verses 12-14; the intemperate and shameless, verses 15-17; and the idolatrous, verses 18-20. Chapter 3 concludes with the prayer of Habakkuk, one of the most precious and sublime portions of Old Testament Scripture.

While Habakkuk's prophecy primarily applies to Judah and Babylon in the dark days following Josiah's death (the same period covered by the major portion of Jeremiah), this book contains crucial principles applicable to all of the Lord's people in all times. As the apostle Paul wrote in Romans, "Whatever things were written aforetime were written for our learning" (15:4). So we would do well to reflect on Habakkuk's searching chapters, listening like the prophet himself to see what the Lord will say to us, and what we shall answer when we are reproved.

That God would so patiently and personally meet the longing cry of His servant's heart is greatly encouraging. As David wrote, He hears the cry of the humble, but "the proud he knoweth afar off" (Psalm 138:6). "The meek will he guide in judgment; and the meek will he teach his way" (Psalm 25:9). Unquestionably, the overriding reason we get so little out of God's Word is our appalling lack of self-judgment and brokenness before its Author. Pride, arrogance, and self-sufficiency, resulting in intellectualism and disputes, abound on all sides. And they are accompanied by moral looseness and a gross lack of discernment. Faithful obedience to God and His Word is very little known or esteemed.

It seems we have largely forgotten that entering into the things of

God requires first a right moral state, for spiritual things "are spiritually discerned" (1 Corinthians 2:14). Consequently, carnal, self-complacent Christians often try to make up for lack of genuine, Spirit-given ministry by filling themselves with empty platitudes. These expressions may be true and precious enough in themselves, but often they are merely learned by rote and given out in a mechanical, parrotlike manner. Instead such Christians ought to be waiting on God until His voice is heard in their souls, thus moving the consciences of speaker and hearer alike.

In a day like the present, when "of making many books there is no end" (Ecclesiastes 12:12), it is very easy for any person of average intelligence to acquire a fair mental acquaintance with the truths of Scripture. It is easy also to pose in the presence of less educated or unspiritual persons as a fount of divine wisdom; when in reality the holy eye of God sees nothing but conceit and self-sufficiency in it all. Truth taken from others' devotion to God is often retailed out to admiring crowds of worldly Christians and Christless churchgoers who are incapable of true, godly discernment. The men who dispense God's truth in this way know little or nothing of its power in their own souls, or of the quiet reverence before God consistent with what they teach.

This is especially true when it comes to Scripture's teaching about the church. How many today talk glibly of the one body and the unity of the Spirit, but they do not appear to have a particle of real concern. They deny the truth of that unity by identifying with unscriptural and heretical systems that in practice deny Christ as the Head of the church, and refuse the Holy Spirit His true place. Instead they construct a human system of clergy and laity that replaces the divine order laid down in the Book of God!

Many who doubtless know Jesus as Savior and the Holy Ghost as the pledge of their inheritance have never learned to truly acknowledge Christ as the church's one Head, and the Holy Spirit as the controlling power in the assembly. For many this is unquestionably due to ignorance, and the great Shepherd of the sheep will take into account their lack of instruction when "we must all appear before the judgment seat of Christ" (2 Corinthians 5:10). But how many of us can really plead ignorance? We boast of our knowledge, even while our concern for the church's condition is glaringly absent. How blind!

Truly, liberalism and self-sovereignty are the order of the day. Spiritual sensitivity is sadly lacking, which accounts for the widespread indifference to Christ and the truth.

In Habakkuk we see the very opposite of all this. He was a man deeply attuned both to the state of his people (as well as his own state) and God's sovereignty. Nor could he rest until he had discovered God's purpose and perspective. His book therefore is of special value in our degenerate and indifferent times, characterized by what someone has called "high truth and low walk." It strikingly portrays spiritual awareness and the divine response to it, found in a man like ourselves, as each chapter will make clear.

HABAKKUK 1: The Prophet's Perplexity

The opening verses of Habakkuk 1 reveal the anguish of the prophet's soul because of Judah's decadent condition. His nation was dear to his heart, not only because they were his people, but because he knew they were Jehovah's special treasure. Now, sadly, the people of His glory were defiled and marred by sin.

> The burden which Habakkuk the prophet did see. O Lord, how long shall I cry, and thou wilt not hear! even cry out unto thee of violence, and thou wilt not save! Why dost thou show me iniquity, and cause me to behold grievance? for spoiling and violence are before me: and there are that raise up strife and contention. Therefore the law is slacked, and judgment doth never go forth: for the wicked doth compass about the righteous; therefore wrong judgment proceedeth (1-4).

In a few graphic touches Habakkuk depicted, as by a master hand, the various evils afflicting the unhappy nation. He took no delight in portraying the sins of those he so tenderly loved. And it was into God's ear, not man's, that he poured out his complaint. For he had been crying to Him for a long time; and now, overwhelmed with a sense of hopelessness for their recovery, he appealed to Jehovah with deepest anguish and concern.

Would his prayer go unheard? If not, how long must he plead before the Lord gave any evidence that He had heard and would intervene? He felt, as many of us have, that it would have been better not to have seen the evil than to see it and feel the unending agony of it in his sensitive soul.

Today, in Christendom's present discordant state, there is a similar danger of those who are able to see things in the light of God's Word desiring to turn a blind eye to it, rather than bear the pain of it. There are some who, conscious of the declining state of the church and aware of the unholy influences at work, can still be indifferent to it all. In doing so, they show their lack of real heart for what so intimately concerns the glory of God and the welfare of His saints. Others, whose eyes have been anointed and whose consciences have been stirred by the Holy Spirit, are in danger of being unduly oppressed and disheartened by the rising power of the mystery of iniquity. Seeing all around them dishonor done to Christ and the truth abandoned, they sink in spirit from the weight of the seemingly irremediable conditions prevailing.

Needless to say, both perspectives are wrong. No spiritually awake soul should or could be indifferent. But none need be disheartened either, for everything has long been under God's control. This was true with Israel; it is true with the church. No failure on our part can thwart the purposes of God.

In regard to Judah, the greatest danger was from the spirit of strife and contention permeating the people, which gave rise to corruption and violence. God's law was ignored, and justice was miscarried. The wicked were in power, and perverted laws proceeded from them.

It was enough to bring one to one's knees, not as a person competent to judge others, but as one who was a part of that which had so grievously failed. This is where Habakkuk found himself. He sighed and cried for the abominations done in what had once been the holy city.

Jehovah did not ignore His servant's cry. He answered him, telling of the punishment He had prepared for the instruction of His disobedient and rebellious people. "Behold ye among the heathen, and regard, and wonder marvellously: for I will work a work in your days, which ye will not believe, though it be told you" (5). Paul quoted this verse at Antioch of Pisidia when he warned the Jews of the danger of rejecting the gospel of Christ (Acts 13:40-41). In Paul's day the wondrous work no one would believe even though it was told to them was the work of grace accomplished on Calvary's cross. In the Lord's reply to Habakkuk, it was His strange work of judgment.

Though it seems inconceivable, the Lord was raising up the Chaldeans—"that bitter and hasty nation"—to "march through the breadth of the land, to possess the dwellingplaces that are not their's" (Habakkuk 1:6). Terrifying and vicious, carrying out what they thought were the purposes of their own hearts, the Babylonians would unleash their armies against Jerusalem, like an eagle hurtling toward its prey! They would be allowed to overrun all the power and dignity of Judah; which would only make them more arrogant, as they ascribed their victory and power to their false gods. This was how Jehovah was about to deal with His wayward people (7-11).

There is a weighty lesson here for us. Long ago, regarding the Egyptians, we are told that God "turned their heart to hate his people" (Psalm 105:25). In our shortsightedness we might only have seen the energy of Satan's power; but it was the Lord who used even Satan to chasten His people. And so it is here in Habakkuk: the Lord is the One who would bring the armies of Nebuchadnezzar to the gates of Zion!

Hasn't God also dealt in a similar manner with the church? We frequently deplore its divisions and the distressing state of Christendom, particularly those of us who know God's desire for the church. But aren't these very things evidences of the Lord's discipline? He loves His people too well to allow them to succeed and remain united when pride and worldliness have displaced humility and heavenly-mindedness. So He permits the power of Satan to work, and the result is scattering. How this should produce confession and brokenness on our part!

In Habakkuk's case, he was amazed that God would deal with the sheep of His pasture in this manner, giving them into the power of the wild beast of the nations. He knew discipline was deserved, but he was astounded to learn who the agent of their punishment would be. So he immediately turned to the Lord again, praying earnestly, "Art thou not from everlasting, O Lord my God, mine Holy One? we shall not die. O Lord, thou hast ordained them for judgment; and, O mighty God, thou hast established them for correction" (12).

His faith was simple and beautiful. Judah was in a covenant

relationship with the everlasting One, who "will not call back his words" (Isaiah 31:2). Therefore, no matter how severely they would be afflicted, they could never be utterly cut off. They needed to be corrected, but they would never be forever abandoned without violating the covenant of David.

Nevertheless, the prophet still could not understand how such an evil nation could be the Lord's instrument for punishing His wayward people. "Thou art of purer eyes than to behold evil, and canst not look on iniquity," he rightly declared. But then he asked in perplexity, "Wherefore lookest thou upon them that deal treacherously, and holdest thy tongue when the wicked devoureth the man that is more righteous than he?" (Habakkuk 1:13) He went on to recount the Babylonians' cruelties and iniquities, their inhumanity, and their gross idolatry—of which Babylon was the mother. If the Babylonians were permitted to take Judah in their net, wouldn't they give the glory to their own prowess and to their false and revengeful gods? How could so perverse a people be Jehovah's instrument? This has perplexed more people than Habakkuk—this toleration and use of the wicked to further God's purposes.

The chapter closes without an answer. But in chapter 2 a reply is given that is altogether worthy of God, far transcending the prophet's highest thoughts and leading to humility of soul in His holy presence.

HABAKKUK 2: On the Watch Tower

There is nothing harder for people to do than wait on God. The restlessness of the flesh will not tolerate delay; it counts time spent in waiting and watching as time lost. Habakkuk, however, was wonderfully different. Since God did not at once reply to his eager, anxious questions, Habakkuk took the attitude of the patient learner, remaining silent until the Master was ready to communicate His thoughts. "I will stand upon my watch, and set me upon the tower, and will watch to see what he will say unto me, and what I shall answer when I am reproved" (1).

His words expressed a right spiritual condition. Acknowledging his inability to pierce the mystery of God's ways, he anticipated that he may require reproof. Still, he took his stand on the watchtower, above the mists of earth and beyond the clamor of humanity, where he could quietly wait to see what God's answer would be.

Such an attitude ensures an answer. God will not leave His servant without instruction if he has a willing mind and a tender conscience.

As Habakkuk maintained his lonely watch, Jehovah answered, telling him, "Write the vision, and make it plain upon tables, that he may run that readeth it" (2). The prophecy about to be revealed was not for the prophet alone but, through him, for everyone. This truth was of great importance and was far-reaching in its application. Therefore Habakkuk needed to write it clearly so that he who read it would proclaim the message far and near.

"For the vision is yet for an appointed time, but at the end it shall speak, and not lie: though it tarry, wait for it; because it will surely come, it will not tarry" (3). The declaration would go beyond the present to have a fuller, wider application at a future time the Lord will appoint. God directed the prophet to look ahead to this day of blessing.

We know from Hebrews 10:37 that Habakkuk really was pointing to Messiah's reign. When the writer of Hebrews quoted Habakkuk, he changed the pronouns from neuter to an intensely personal form. To Christ alone do these prophetic words refer. "For yet a little while, and he that shall come will come, and will not tarry." At the time the apostle wrote, Jesus had already come the first time, only to be rejected and crucified. But He is coming back again, coming in a "very, very little while," as the words might be rendered. When He returns He will abolish all wrongdoing, and see that justice triumphs at last. Then the prophet's yearnings will be fulfilled. The mystery of God's long toleration of evil will be ended, and the reign of righteousness shall have come in.

Habakkuk looked forward to this period of blessing, but self-willed people would not. Of them it could be said, "Behold, his soul which is lifted up is not upright in him." Yet, no matter how much wickedness may triumph, Habakkuk was assured that "the just shall live by his faith" (4).

This was the prophecy Habakkuk was constrained to write so clearly. This was the word the reader would run to declare.

Such a reader, and such a runner, was the apostle Paul. This verse was the keynote of his instruction to both saint and sinner. Having read the prophet's words with eyes anointed by the Holy Ghost, he ran the rest of his days to make them known to others. These words occur three times in his Epistles, and in each place they were used with a different object in view.

In Romans, as Paul expounded the glorious doctrine of the righteousness of God as revealed in the gospel (1:16-17), he found in Habakkuk's words the inspired answer to the question raised ages ago in the book of Job, "How then can man be justified with God?" (Job 9:2; 25:4) Triumphantly Paul pointed to the revelation of the watchtower and exclaimed, "The just shall live by faith"!

In the Galatian churches Judaizing teachers sought to turn the Christians away from the simplicity of Christ, implying that while it was by faith they were saved, the law was the rule of life afterwards. Paul indignantly repudiated their false assertion by declaring that faith was not only their foundation with God, but their life: "the just shall live by faith" (Galatians 3:11). He immediately showed that "the law is not of faith"; therefore it could not be the Christian's standard. Christ, and Christ alone, is that. In Him we are a new creation. "And as many as walk according to *this rule*, peace be on them, and mercy, and upon the Israel of God" (Galatians 6:16, emphasis added).

The third use occurs in Hebrews, where Paul traced the pilgrim's path through this world from the cross to glory. Here he showed that only by entering into the power of the unseen can the believer be sustained through a life of trial and conflict. Once more he declared, "The just shall live by faith" (Hebrews 10:38). He added, "But if any man draw back, my soul shall have no pleasure in him," which is the first half of the verse in the Septuagint's rendering.

So the secret made known to Habakkuk so long ago has become the watchword of Christianity. At the Reformation, it very fittingly became the battle cry of Luther and his colleagues.

It was crucial then for Habakkuk to look beyond and above what his natural eyes could see. Only in this way could he endure "as seeing him who is invisible" (Hebrews 11:27). And we need to do this today. There is much in life to dishearten and discourage us. But as dark as the times may be, the man of God by turning in faith to the Holy Scriptures will find the mind of the Lord. He will obediently act on what is written, no matter what others may do. The path may be lonely, and the heart often sad, but with hopeful anticipation the person after God's heart will look forward to the day of the Lord's coming and seek to walk *now* in the light of *then.*

Because Habakkuk lived each day in light of God's future, he could see everything clearly and was able to judge ungodly and spiritual men at their true value. The Babylonians proudly boasted of their god's help in overthrowing the people of Jehovah. Habakkuk, however, was shown that they were only an instrument used for Jehovah's present discipline, and they would soon be paid double for all their sins.

Self-important like the false world-church of today, Babylon would gather the world into its fold and stifle everything of God. The hour of doom, though, was coming, when the nation would be the sport of the people, who would taunt, "Woe to him that increaseth that which is not his!" Suddenly Babylon's enemies would arise, and destroy them because of their bloodguiltiness and blasphemy against Jehovah (5-8).

In the meantime, though times were hard for the little flock who sought to walk in obedience to God, the trusting soul looked up in holy confidence, and knew that the triumph of the wicked was short. This was how "the just shall live by his faith."

In every age, when deterioration sets in, those who would live for God have found themselves in a position similar to that of Habakkuk. Jeremiah, his companion-prophet, felt the decline most keenly, but grace sustained him through it all. We would be wise to follow their example in our day, when the Word of God is in large measure abandoned, and human resources take the place of divine precepts. We should be found walking humbly in the path of faith, able to say, "All my springs are in thee" (Psalm 87:7).

The woes that follow in Habakkuk 2:9-20 apply not only to Babylon's king and his cruel, relentless armies, but they also reveal God's mind regarding any who walk in the same unholy ways.

"Woe to him that coveteth..."! The sentence, uncompleted, makes this sin stand out all the clearer. It was covetousness that drew the hordes of Babylon to the gates of Jerusalem. Nebuchadnezzar would add "an evil gain to his house" (literal rendering) so he could exalt himself and "set his nest on high." Though he might build an opulent palace by means of the spoil he had taken, the very stones of the walls would cry out, and the beams would answer, "Woe to him that buildeth a town with blood, and stablisheth a city by iniquity!" (9-12) Sin springs out of covetousness, as Paul wrote, "The love of money is the root of all evil" (1 Timothy 6:10). That is, lust for wealth is a prolific root for every kind of iniquity to spring from.

Covetousness is unquestionably the definitive sin of today. It insidiously creeps in and latches onto God's people as well as the world's. Yet it is a sin that the Word of God solemnly warns against. It has been the downfall of many principled people and has destroyed the pilgrim character of thousands.

What exactly is covetousness? And how do we distinguish it from sensible thrift and a proper use of honest opportunities? In our King James Bibles four words express the one sin—*covetousness*, *concupiscence*, *lust*, and *desire*. Believers are exhorted to "be content with such things as ye have" (Hebrews 13:5). We also read, "Having food and raiment let us be therewith content" (1 Timothy 6:8). Covetousness is the opposite of contentment. It is the heart's unsatisfied craving for more than God has been pleased to give. "Covetousness," we are told, "is idolatry" (Colossians 3:5). It is plain then that the covetous person puts gain between his soul and God. Anything that turns our hearts away from Him is an idol. By this we may readily test ourselves as to where we stand.

The Bible doesn't praise the lazy and the shiftless but denounces them, recommending instead thrift and energy. But to run to the other extreme and set our hearts on business and the accumulation of wealth is equally fatal to spirituality. The happy medium is presented by the Holy Spirit, who tells us to be "fervent in spirit, serving the Lord" (Romans 12:11). When *He* is served, everything else will fall into place. We can then use this world, not directing it as if it were our own, but in recognition of being God's stewards.

One cannot help feeling that, if we really took this to heart, we would hear less of Christians getting involved in doubtful (not to say shady) business schemes because of alluring profits. The failure of these plans often brings dishonor on that holy name by which we are called. It may be prescribed as an axiom that no saint should be in any way connected with any business, however profitable, that could not bear the searching inspection of the One whose "eyes [are] like unto a flame of fire" (Revelation 2:18).

Otherwise, it may seem that success and prosperity are assured, but it will ultimately turn out like Habakkuk wrote, "Behold, is it not of the Lord of hosts that the people shall labour in the very fire, and the people shall weary themselves for very vanity?" (Habakkuk 2:13) Another passage says, "Behold, all ye that kindle a fire, that compass yourselves about with sparks: walk in the light of your fire, and in the sparks that ye have kindled. This shall ye have of mine hand; ye shall lie down in sorrow" (Isaiah 50:11). How many have fulfilled this prophecy! Laboring in the very fire, they have exhausted themselves pursuing emptiness. Kindling their own fire and walking in the light of its sparks, they have had to lie down in sorrow because they neglected God's Word.

However great the apparent triumph of sin in the present time may be, the outlook is bright for people of faith. When the present evil age passes away, "the earth shall be filled with the knowledge of the glory of the Lord, as the waters cover the sea" (Habakkuk 2:14). Whoever would have a part in the coming day of glory would gladly have surrendered all present gain if they could only live once more a life of faith instead of rejecting the Lord and Redeemer! But it will be too late then to be faithful. Because for all of our self-seeking we will "suffer loss" (1 Corinthians 3:15), while those who have kept the end in sight will have a glorious entrance into God's everlasting kingdom.

The next woe is directed at those who get their neighbors drunk in order to take advantage of and shame them. This pictures the grossest hypocrisy: speaking kindly while hatred fills the heart. It is an unholy deception that leads one to offer a seemingly pleasant but intoxicating drink to others in order to accomplish their ruin (Habakkuk 2:15-17). How terrible will Jehovah's vengeance be! To be the cause of someone's stumbling is to draw down judgment on one's own head. It would be better for the person who causes one of Christ's little ones to fall to have a millstone tied to his neck and be thrown into the depths of the sea (Matthew 18:6).

The final woe Habakkuk announced was against idolatry. Babylon boasted in the making and worshiping of idols. But the idol and its worshiper would perish together in the hour of Jehovah's fury (Habakkuk 2:18-19). The Lord alone is God over all, blessed forever, now revealed in flesh in our Lord Jesus Christ.

"The Lord is in his holy temple: let all the earth keep silence before him" (20). When the Lord speaks, it is for us to hear and bow in submission to His Word. When Habakkuk heard His voice, his anxious questions vanished. His heart was at rest, and his soul bowed in awe before the majesty of Jehovah's glory. May we too be of the same chastened and humbled spirit!

HABAKKUK 3: The Prayer of Habakkuk

The true purpose of ministry is to move people to humble their souls in the presence of God and draw their hearts to Him in worship and adoration. This was what Habakkuk did. He had been admitted into the secret counsels of Jehovah. God's word had entered his soul with power. The result was that he prostrated himself before the Lord in prayer and worship. His prayer-poem is one of the most sublime portions of the Old Testament. He was, as it were, overpowered by God's majesty and omnipotence so that he trembled before Him. Nevertheless he looked up with confidence to the only One who could bring revival and blessing to His chastened people, who were so rightfully under His rod because of their sins.

The term *Shigionoth* in the introductory line indicates that this prayer-poem was set to music. How blessed it is when our prayers and supplications take on the character of praise!

> Be careful for nothing; but in everything by prayer and supplication *with thanksgiving* let your requests be made known unto God. And the peace of God, which passeth all understanding, shall keep your hearts and minds through Christ Jesus (Philippians 4:6-7, emphasis added).

Praise is fitting to the lips of sinners saved by sovereign grace, however trying and perplexing their circumstances may be at times. David, for example, composed a psalm when he was in deep affliction. Psalm 7 is described as "Shiggaion of David, which he sang unto the Lord, concerning the words of Cush the Benjamite." Cush is generally thought to be another name for Shimei, who cursed David as he fled from his son Absalom. *Shiggaion* is the singular of *Shigionoth.* The actual meaning is not known with certainty, though many believe it means, "A wandering ode." In this way, then, the prophet poured out his heart to the all-glorious One, who from of old had been the deliverer and the support of His redeemed people.

> O [Jehovah], I have heard thy speech, and was afraid:
> O [Jehovah], revive thy work in the midst of the years,
> In the midst of the years make known;
> In wrath remember mercy (Habakkuk 3:2).

The word of the Lord filled Habakkuk with fear as he realized something of the depravity of his own heart and the state of his people. Like Isaiah, he could cry, "Woe is me! For I am undone; because I am a man of unclean lips, and I dwell in the midst of a people of unclean lips" (Isaiah 6:5). He could not plead on the ground of his merit. But as he remembered the God to whom he was supplicating, he could plead with confidence and assurance for revival and blessing.

Because a people are under God's judgment for their failure to carry out His revealed will is no reason to sink in despair and conclude that their light has been extinguished and their testimony nullified. It is unbelief, not godly submission, that leads saints to take this view. To make failure a reason for further unfaithfulness is to walk in self-will and lose the force of the very lesson that God wants us to learn. Like Habakkuk, we have reason to be dispirited; but, like him too, we can count on God to be with us when we are low.

Habakkuk pleaded for revival—revival, which we know God was pleased to grant when the discipline had accomplished His purpose for His people. The remnant, delivered from Babylon, confessed God's grace in giving "a little reviving" in their bondage (Ezra 9:8). We may be assured that our God would be delighted to give us revival now if He discerns that same spirit of humble submission to His will that we see here.

The wondrous way Jehovah led Jacob like a flock through the wilderness during the ancient exodus is the basis of Habakkuk's prayer for mercy. "God came from Teman and the Holy One from mount Paran....His glory covered the heavens, and the earth was full of his praise." The mighty One of Israel marched through the desert, spreading terror among the pagan nations while filling His redeemed with rejoicing (Habakkuk 3:3-6). He who had cared for His people before, would care for them still, no matter how the enemy might rage.

Like a glorious panorama, the scene unfolded before Habakkuk's eyes. He saw the fiery pillar driving out the hostile nations before Israel and lighting a path for the armies of the Lord. He watched the floods rolling back to permit the Lord's chosen to pass through the dry seabeds. He saw the mystic river springing from the rock Moses struck. He resumed the song of the book of Jasher, which told of the day the sun and moon stood still in their courses so Israel could rout their enemies (Joshua 10:13). He heard the shout of the victor and the wail of the vanquished. And when he realized that the Shepherd of Israel was still faithful, though so dreadfully dishonored, his heart trembled and his lips quivered at the voice of the Majesty. All of his self-confidence slipped away, and his heart trembled as he waited patiently for the day of trouble that was so soon to come upon the land. Truly it had begun, for the invader had already come up with his troops.

All this is proof that revival had already taken place in Habakkuk's soul at least. Oh, if we would only enter more fully into the same spirit!

The last three verses are the expression of a truly revived man who has learned to find all his springs in God. The apostle Paul spoke in a similar strain in the fourth chapter of Philippians. In fact, his words parallel so closely the idea we have here that, as noted in the introduction, it would seem that he had this very Scripture in mind when writing his Epistle. Habakkuk wrote:

> Although the fig tree shall not blossom,
> Neither shall fruit be in the vines;
> The labour of the olive shall fail,
> And the fields shall yield no meat;
> The flock shall be cut off from the fold,
> And there shall be no herd in the stalls:
> Yet I will rejoice in the Lord,
> I will joy in the God of my salvation.
> The Lord God is my strength,
> And he will make my feet like hinds' feet,
> And he will make me to walk upon mine high places.
> To the chief singer, on my stringed instruments.

How great the difference in the opening and the closing of Habakkuk's prophecy! He began as a troubled man, bewildered and confused, filled with questions. He closed as one who had found the answer to all his questions, satisfying his soul in God Himself. This is most blessed. As we journey with Habakkuk from perplexity to resolution, we get a sense of what God could do to strengthen our own hearts—if we will permit Him to have His own way with us in all things. For Habakkuk, crops might fail, flocks be destroyed, fields be barren, and cattle be cut off; but God would abide, and in Him was an abundant supply to meet every need. He is the God of our salvation too. He is the strength of our hearts. What more can we desire?

Content in this glorious realization, Habakkuk—and we too—could walk in faith on our high places, far above the mists and snares of earth. Like the wild goats of Psalm 104:18, we will be enabled to climb to the top of the rocks and dwell in the high hills. Surely if a child of God from a past dispensation could so triumph over all circumstances, we who live in the full blaze of the day of grace may very well be stirred to a holy jealousy. Because we continually dwell in the heavenlies, we can overcome through the power of faith every day (Ephesians 2:4-7)!

The closing line is the dedication, and it is unspeakably precious. The Chief Singer on the stringed instruments is, for us, none other than our Lord Jesus Christ, who as the risen One now leads the praises of His redeemed. As His hand sweeps the strings of the hearts of His people, what strains of heavenly music greet the ear of our God and Father. Even angelic hosts learn through the church the manifold wisdom of God. "In the midst of the congregation will I praise thee," He has said, as His Spirit spoke through the prophet-poet in Psalm 22:22. Whenever His people are gathered in His peerless name, He is in their midst as the director of their worship as well as the object of their adoration.

How sad that so many of our hearts are so often out of tune. Only by constantly examining ourselves and our walk in the Spirit will we be prepared to add to the sweetness of the great orchestra of the Chief Singer!

ZEPHANIAH

A PROFILE
ZEPHANIAH
THE ROYAL PROPHET
BY JOHN PHILLIPS

Zephaniah (634-625 B.C.) gives his ancestry more fully than any of the other prophets. Mention is made of "Hizkiah" in his opening sentence, and there is every reason to believe that this name is the same as Hezekiah. Zephaniah would therefore be the great-great-grandson of that illustrious and godly king of Judah. He would also be related to good King Josiah in whose reign he ministered. This would make Zephaniah a contemporary of Jeremiah and, probably, a leading figure in the great religious revival in Josiah's day.

Background of Zephaniah

The kings of Judah vacillated between good and evil, between the worship of the living God and the worship of idols. Each revival and reformation was followed by a lapse back into idolatry; only with each return to paganism, Judah sank lower than before. Little lasting effect resulted from the various reforms, for it always seemed to be the old story of "too little and too late." Josiah's valiant attempts to bring the nation back to God represented the last flicker of the nation's candle before it was finally extinguished. In Babylon, the cradle of idolatry, the nation would have to learn the hard and bitter way that idolatry is a mockery and a lie.

Themes of Zephaniah

Zephaniah's prophecies were pronouncements of wrath to come, and over and over again he spoke of "the great day of God." He looked squarely at the coming Babylonian invasion with all its horrors and then, borne on the wings of divine inspiration, looked far beyond that terrible event to even worse sufferings for the Jews at the end of the age. Like Jeremiah, Zephaniah's clear prophetic vision took in other nations besides Judah. So far as his main subject is concerned, he stands shoulder to shoulder with Joel, mentioning "the day of the Lord" some twenty times within the compass of his short book.

Zephaniah can be divided into discussion of the determination of the Lord, the day of the Lord, and the deliverance of the Lord.

I. The Determination of the Lord (1:1-6)
  A. To Judge Fully (1:2-4)
  B. To Judge Fairly (1:5-6)
II. The Day of the Lord (1:7—3:8)
  A. The People Mentioned (1:7-13)
    1. The Mighty: Too Independent to Listen (1:7-8)
    2. The Mob: Too Iniquitous to Listen (1:9)
    3. The Merchants: Too Involved to Listen (1:10-11)
    4. The Majority: Too Indifferent to Listen (1:12-13)
  B. The Period Mentioned (1:14-18)
    1. Its Nearness (1:14)
    2. Its Nature (1:15-18)
  C. The Places Mentioned (2:1—3:8)
III. The Deliverance of the Lord (3:9-20)
  A. Israel's Regathering (3:9-10)
  B. Israel's Repentance (3:11-13)
  C. Israel's Rejoicing (3:14-15)
  D. Israel's Redeemer (3:16-20)

It is interesting to see how God asserts His sovereignty both in terms of judgment (1:2-4) and in terms of mercy (3:18-20). The emphasis in both these portions is on the divine assertion, "I will."

Joel, Hosea, Amos, Micah, Isaiah, and other prophets besides Zephaniah make mention of the "day of the Lord." It is toward this great focal point of Hebrew prophecy that world events are surely moving so rapidly today. The same theme is picked up in the New Testament in 2 Thessalonians 2:2. The nature of the "day of the Lord" should not be confused with the nature of the "day of Christ." The first has to do with Israel and the nations, the second with the church. The day of the Lord has to do with that coming time when the wrath of God will be poured out upon the earth and to the time of blessing thereafter. It is one of the chief themes of the book of Revelation.

Zephaniah has none of the tender wooing of Jeremiah. Instead, he hammers hard at the nation's conscience. However, he does end on a happier note, looking beyond the time of wrath to the blessings that follow. His message was pertinent to his own day and generation, and it is pertinent to ours as well.

CHAPTER NINE

THE PROPHECY OF ZEPHANIAH

Practically nothing is known about the prophet Zephaniah beyond what he himself told us in the first verse of his book. He traced his lineage back through four generations, and he ministered "in the days of Josiah the son of Amon, king of Judah." Those were days of blessing and revival for a remnant; but the majority of the people, though outwardly reformed, were in the sad state described in this book and in the early chapters of Jeremiah. The Holy Spirit's aim in Zephaniah was therefore to warn the formalists of coming judgment and comfort the hearts of the godly remnant who had little strength, yet had not denied God's name.

The prophecy of Zephaniah has much in common with Christ's letter to the church at Philadelphia in Revelation 3:7-13—and with our day as well. Many boast in Laodicean pride (see Revelation 3:14-22), walking in complete indifference to the Word of God, while a feeble remnant clings to that Word and seeks to honor Him who gave it. Such devoted people may be like Zephaniah himself, whose name means, "Hidden of Jehovah." Though this faithful remnant is unknown to the world, they are well known to God who speaks of a coming hour when the proud opposers of truth will "come and worship before thy feet, and...know that I have loved thee" (Revelation 3:9).

The very fact that a remnant is at any time distinguished from the majority implies that the latter are ripe for judgment. For when all goes as it should, there is no reason for the faithful to be set apart in this way. Therefore this prophecy has much to say about the coming of the Lord when everything will be dealt with in the light of

His revealed will. Zephaniah spoke of judgment about to fall—first on Judah and Jerusalem (the ten tribes had been carried into Assyria nearly a century earlier), then on all the surrounding nations. For, if God begins with His people, He will not stop there. All must know the power of His anger when He holds them accountable for their ways.

The three chapters of Zephaniah may be considered as three topical divisions. Chapter 1 presents the general truth about the coming day of judgment upon Judah. Chapter 2 gives the judgment of the nations. Chapter 3 is the indictment of Jerusalem, with the customary promise of restoration after the purging of the tribulation.

Zephaniah was contemporary with Jeremiah for at least a part of the latter's ministry, but he probably passed off the scene before the predicted destruction of Jerusalem was fulfilled.

ZEPHANIAH 1: The Day of the Lord

We find in Zephaniah 1:2-6 the declaration of Jehovah's impending judgment against His chosen people. He was about to consume everything in the land. Man and beast, fowl and fish, all would feel the stroke of judgment. These verses speak of utter desolation—the result of bloody warfare. Judah and Jerusalem would be given up to the woes of which they had been warned for so long. They had turned away from the Lord who would have been their Savior, to follow Baal, the demon of the heathen. God would not stop until He had wiped out every vestige of Baal-worship from the land. The idolatrous priests who had deceived the people would be eliminated until their very names would be forgotten. Those who worshiped the heavenly bodies, along with those who professed to follow the Lord but also swore by Malcham—all would be included in the coming doom. Malcham is generally identified with Milcom or Molech. The Israelites were warned against his abominable worship, with its human sacrifices, when they first entered the land (Leviticus 20:1-5). However, many adopted his vile service early on.

Those appointed to die were divided into two groups in the sixth verse: "Them that are turned back from the Lord: and those that have not sought the Lord, nor inquired for him." Some had initially heeded Josiah's call to repentance, and they tried to obey the Lord's voice for awhile. But, putting their hand to the plow, they looked back and reverted to their old, idolatrous ways. Others had never known, nor cared to know, the mind of God. All would perish in the approaching destruction.

Beginning with verse 7, we have a more detailed account of the manner in which the awful judgments would be carried out. Notice that, while the prophet doubtless had in mind the Babylonian conquest, the Holy Spirit who empowered him to speak and write had something far more serious in His mind. The day of the Lord was at hand, a day that will only be known in its fullness when man's day has come to a close. At that time, the Lord will prepare a great sacrificial feast. He had already "bid his guests." (The language reminds us of "the supper of the great God," or, as it should be rendered, the great supper of God, in Revelation 19:17-18.) He would inflict the sins of the princes and the king's household and all of foreign birth who were in Palestine back on them. Violence and deceit would be their just deserts, and evil would be overthrown everywhere (Zephaniah 1:7-9).

From gate to gate the cry of anguish would be heard. The merchants and affluent who had lived in pleasure on the earth would not escape the day of God's wrath. James 5:1 seems to be intimately connected with verse 11 of Zephaniah 1. Both deal with the collapse of the great economic system, which in our own day has assumed such gigantic proportions.

The attention given in Scripture to the mad rush for silver and gold in the last days is significant. The world today presents an amazing spectacle if viewed from this standpoint. Business is the Baal of the hour. In the accumulation of wealth, conscience and Christianity are pressed to the wall. Gold is king and god. For gold, people will sacrifice every principle, human and divine. Covetousness is the ruling passion of this age—all else must bow before it. And Scripture tells us to expect this, and emphasizes that it is a sign of the approaching end. Happy are those saints who are preserved from this unholy spirit of the times, and who, having food and clothing, seek to be content with them.

With a lighted lamp the Lord would search Jerusalem—not, as now, to find the lost piece of silver that typifies the poor sinner lying in dust (Luke 15:8-10). He would be ferreting out every person who had been indifferent to His truth and had sought to make God a nonentity in His own creation, saying, "The Lord will not do good, neither will he do evil" (Zephaniah 1:12). This is likewise characteristic of the present times. People no longer believe in a personal providence. Even the so-called clergy often ridicule the idea of divine intervention in human affairs. The law, hard and unbending, is supposed to control all things—human responsibility and a prayer-hearing God are practically denied. But the hour of awakening is nearing when, too late, people will know the reality of God's rule and the truth of His Word. Their possessions will be ravaged and their homes destroyed when they are consumed by the fierce anger of the Lord, whose power and hatred against sin they have contemptuously ignored (13).

With impassioned tones the prophet wound up the first section of his book with a fearful description of the day so long expected—the day of the Lord. It is near, approaching speedily—that day in which the mighty man shall cry bitterly when he sinks beneath the weight of divine wrath. It shall be "a day of trouble and distress, a day of wasteness and desolation, a day of darkness and gloominess, a day of clouds and thick darkness, a day of the trumpet and alarm"! There will be no refuge, no high tower to run to for protection from the avenging hand of Him whom people have insulted to His face for so long. Like the blind who stumble in the daytime, they will grope in their distress. They will fall into the pit God has prepared for them, "because they have sinned against the Lord." The riches for which they have labored will be useless to save them. "Neither their silver nor their gold shall be able to deliver them in the day of the Lord's wrath." He will not stop until He has made "a speedy riddance" of all who have defiled His land. The fire must burn until all the chaff is consumed (14-18).

The human race is hurtling toward this judgment. The Jews are even now returning in unbelief to their ancient home. People are sacrificing every right and noble instinct to build, as has been well said, everything for the fire!

What solemnity and otherworldliness the Christian will need in view of this fast-approaching end! I say "otherworldliness" because we need to walk, not just separate from this world, but in the power of another world to be true ambassadors of Christ. The day of the Lord is near. The Morning Star will soon shine forth. It is our task then to live and act as disciples who wait for their Lord!

ZEPHANIAH 2: The Judgments of the Nations

Over and over again, Scripture emphasizes the principle that while God will not overlook His people's sins, He will also severely judge all who lift their hands against His chosen. Philistia, Moab, Ethiopia, or Assyria might have been His tool to chastise Israel; but they should not have delighted in such service and gloried over them. Because of their unholy hatred and vindictive spirit, their own punishment would be all the more severe.

All of this pictures the end time. Judah will be in much the same position it occupied in Zephaniah's day—in the land, surrounded by enemies, with a feeble remnant crying, "How long, O Lord?" The majority of her people will be apostate and swayed by antichrist. All this is because of their rejection of Messiah when He came in grace. Therefore they must drink the cup of retribution to the dregs. When that cup is emptied, however, the Lord will arise in His might as their Deliverer. Their enemies who have gloried over their helplessness will become the objects of His avenging wrath as a prelude to the ushering in of the world-kingdom of our God and His Christ.

The three opening verses of Zephaniah 2 are addressed to Judah, with a singular call to the Godly remnant. The nation itself was not desired; they were no longer lovely in His eyes. Polluted by sin and bearing the marks of apostasy, Judah had become like a vessel that gave no pleasure. However, before God's judgment would take place, the faithful were summoned to gather together. As in Malachi's day, they would often meet together, drawn to each other's company by a common tie and common interests. Here they were told to seek the Lord, to seek righteousness and meekness. Indeed, they were distinctively called, "Ye meek of the earth, which have wrought his judgment" (3).

Pride is never attractive in fallen creatures, much less in a remnant in days of apostasy. They should not seek power or greatness, but Jehovah Himself should be the object of their desire. Therefore righteousness must be coupled with humility. It is the only appropriate position at such a time. No matter what judgments have fallen in each succeeding dispensation, God has always had a remnant who have sought grace to walk in His truth. There is always a danger though of pride destroying their testimony: they become absorbed with their position and proud of being a faithful remnant.

The truly faithful, however, will not be occupied with their remnant character but with Him to whom they are consecrated. They will not talk of being "the testimony," or "Philadelphia." They will instead testify of Christ and will exhibit Philadelphia ("brotherly love") in their ways while holding fast Christ's Word and not denying His name. In this way they will have His approval in *that* day, if they are content to be unapproved by the world in *this* day. Satisfied to let the Lord act for them, they will be concerned about acting for Him. In His own time He will show who is truly His; just as, regarding Judah in Zephaniah's time, the hour was about to strike when He would deal with the surrounding nations and the apostate majority, bringing to light the hidden things of darkness and making known the counsels of the heart.

Philistia, symbolizing corrupt Christendom, would be one of the first powers destroyed because the Philistines, of Egyptian origin, sought to keep all of Canaan for themselves—apart from divine permission. They even arrogantly gave their name, Palestine, to the whole land. This is religious pretension seeking to control all that stands for God. Verses 4-7 relate to Philistia's judgment and the deliverance of the Jewish remnant. This pictures for us the overthrow of hierarchical domination and the setting free of a Thyatiran remnant at the coming of the Lord (Revelation 2:24). For Judah and Philistia, there has already been a carrying out of this prediction literally. A more complete fulfillment will take place in the last days.

Moab and Ammon (verses 8-11) are often linked together, since both were illegitimately descended from fallen Lot (Genesis 19:33-38). They too will be judged nationally in the last days, when the remnant of Jehovah's people will conquer them. "This shall they have for their pride, because they have reproached and magnified themselves against the people of the Lord of hosts" (Zephaniah 2:10). Moab and Ammon have been under God's hand for centuries. They will be fully dealt with at the endtime. For us, they speak of those who, appearing to be alive, are really dead. They are those who, professing to be of the family of God, were never truly born again but are "strange children," in whom is no faith (Psalm 144:7-8). We see them all around us in the so-called church, saying, "I am rich, and increased with goods, and have need of nothing," while in God's sight they are "wretched and miserable, and poor, and blind, and naked" (Revelation 3:17). They are the proud, Christless "Christians" of the day who look with contempt and pity on any who seek to be guided only by the Word of God and emphasize the need of new birth for eternal life.

Ethiopia and Assyria were also appropriately joined together, with Nineveh having been the chief city of the latter (Zephaniah 2:12-15). These two nations represent humanity in the darkness of a fallen nature and in its pride and haughtiness, having no sense of need whatever. Desolation would fall on them soon. We get a full description of Nineveh's doom in Nahum's prophecy. She would never rise again. However, for Ethiopia there was still hope, when she would "stretch out her hands unto God" (Psalm 68:31).

The true significance of Nineveh is given in Zephaniah 2:15: "This is the rejoicing city that dwelt carelessly, that said in her heart, I am, and there is none beside me." This is human all-sufficiency at its worst, utterly indifferent to God. Though the Assyrians lived in pleasure on the earth, fattening themselves for the slaughter, as it were, the hour of their doom was about to strike—when they would learn that power belongs to God alone.

ZEPHANIAH 3: The Remnant and the Lord in the Midst

The remnant's resemblance to the church at Philadelphia in Revelation 3:7-13 is even stronger in Zephaniah's final chapter. Here the majority of Judah's people had utterly rejected the truth; but the remnant, though weak, still held fast the Word and the Name. The Lord Himself was "in the midst" (Zephaniah 3:5), just as He had declared when He was on earth, "Where two or three are gathered together in my name, there am I in the midst of them" (Matthew 18:20).

In Zephaniah 3:1 Jerusalem, the most highly privileged of all cities, is described as "filthy and polluted." A fourfold indictment is drawn up in verse 2: "She obeyed not the voice; she received not correction; she trusted not in the Lord; she drew not near to her God." These statements are intensely sobering. We would do well to search ourselves before the One who is called, "He that is holy, he that is true" (Revelation 3:7) to discover any similarities between our ways and the charges brought against Jerusalem. Have we obeyed the voice? Have we accepted correction from the Word of God? Do we truly confide in the Lord and draw near to our God? Serious questions. May we answer them in the fear of the Lord!

Zephaniah 3:2 is collective regarding the whole nation. In verses 3-4 the various classes who should have been the leaders in righteousness are individually indicted. The princes were roaring lions, seeking only for prey. That is, they sought their own profit, not the welfare and blessing of the flocks they should have shepherded. The judges were even worse—evening wolves, secretly devouring all they could while professing to administer justice. The prophets were triflers with holy things, handling the Word of God deceitfully, traitors to their trust. The priests, who should have been holy and undefiled, had polluted the very sanctuary itself with their uncleanness and done violence to the law.

Therefore everyone God had established in responsibility had failed. What then remained? Only this: "The just Lord is *in the midst* thereof; he will not do iniquity." He remained "the faithful and true witness" (Revelation 3:14). He, the Amen, was still the resource of every faithful heart, and in Him the heart of God could rest.

This pictures Christ, the Man of God's pleasure, when all else has been, humanly speaking, a disappointment. This passage applies to the millennium, when God's deliverance will be seen in its fullness. It is then that the words will be fulfilled: "Every morning doth he bring his judgment to light, he faileth not; but the unjust knoweth no shame" (Zephaniah 3:5). Never will wickedness have risen to such a height as when the Lord descends to take the kingdom. Righteousness, however, will then be firmly established, and morning by morning the wicked will be cut off. For centuries men have been warned of this, but at that time it will actually be fulfilled (6-8).

Then the confusion of Babel will be undone, and the Lord will give to all peoples "a pure language, that they may all call upon the name of [Jehovah], to serve him with one consent" (9). He will bring His redeemed earthly people home to Zion from all the lands to which they have been scattered. He will purge out pride and arrogance, making them willing to serve in the day of His power (10-11).

The apostate portion of Judah will be destroyed in the time of Jacob's trouble, when the Son of man appears. But He says,

> I will also leave in the midst of thee an afflicted and poor people, and they shall trust in the name of the Lord. The remnant of Israel shall not do iniquity, nor speak lies; neither shall a deceitful tongue be found in their mouth: for they shall feed and lie down, and none shall make them afraid (12-13).

The faithful—weak and dependent, acknowledged by the Lord, preserved in the midst of all the surrounding corruption—will be made the nucleus of the kingdom when Gentile dominion and Jewish and Christian apostasy have been overthrown forever. These verses picture the preserved virgin-company of Revelation 14:1-5, who will stand with the Lamb on mount Zion when the glory is about to be displayed.

In our day it is also part of God's ways to preserve an afflicted and poor people who trust in His name. Such people will be characterized by loving devotedness to Christ, brotherly kindness, integrity of heart, striving to maintain a clear conscience, holding fast the faithful Word, not denying the name of the Lord, consistent testimony to the world and the world-church for the absent One now rejected, separation from evil, following "righteousness, faith, [love,] peace, with them that call on the Lord out of a pure [or single] heart" (2 Timothy 2:22). This is the Philadelphian position. This alone constitutes a true remnant. Such a path can only be maintained in the energy of faith. Our human nature can form an alliance of churches based on mutual acceptance of certain guiding principles, but this is not faith. This only results in the formation of a system as rigid and unscriptural as any worldly sect. Such a system does away with individual exercise of conscience, and substitutes the voice of the church for the voice of God in His Word.

The last part of Zephaniah 3 brings the prophecy to a fitting close by describing God's blessing on the faithful remnant. Faith appropriates this blessing for us now, and we can enter into the enjoyment of it in spirit.

Zion is called upon to sing; Israel, to shout. The day of gladness and rejoicing has arrived for Jerusalem; for the Lord will then have taken away her judgments and cast out her enemy. He Himself, the glorious King of Israel (once crucified outside the gate on a felon's cross beneath the title, "Jesus of Nazareth, the King of the Jews"), will then dwell *in the midst* of the restored city and people, and they will not experience evil anymore (14-15).

This will be their joy and blessing throughout the millennium. Jerusalem will be told, "Fear thou not"; and Zion will hear, "Let not thine hands be slack." Loving service will follow deliverance from all her foes (16). Again Zephaniah stated, "The Lord thy God *in the midst* of thee is mighty" (emphasis added). To Him salvation is ascribed. He will rejoice over them and rest in His love, even singing in joy over them. It will be "the time of the singing," spoken of in the Song of Songs (2:12), when all redeemed creation, heavenly and earthly, will resound with songs of praise and exultation.

Once more Israel will keep her solemn assemblies, and her griefs will be changed to gladness. All who have afflicted her will be destroyed, and she who was driven away in weakness will be regathered in power. In every land where the scattered people had been put to shame, they will become objects of praise and fame (Zephaniah 3:18-19). The Lord Himself will make them "a name and a praise among all people of the earth, when I turn back your captivity before your eyes, saith the Lord" (20).

So we see again how God deals with Israel on the earth. Whatever their failures, they remain beloved for their fathers' sakes.

Their portion is earthly. Ours is heavenly. But both will contribute to the glory of our Lord Jesus Christ, and both will be vessels to display God's matchless grace throughout all the ages to come.

HAGGAI

A PROFILE
HAGGAI
FIRST THINGS FIRST
BY JOHN PHILLIPS

The prophets Haggai, Zechariah, and Malachi are known as "postexilic" prophets because they prophesied to the returned remnant after the Babylonian exile was over. Haggai and Zechariah were contemporaries, and Malachi prophesied about a century later.

The prophecies of Haggai (520-504 B.C.) are all dated and were given over a period of four months against the background of Ezra 5 and 6. Zechariah's prophecy began midway between Haggai's second and third messages.

There can be no doubt that the returned remnant had become greatly discouraged. For one thing, the prophets had painted glowing pictures of the promised land. But it was a far cry from the refinements of the Babylonian culture to which they had grown accustomed, to the rigors of pioneer life in the homeland. There was nothing romantic about having to hoe the flinty soil, quarry stones and stay up nights on watch against a bitter and persistent foe. For some years before the voice of Haggai was raised in the land, things had been allowed to drift. Poor harvests, declining income, and repeated discouragements had taken their toll.

Theme and Structure of the Book of Haggai

The chief theme of Haggai was the rebuilding of the temple, work on which had ceased. Fourteen years had passed since the remnants had returned, and not only was the temple unfinished but its foundation had become overgrown with weeds. At the same time the people were building and ornamenting their own houses. Haggai insisted that first things be put first.

I. A Call to Build (1)
   (First Day, Sixth Month)
   A. The Background of the Message (1:1-2)
   B. The Burden of the Message (1:3-11)
   C. The Blessing of the Message (1:12-15)
II. A Call to Behold (2:1-9)
   (Twenty-first Day, Seventh Month)
   A. The Present: Dealing with the Temple (2:1-3)
   B. The Past: Dealing with the Covenant (2:4-5)
   C. The Promise: Dealing with the Messiah (2:6-9)
III. A Call to Behave (2:10-19)
   (Twenty-fourth Day, Ninth Month)
   A. The Blessing Wanted (2:10-14)
   B. The Blessing Withheld (2:15-17)
   C. The Blessing Waiting (2:18-19)
IV. A Call to Believe (2:20-23)
   (Twenty-fourth Day, Ninth Month)
   A. God Will Manifest His Power (2:20-22)
   B. God Will Manifest His Prince (2:23)

A Call To Build

Haggai appeared at a critical time in the history of his people. The incomplete temple was not only a bad testimony to the surrounding nations but a source of spiritual peril to Israel. With the throne of David gone it was imperative that the nation realize its true center in the temple. Within the compass of his brief book Haggai mentions three temples: Solomon's (2:3a), Zerubbabel's (2:3b-5), and the Messiah's (2:6-9).

A wrong attitude toward prophecy on the part of the people was somewhat responsible for the national lethargy. "The time is not come, the time that the Lord's house should be built," was their excuse (1:2). This fatalistic attitude toward the work of God has its counterpart in the church today. Prophecy is never intended as an excuse for inaction but always as a spur to holy, consecrated living.

The prompt obedience on the part of prince, priest, prophet, and people must have been a tremendous encouragement to Haggai. Not all the prophets by any means had the joy of seeing the people respond thus to their messages, but Haggai did. Within three weeks of his first message, Zerubbabel was stirred up by God to give fresh leadership to the work.

A Call to Behold

The completion of the temple was not looked upon with undiluted joy by all. Some of the senior citizens lamented the fact that it was far inferior to Solomon's, so Haggai's second message was to remind the people that the Messiah Himself would grace the courts of Zerubbabel's temple, something which could not be said about Solomon's.

A Call to Behave

Haggai's third message was addressed to the priests and called for a renewal of consecration. The blessing of God, long wanted and long withheld, was waiting for them. "From this day and upward" is the key expression in this section, signifying, according to some, that this date terminated the "desolations" to come upon Jerusalem as predicted by Jeremiah. "From this day will I bless you." God is ever more willing to bless than we are to receive His blessing.

A Call to Believe

Haggai's final message was apocalyptic in character. Looking down the long ages, he finished his book by pointing to the coming golden age. This part of his prophecy remains unfulfilled, and we are called upon to believe it just as much today as Israel was then.

CHAPTER TEN
THE PROPHECY OF HAGGAI

There are six books of the Old Testament that may be read together most profitably. I refer to Ezra, Nehemiah, and Esther, of the historical part of the Bible, coupled with the prophetic messages of Haggai, Zechariah, and Malachi. To these a seventh might be added—the book of Daniel, showing the spiritual preparation that led up to the restoration.

The book of Ezra opens with the people of the Lord in captivity to the Persians, living in the provinces once controlled by the kings of Babylon. God's center, Jerusalem, where He had set His name, was a blackened ruin. The walls of the holy city had been thrown down, and the very stones buried beneath piles of rubbish.

All this pictures the subjection of the church of God to human systems of error and superstition. For long centuries, the truth of simply gathering in the Lord Jesus' name had been lost. The place of the name, we may say, had become a Jerusalem destroyed by her enemies. The walls, representing godly separation from the world that should have kept the church as "a garden enclosed," had been completely demolished, and ecclesiastical rubbish of all descriptions had so buried the truth that it seemed as though it was lost beyond all recovery. Separation from evil is always God's principle for His people.

However, God was watching over all, and in His grace He raised up a testimony to these precious and important teachings of His Word that had lain dormant for so long. The result was a movement very much like that detailed in the record made by Ezra. From the confusion of human theologies and man-made sects and parties, there was a returning to the simplicity of early days by some whose hearts God had touched. In much weakness, yet in much eagerness too, with a deep sense of the church's ruined testimony for God in the world and their own sad part in it, a remnant returned to the Lord. They found in His name their center of gathering and rejected everything for which they could not find a "Thus saith the Lord."

This is all foreshadowed, one might say (or at any rate a similar movement is pictured), in the book of Ezra. There was a separation of the clean from the unclean, a removing of the precious from the vile, and a setting up of the altar, called by Malachi "The table of the Lord" (Malachi 1:7) around which gathered the recovered remnant. This remnant was great in nothing but the faith that led them to put Jehovah's claims before all else, for we remember that their circumstances in the land of their captivity were more comfortable than freedom in the land of Israel.

Nehemiah emphasized the need for complete separation from all that is contrary to God's will. He came later than Ezra, and his special work was to restore and rebuild Jerusalem. Led on by this faithful servant, the remnant engaged in the building of the wall that was to shut them in to God. That angered their neighbors by its, in their eyes, sinister exclusiveness. Bit by bit the rubbish of years was cleared away, and one by one the stones of the wall were brought to light and fitted into their appointed places.

Surely in this picture there is something analogous to those who first gathered with little light around the table of the Lord. Gradually, yet clearly showing the work of the Holy Spirit, human thought was put to one side, the rubbish of traditionalism was cleared away, and the stones of divine truth were recovered and built up—shall I say?—into a wall of separation that angered the "societies," who could not bear to think of a work of God carried on apart from their organized control. However, unmoved by mockery, undeterred by threats, and unseduced by proffers of help from those who had neither part nor lot in the matter, the work went on until the wall was finished. The truth as to the individual believer's standing and state; the unfolding of the great mystery of Christ and the church; the cluster of precious truths connected with the second coming and the day of the Lord, with their sanctifying effect on heart and life—one by one, these stones of the separating wall were recovered. The rebuilding often came at great cost; it took the deepest soul-searching and the ability to endure severe conflicts with the enemy within and without. But in the end, God was glorified and His people were blessed.

The book of Esther describes God's gracious care over those who, while equally His, chose to remain in Persia rather than return to God's center.

It would have been wonderful if the problems traced in the records of Ezra and Nehemiah were the only problems we need be concerned about. Sadly, that is not the case. It was not long before almost all the evils that had once been on the *outside* of the wall, appeared *within*. Pride, dissension, covetousness, worldliness in its various forms, self-seeking, and a myriad of other unholy things no walls could shut out (because they dwelt within the heart and were allowed to exist unjudged) soon marred the lovely scene. Who with eyes to see and a heart to understand and mourn can fail to see the sad similarity to some today who claim Christ alone as their center, and His name their tower of strength?

But blessed be the God of all grace; He did not leave His people without the needed conscience-stirring ministry. Among the returned remnant He raised up prophets whose messages led to self-examination and humbling before God's presence. Haggai and Zechariah come in here, as polished shafts from the quiver of the Lord. Their mission was to call back to God the hearts of those so privileged to be His people. Zechariah's calling was to unfold the glories to come so that the people might be encouraged to live in the light of that coming day. He is emphatically "the prophet of the glory." Haggai, on the other hand, pressed home to the conscience the actual moral conditions of the time. With trumpet voice he recalled the people to ways of practical holiness, with striking blessings to follow.

That Malachi comes a generation later, mourning the complete moral breakdown of the people, is pregnant with warning. It should cause us to search our ways. Truth alone will not preserve us if we do not correspondingly live in its power and control. Nothing is more wretched than to see unspiritual, carnal people debating questions involving fine distinctions of truth, when their unholy ways are a reproach to the One whose truth it is.

It is important to remember that God teaches through the

conscience, not merely through the head. That's why we so often see brilliant, gifted men floundering, while humble, godly men walk securely. Blessed it is when gift and godliness go together—unhappy indeed when they are divorced!

Of Haggai himself little is recorded in Scripture. Even his father's name is not given, nor his tribe in Israel. He appears suddenly on the page of inspiration in Ezra 5:1, in all the dignity of a Heaven-appointed messenger. His only credentials were that the word of the Lord was on his lips and the power of the Lord was apparent in his ways. These credentials are surely enough. God had equipped him to be, as he himself put it, "the Lord's messenger in the Lord's message" (Haggai 1:13). There is something wonderfully revealing in this. It brings before us the divine character of prophetic ministry—a ministry much needed in our day and for which we should give thanks. "He that prophesieth speaketh unto men to edification, and exhortation, and comfort" (1 Corinthians 14:3). Such ministry is Spirit-given and sure to result in blessing, for what God Himself gives will never return to Him void. What that ministry was in Haggai's particular case we will now explore.

HAGGAI 1: Consider Your Ways

The date given in verse 1 corresponds with the statement recorded in Ezra 4:24. There we learn that, because of opposition from the adversaries of Judah and Benjamin, the work of rebuilding the house of the Lord stopped "unto the second year of the reign of Darius king of Persia." The letter that spurred the prohibition to build was written in the reign of Artaxerxes, so several years had passed in which nothing had been accomplished. A period of lethargy had settled in, which ended only when a God-appointed ministry stirred up the consciences of the people.

In the second year of Darius's reign, on the first day of the sixth month, Haggai addressed the rulers: Zerubbabel, the governor, who was of David's line, and Joshua, the high priest (Haggai 1:1). His message began "Thus speaketh the Lord of hosts, saying, This people say, The time is not come, the time that the Lord's house should be built" (1-2). It is evident from this that the people were only too ready to refrain from the work of rebuilding the temple. Had there been the energy of faith, the decree of Artaxerxes (apparently contradicting that of Cyrus) would have been no real hindrance. The unalterable character of Persian decrees would have rendered the second one invalid anyway. But already a self-seeking spirit and its consequent listlessness toward the things of God had set in, which made it possible for them to build their own houses while neglecting the house of the Lord. But Artaxerxes' decree, rightly read, contained no direct prohibition against building the temple; rather, it was directed against restoring and fortifying the city.

When the conscience is not active, people readily interpret circumstances to suit themselves. At such times an often amazing amount of energy is spent on one's own comfort, while utter indifference is connected with the Lord's glory. In this way saints have time and means for much that is not spiritually profitable. We find it difficult to get a few hours for a meeting, or to spare our resources to further the gospel. However, once we let our conscience have some exercise, all will be in place.

"Is it time for you, O ye, to dwell in your ceiled houses, and this house lie waste?" is the Lord's challenge through His prophet (3-4). No Persian decree hindered their providing warm and even expensive houses for themselves; but it was readily made the excuse for indifference to what should have had the first place in their thoughts.

> Now therefore thus saith the Lord of hosts; Consider your ways. Ye have sown much, and bring in little; ye eat, but ye have not enough; ye drink, but ye are not filled with drink; ye clothe you, but there is none warm; and he that earneth wages, earneth wages to put it into a bag with holes (5-6).

This is intensely serious. May reader and writer weigh it well. Undoubtedly, it reveals the secret of many failures and disappointments among Christians today, as well as among the Jews of old. God cannot bless self-centeredness. He calls on each one to "consider your ways." It is a summons to self-examination, for our ways reveal the state of our soul.

This call to self-examination applies to every area of life.

Consider your ways, you in the business world in its present condition. How much we tolerate that would not bear the all-searching eyes of the One who sees not as mere humans see! The greedy spirit of the age is eating the very life out of many companies of the Lord's people. The grasping avarice prevalent in the world is making dreadful inroads among Christians. How much is sacrificed for money! We sacrifice Christian fellowship, the joys of gathering at the table of the Lord, gospel work, and privileges of mutual edification and instruction in divine things for the opportunity to add a few paltry dollars to the monthly income and savings. Christian brothers and sisters with families will even leave a town where they have spiritual support and fellowship, where their children have the privileges of a good church and Sunday school, simply because they fancy they see an opportunity to better their earthly circumstances. Sadly, in many instances they miss all they had hoped for and lose spiritually what is never regained!

Next, consider your ways in the home life. What place do you give the things of God there? Do the children see the Bible habitually neglected and the knee seldom bowed in prayer? Little wonder that they grow up to think lightly of what you seem to place so slight a value on. Do you discuss Christ's servants and His people in a cold, hard, critical manner in front of these same children? Then do not be surprised if they learn to despise all ministers of the Word and disrespect all those who bear the name of Christ.

Also consider your ways in connection with the service of the Lord and the assembling of His people. Do petty circumstances keep you from gathering with God's people to remember our Lord in His sufferings for us? Do you neglect the preaching of the Word on the plea that "it is only the gospel?" Are you generally missed at the prayer meeting, and seldom found at the Bible study? Is it months, or years, since you handed out a tract or spoke to others of Christ? How then can you expect God's blessing to be on you and your plans while you are so indifferent to Him and His purposes?

"Thus saith the Lord of hosts; Consider your ways. Go up to the mountain, and bring wood, and build the house; and I will take pleasure in it, and I will be glorified, saith the Lord" (7-8). Awakened from the deadening effects of self-seeking, judge yourself and your past in God's presence; then, "Put first things first," as one has said, and give the Lord the supreme place in heart and life. Because of the lack of this determination to cling to Him, He could not bless as He otherwise would. Therefore, "Ye looked for much, and, lo, it came to little; and when ye brought it home" God blew upon it, and it fled away (9). Do you wonder why failure follows failure, and plan after plan does not result as you hoped? Because you have not given God His place; His house is neglected. "Therefore the heaven over you is stayed from dew, and the earth is stayed from her fruit," and drought and barrenness prevail instead of blessing and refreshment (9-11).

The effect of Haggai's words was immediately apparent. If only they would have the same effect today—to arouse those of us who are sleeping among the dead! Both leaders and people immediately "obeyed the voice of the Lord their God," and the neglected work was at once resumed (12).

"Then spake Haggai the Lord's messenger in the Lord's message unto the people, saying, I am with you, saith the Lord" (13). This is a word of encouragement, and the way it is introduced communicates great strength—"the Lord's messenger in the Lord's message"! It is quite possible to be truly the Lord's messenger and yet to miss the Lord's mind. To give His message, one must be in touch with Him. Such was Haggai's happy state.

Rallied by the stirring call to consider their ways, and comforted by the knowledge of the Lord's presence with them, the remnant willingly returned to work so that the actual labor on the house of God was resumed in twenty-four days (14-15).

HAGGAI 2: Be Strong

The work of building the long-neglected house of the Lord had been going on less than a month when the word of Jehovah came a second time through the prophet Haggai. On this occasion it was a message not of rebuke but of encouragement to both rulers and people (Haggai 2:1-2). Here we see that God delights to comfort and sustain the hearts of those who, however poor and weak, still seek to honor Him.

Three questions are asked: "Who is left among you that saw this house in her first glory? and how do ye see it now? Is it not in your eyes in comparison of it as nothing?" (3) We know from Ezra 3:12 that there were among the restored remnant "ancient men, that had seen the first house," and who wept bitterly when they contrasted its former glory with the smallness of the present house among the ruins. Yet there was also the gladness of the younger ones, who had just been delivered from Babylon and whose whole past lives had been in the midst of idolatry and oppression—their voice, however, was almost drowned out in the noise of the weeping.

So God assured them that the future had brighter things in store than the past had ever known; and He made this hope the basis for the encouragement. "Yet now be strong," was His message, "for I am with you...my spirit remaineth among you: fear ye not" (4-5).

Ruin and desolation may have come in, and division and scattering may have taken place; but those who gather again around Jehovah's center have the joy of knowing—on the authority of His own Word—that He is in the midst and His Spirit remains among them. What better reason is there to be strong and unafraid.

A similar assurance was given to the church in Philadelphia in the last book of the Bible. The saints may have only "a little strength"; but God's Word and His Name abide, and He, the holy and the true, is in their midst. Division and strife cannot alter this; nor can any particular company of believers claim it to the exclusion of others as though they alone composed "the remnant." "For where two or three are gathered together in [or unto] my name, there am I in the midst of them." Every little company of saints who find themselves in the same position as the remnant in Haggai's day may be comforted by this truth.

Not only did the people have the Lord's presence through His Spirit among them, but His coming in person was to be their hope. Because of this their hearts could be lifted above their circumstances as they waited for the coming glory. In "a little while" the heavens and earth, the sea and the dry land, together with all the nations, would be shaken by the power of Jehovah. Then "the desire of all nations shall come: and I will fill this house with glory, saith the Lord of hosts" (6-7). The long-desired One is none other than our Lord Jesus Christ. He came once in grace only to be rejected. He is coming again to bring in the glory long foreseen by the prophets of old. To that temple (albeit refurbished and enlarged by King Herod) He came, only to be unrecognized and cast out. To that house, rebuilt in the last days, He will come again to take the kingdom and reign in righteousness.

The remnant might be too poor to adorn the rebuilt temple, but God owns the silver and the gold. Nothing will hinder the manifestation of His glory when the set time has come. "The [latter glory of this house] shall be greater than of the former, saith the Lord of hosts: and in this place will I give peace, saith the Lord of hosts" (8-9). The interpretation of the King James version—"the glory of this latter house"—is misleading, and has generally been taken by commentators to mean that the rebuilt temple, being hallowed by the personal presence of the Son of God, was thus far greater than that of Solomon's, despite the grandeur of the one and the deficiency of the other. Some have also supposed that the architectural beauty of the temple after Herod's embellishments even surpassed that of the temple "exceeding magnifical," built by the wise king. But this was by no means the case.

To the first interpretation there could be no real objection. It is beautiful and true in itself, but it does not seem to be what is really meant here. "The latter glory of this house" refers undoubtedly to the millennial splendor of the temple depicted prophetically in Ezekiel 40–48. People may speak of temples or houses of God; but He speaks of *the* temple or *the* house. Whether the building erected by Solomon, Zerubbabel, or Herod is in mind here; or whether it is the one to be rebuilt by unbelieving Judah in the coming tribulation; or the final millennial temple—all are called "the house" and "the temple" of God. They are all one in God's eyes. In that temple of old, every bit of it uttered His glory. In that temple the man of sin will yet sit. Once cleansed, that temple will be the center of earth's worship and thanksgiving for the millennium. At present, in this interval of "the dispensation of the mystery," God claims no material building as His home. Believers on the whole, through the entire church period, are growing into a holy temple in the Lord. All saints on earth at a given time form the house of God, composed of living stones, who have come to *the* living Stone.

Haggai's prophecy is not occupied with this spiritual building. His message has to do with the earth, and earthly things.

Verses 10-14 bring in another line of truth. The transition from what we have been considering seems abrupt, but doubtless the state of the people demanded it. In reply to a question by Haggai, the priests assert that if one "bear holy flesh in the skirt of his garment, and with his skirt do touch" articles of common food, the latter are not sanctified by the touch and rendered holy. On the other hand, they bear testimony to the fact that one who is unclean from touching a dead person defiles everything he touches, making everything else unclean. Such was the condition of the people. They were all defiled, and all their actions were unclean before God. But this only gave occasion for grace to act—despite their uncleanness, the Lord had blessed them. But He would have them remember that everything has come from His own heart, apart from what they deserve. Though defiled, when they turned to God and bowed in subjection to Him, He showed Himself strong on their behalf.

So in verses 15-19 their formerly apathetic attitude in regard to His house is contrasted with their present hard work and obedience to His word. Before, poverty, blasting, and mildew were their portion. Now, He has "from the day that the foundation of the Lord's temple was laid" given increase and plenty, even as He had declared long before that "them that honour me I will honour, and they that despise me shall be lightly esteemed" (1 Samuel 2:30).

We may be sure that no one who puts God first will ever be the loser. "From this day will I bless you" is a promise for all who judge what is evil and seek to walk in the truth.

The prophecy of Haggai concludes with another message given the same day. It is addressed to Zerubbabel, the uncrowned son of David, who had been appointed governor of Judah. To him the Lord announced the shaking of the heavens and the earth and the final overthrow of all the kingdoms of the Gentiles. He assured him, however, that he will remain as a signet before Him, "for I have chosen thee, saith the Lord of hosts."

From Zerubbabel's descendants shall spring "the prince," who would seem to be the earthly representative of "great David's greater Son," in the day when all nations will acclaim the splendors of "the latter glory of this house."

ZECHARIAH

A PROFILE
ZECHARIAH
LOOKING AHEAD
BY JOHN PHILLIPS

Zechariah (520-489 B.C.) was a priest as well as a prophet. His grandfather, Iddo, was one of the priests who returned from the Babylonian exile with Zerubbabel and Jeshua (Nehemiah 12:1,7). Zechariah was probably a very young man when he began to prophesy. The difference in style between chapters 9–14 and the earlier part of his book is usually explained on the grounds that these later chapters were probably written when the prophet was a much older man. Also the circumstances would probably be much different.

The original circumstances which called for the ministries of Haggai and Zechariah were the same. Zechariah began to prophesy two months later than his contemporary, and although Haggai concentrated on the need for finishing the temple, Zechariah had a wider vision. He saw Israel in a world context and looked far ahead to the end times with great clarity.

Structure of Zechariah

The book of Zechariah deals with Israel's future, fasts, and folly.

I. Revelations concerning Israel's Future (1–6)
  A. The Voice of Zechariah (1:1-6)
  B. The Visions of Zechariah (1:7–6:15)
    1. God Sees (1:7-21)
      a. Distressing Indifference of the Nations (1:7-17)

The Vision of the Red Horse

b. Diminishing Influence of the Nations (1:18-21)
   (1) The Vision of the Four Horns
   (2) The Vision of the Four Carpenters

2. God Speaks (2–4)
   a. The Matter of Israel's Restoration (2)
      The Vision of the Man with the Measuring Rod
   b. The Matter of Israel's Righteousness (3)
      The Vision of Joshua's Garments
   c. The Matter of Israel's Revival (4)
      The Vision of the Candlestick and Olive Trees
3. God Stirs (5–6)
   a. Implicitly to Convict (5:1-4)
      The Vision of the Flying Roll
   b. Impartially to Condemn (5:5-11)
      The Vision of the Ephah and the Woman
   c. Imperially to Conquer (6)
      The Vision of the Four Chariots and the Branch

II. Revelations concerning Israel's Fasts (7–8)
   A. The Question concerning the Fasts Asked (7:1-3)
   B. The Question concerning the Fasts Argued (7:4-14)
      1. The Reason for Fasting (7:4-7)
      2. The Result of Fasting (7:8-14)
   C. The Question concerning the Fasts Answered (8:1-23)
      1. Exile Will Give Place to Exaltation (8:1-17)
      2. Fasting Will Give Place to Feasting (8:18-23)

III. Revelations concerning Israel's Folly (9–14)
   A. The Coming of the King (9)
   B. The Call of the King (10)
   C. The Crucifixion of the King (11)
   D. The Curse of the King (12)
   E. The Compassion of the King (13)
   F. The Coronation of the King (14)

Zechariah's task was not only to support Haggai in his urgent call to the nation to complete the temple but also to put the restoration in its proper perspective. There was every reason for the returned remnant to be discouraged. The glowing predictions of Isaiah and Jeremiah had not materialized, and Zechariah had to show that God's promises were not forgotten, though they might indeed be postponed.

Zechariah's Visions

Zechariah's visions savor of the apocalypse. First, God sees: the vision of the four horsemen tells us that. He has not failed to observe the attitude of the Gentiles toward His people, neither will He allow it to continue indefinitely. The vision of the four carpenters guarantees redress.

The vision of the man with the measuring rod promises great future prosperity for Jerusalem. The vision of Jeshua (or Joshua), the high priest, defended against Satan by Jehovah Himself, gives comforting assurance that divine favor has returned to His people. The vision of the candlestick speaks of spiritual revival.

The vision of the flying roll is essentially one of conviction, for evil must be expelled if God is to bless. The vision of the ephah (the largest of the dry measures used by the Jews), together with the woman (often used as a symbol of religious error in the Scripture), is next seen. The ephah is returned to Babylon from whence, in the beginning, all religious error stemmed. The coming of divine judgment upon the nations is symbolized in the vision of the four chariots.

The Branch is one of the great Old Testament titles of the Lord Jesus. There are twenty-three words translated "branch" in the Old Testament, but one, occurring twelve times, is used specifically of the Messiah on four great occasions: Jeremiah 23:5-6; 33:15; Zechariah 3:8; 6:12; and Isaiah 4:2. It will be seen from the context of these references that the Messiah is referred to as King, Servant, Man, and Jehovah; and it is from those four viewpoints exactly that the four Gospels are written.

Fasts and the Returned Remnant

Zechariah's visions are followed by a discussion of the relationship of fasts to the returned remnant, and the glad conclusion is that the time will come when all fasting will give way to feasting. Zechariah's closing chapters, probably written some thirty years after the earlier portions of his book, deal with the coming, rejection, and ultimate triumph of the Messiah. The greatest national folly of Israel was the rejection and crucifixion of Christ, and it is this folly which would be unbelievable were it not for the fact that, although it is now past history, millions today are perpetuating it by rejecting Christ and, as it were, crucifying afresh the Son of God. But God will not allow human folly to thwart His own good purposes concerning His Son, and the day will come when Jesus shall reign as Zechariah also foretold. The nations will one day "worship the King" (14:17), and "Holiness unto the Lord" will yet pervade the earth (14:20).

CHAPTER ELEVEN

THE PROPHECY OF ZECHARIAH

Zechariah, like Haggai and Malachi, was a post-captivity prophet. He was one of those who came up from Babylon with Zerubbabel, having been born in a foreign land, and he gave the word of the Lord to the returned remnant. Haggai's mission had been to arouse the people to action when they were overcome by sloth and self-seeking. Zechariah followed with messages of encouragement designed to bring the souls of the people into the power of the coming glory. He was therefore largely occupied with the appearing of Messiah and His reign of righteousness.

There is blessing in having heart and mind transported to the days of Heaven on earth. It is then that one is able to put into proper perspective the passing glories of this present evil age. The hope of the Lord's coming has a purifying effect on the lives of those held by it. "Every man that hath this hope in him purifieth himself, even as he is pure" (1 John 3:3).

The church has lost much by neglecting the study of prophecy. It should be remembered that, while the prophets of the Old Testament do not speak of the assembly of the present dispensation, nevertheless those who compose the body of Christ and the bride of the Lamb may be built up and blessed through a study of Jehovah's word to Israel. It should also be enough for the devoted soul to know that Christ will be the center of all the glory soon to be revealed. All who love Him will find spiritual delight in tracing the steps leading up to His exaltation and the establishment of His kingdom.

This is what characterizes Zechariah. He delineated the various stages leading to the Messiah's advent, thus opening up, in large measure, "the sufferings of Christ and the glory that should follow" (1 Peter 1:11). His book falls readily into two main parts. The first six chapters relate the visions of the prophet. The last eight are devoted to instruction based on these visions. There are also numerous subdivisions we will notice as we proceed.

It appears as though Zechariah, like many of his predecessors, died a violent death at the hands of the Jews returned from Babylon, when faithlessness had again set in. At least our Lord Jesus spoke of "the blood of Zacharias son of Barachias, whom ye slew between the temple and the altar," which would be required of the men of His generation because they had filled up the iniquity of their fathers (Matthew 23:35-36).

It is possible, though not probable, that our Lord was referring to the martyrdom of Zechariah the son of Jehoiada, who was stoned to death in the court of the temple (see 2 Chronicles 24:20-21). But in that case we have to suppose a Berechiah in the genealogy of Jehoiada or a copyist's error in transcribing the Greek text. In the absence of proof to the contrary, it seems safer to assume that Zacharias the son of Barachias is none other than the prophet to whose writings we are about to turn for instruction and warning.

In addition the Jews have a tradition that Zechariah perished in the manner Jesus described. J. N. Darby, in his *Irrationalism of Infidelity*, wrote that "the Jewish Targum states that Zechariah the son of Iddo, a prophet and priest, was slain in the sanctuary." Since the rabbis could have no possible reason for seeking to confirm the words of the Lord Jesus, it seems as though their testimony is conclusive.

ZECHARIAH 1: Israel and the Divine Government

By comparing Zechariah 1:1 with the opening words of Haggai's prophecy, we will notice that about two months passed between the beginning of the recorded ministry of the two prophets. Conscience was aroused and the work of building the house of the Lord was begun as a result of Haggai's stirring message. In the seventh month he had sought to encourage the now awakened people by directing their attention to the future day of Messiah's glory. Then in the following month, in Darius's second year, God called Zechariah to speak to the remnant, first in a rousing call to repentance and then by a remarkable unfolding of what Haggai had so briefly outlined in Haggai 2:6-9.

Others have long since noticed the striking significance of the names in Zechariah's first verse: "Zechariah the son of Berechiah, the son of Iddo." *Zechariah* means "Jehovah remembers"; *Berechiah* is "Jehovah blesses"; and *Iddo*, "the appointed time." We could then read this as: "Jehovah remembers; Jehovah blesses at the appointed time." Thus, when the set time to favor Zion has come, all the promises of the Lord will be fulfilled and carried out in blessing. If anyone thinks such an interpretation is fanciful, let them remember how the apostle, by the inspiration of the Holy Ghost, dwelled on the meaning of names, and their order in the case of Melchizedek, King of Salem, in Hebrews 7:2. There is surely more than a hint in that remarkable passage that there are vast stores of instruction in the names of people and places throughout the Scriptures which many of us have little dreamed of.

Zechariah 1:2-6 comprises Zechariah's first message and is a fitting introduction to the book. In view of the return from captivity and the rebuilding of the temple, the people were warned not to repeat the errors of their fathers—a warning sadly soon forgotten.

The Lord had been greatly displeased with their ancestors. Because of their sins He had given them into the hand of their Gentile enemies. Now if the children of those who had failed so repeatedly would turn to God with all their hearts, He would turn to them and openly act on their behalf as Jehovah of hosts. They must not refuse to listen, like their fathers refused to obey the messages of the prophets when God urged them, "Turn ye now from your evil ways, and from your evil doings." They had despised His words. But where were they now? They had been made to know the power of God's displeasure, finally confessing that His word was infallible. In the land of the enemy they sadly confessed, "Like as the Lord of hosts thought to do unto us, according to our ways, and according to our doings, so hath he dealt with us" (6). In this way, God had been glorified even in their downfall. In all this how serious and important the lesson for us!

In verse 7, Zechariah began to relate a series of eight visions, all closely connected. All of them seem to have been given to him on the twenty-fourth day of the eleventh month, in the same year as that of verse 1. The first vision and its partial explanation appears in verses 7-17. For convenience we will call it, "The Man among the Myrtle Trees."

The prophet saw a man riding a red horse in a deep valley among a grove of myrtle trees, "and behind him were there red horses, speckled, and white." In surprise, he asked, "O my lord, what are these?" An angel replied, "I will show thee what these be." Then the rider, twice called a man but in verse 11 identified as the angel of Jehovah, said, "These are they whom the Lord hath sent to walk to and fro through the earth" (8-10).

As if summoned to give an account, the unmentioned riders on the attending horses answered the angel of the Lord, "We have walked to and fro through the earth, and, behold, all the earth sitteth still, and is at rest" (11). (Some suppose the other horses to be riderless and see in this a significant picture of the restless energy of Gentile dominion. However, this involves speaking horses, an image, it seems to me, grotesque and unimplied here.)

The rider on the first horse would seem to be the covenant-angel, standing for Jehovah's chosen people. The other horses represent the providential agencies, possibly angelically directed, working among the Gentile nations. Notice, the Lord had sent them. The powers that be are ordained of God. They had just been used for the discipline of sinful Israel. Now all the world was at peace, and the nations were utterly indifferent to the reduced condition of the seed of Abraham.

This is why the angel of Jehovah cried out, "O Lord of hosts, how long wilt thou not have mercy on Jerusalem and on the cities of Judah, against which thou hast had indignation these threescore and ten years?" (12) The Babylonian captivity had come to an end. Cyrus had given permission for the Jews to return to Jerusalem. But though a remnant had gone back, the great powers were utterly indifferent about recognizing nationally the people who were destined to be the chief of the nations. This is what was behind the angel's question, and Jehovah answered him with comforting words (13).

It is a little difficult here to distinguish between the angel of Jehovah riding on the horse among the myrtles (who really represents Messiah Himself as the angel-intercessor on behalf of Israel, as in Revelation 8:1-4), and the interpreting angel who explained the visions to Zechariah. It is the latter in verses 14-15, who gives the seer a prophetic message, telling him, "Cry thou, saying, Thus saith the Lord of hosts; I am jealous for Jerusalem and for Zion with a great jealousy. And I am very sore displeased with the heathen that are at ease; for I was but a little displeased, and they helped forward the affliction."

Proud and self-sufficient, the Gentile powers promoted only their own interests, and regarded God's chosen with contempt. But God was watching, so they only added to the cup of their iniquity.

In His own set time, as hinted at already in connection with the prophetic character of the three names in verse 1, Jehovah will arise on behalf of His people and return to Jerusalem, so long trodden underfoot by the nations. He will come with great mercies, bringing in all the blessings of the new covenant for the long-despised nation. His house will be built in the land once more, on a more magnificent scale than ever, as set forth in the last nine chapters of Ezekiel. Jerusalem will become a glorious city, unequaled in splendor by any of the cities of the nations, when "the Lord shall yet comfort Zion, and shall yet choose Jerusalem" (16-17).

It is important throughout to distinguish between vision and interpretation. Verses 8-13 give the vision. Verses 14-17 are the divine explanation. Judah and Jerusalem form the subject. There is no reference to the church of the present dispensation whatsoever. Spiritualizers have always been fond of applying the message this way, but to do so is to violently wrest the passage out of its context.

The second vision, concerning the four horns and the four carpenters (or four smiths), is given in verses 18-21. The four Gentile empires, made familiar to us in Daniel's prophecy, are represented by horns (symbols of power). These empires are Babylon, Medo-Persia, Greece, and Rome. But for every horn there is a carpenter. As the horns agreed together to oppress and destroy Israel and Judah, so shall God use these carpenters to destroy them. Israel's enemies are God's enemies, and must be broken when their appointed course is run. God's goal is the full deliverance of His chosen remnant.

In the Hebrew text this vision belongs to the next chapter, with chapter 1 ending at verse 17. It requires no further comment. For the saint of any dispensation it ministers blessed truth, reminding him that God works all things according to His own will; and evil is only permitted insofar as it will serve in accomplishing His wondrous purposes of blessing.

ZECHARIAH 2: Jerusalem's Restoration

Chapter 2 contains only one vision—that of the man with a measuring line in his hand. On seeing him, Zechariah asked, "Whither goest thou?" The man replied, "To measure Jerusalem, to see what is the breadth thereof, and what is the length thereof."

The interpreting angel then left the prophet's side and advanced to meet another angel who was coming toward him. The latter cried, "Run, speak to this young man, saying, Jerusalem shall be inhabited as towns without walls for the multitude of men and cattle therein; For I, saith the Lord, will be unto her a wall of fire round about, and will be the glory in the midst of her" (3-5; see also Zephaniah 3:5,14-20).

The young man is Zechariah himself, who is to be informed of Jehovah's purposes concerning Jerusalem so that he may write it down for future generations. The city that he knew was small and inconsequential compared with the Jerusalem that was yet to be. In the day of its glory, there will be no need of a wall of masonry. The Lord Himself will be her wall of fire, protecting her from every assailant and dwelling in her midst in the Shekinah glory.

Zechariah 2:6-9 summons the remnant to return to their land in the day when all that God has promised is about to be fulfilled. Morally, they will still be dwelling with the daughter of Babylon, for Gentile dominion was established with Nebuchadnezzar, and the powers that have succeeded him are all of his spirit and character. For more than two millennia they have been the persecutors and haters of the Jews. And though in our day the Jews' position is much more tolerable than ever before since their dispersion, anti-Semitism still thrives in many parts of Europe. This malicious spirit is destined to start a conflagration of unequaled fierceness in the time of Jacob's trouble, which follows the translation of the church to Heaven. But when His people appear friendless and helpless, the Lord will send His angel to gather His elect from the four winds of heaven and reestablish them in peace in their long-promised inheritance, the land of their fathers.

The exact time this will take place is given in verse 8: "*After the glory* hath he sent me unto the nations which spoiled you: for he that toucheth you, toucheth the apple of his eye" (emphasis added). The expression "after the glory" refers to the period immediately following the revelation, or apocalyptic appearing of Christ from Heaven, when He descends in power and great glory to take the kingdom and assert His rights (see Psalm 2). Then the world will know that the Israelites are the people of His choice, and the sheep of His pasture. As in Esther's time, the Jews will have light and joy, gladness and a good day, while their enemies will be humbled in the dust before them and made to know that in oppressing the seed of Jacob they have been fighting against the living God.

Zechariah 2:10-13 forms a fitting close to such a prophecy. The daughter of Zion, who has hung her harp on the willow for so long, as she wept by the rivers of Babylon, is called to sing and rejoice (see Psalm 137:1-4)! For her glorious Lord will dwell in her midst, and they will all know Him, from the least to the greatest.

Many nations will then become Jehovah's people, being brought into the same blessed knowledge granted to Israel. This is far different from the call of the Gentiles in the present dispensation. Now God is taking out from among the nations a people for His name and uniting Jew and Gentile into one body. But at the later time, Israel will be supreme in the earth, and all the nations will find their blessing through her, when "the Lord shall inherit Judah his portion in the holy land, and shall choose Jerusalem again" (12).

So shall the years of Israel's mourning be ended and Israel's long warfare be over. In that day, the portion of the church will be in Heaven, while the earthly people will find their blessing in the land promised to Abraham, Isaac, and Jacob as an inalienable inheritance, from which their seed will never be expelled.

The last verse expresses the attitude of all the world in the day when the Lord will do this: "Be silent, O all flesh, before the Lord: for he is raised up out of his holy habitation."

It is sweet to know that the rising tide of evil will soon be checked, that sin and rebellion in every form will be eliminated from the earth. The spared of all the nations will bow to the benevolent yet righteous rule of the now-rejected Savior, and Jehovah of hosts will be worshiped and obeyed everywhere.

ZECHARIAH 3: A Brand Plucked out of the Fire

The fourth vision may be looked at in two ways. Primarily, it sets forth Israel's cleansing, judicially and morally, in the last days. It is also a lovely picture of the gospel.

Joshua the high priest, the associate of Zerubbabel (the uncrowned heir of David's line), was seen standing before the angel of Jehovah, as if for judgment. At his right hand appeared Satan, the adversary, ever the accuser of the people of God. But Satan was not permitted to bring any charge, though Joshua was clothed in filthy garments; for the Lord Himself spoke, saying, "[Jehovah] rebuke thee, O Satan; even [Jehovah] that hath chosen Jerusalem rebuke thee: is not this a brand plucked out of the fire?" (1-3).

It is a striking yet lovely scene. Joshua represented the entire remnant; for as priest, he went before God on their behalf. But he was clothed, not in the unsullied robes prescribed by the law, but in filthy garments—depicting the moral pollution of the whole nation. Isaiah's description complements this significant picture:

> Why should ye be stricken any more? ye will revolt more and more: the whole head is sick, and the whole heart faint. From the sole of the foot even unto the head there is no soundness in it; but wounds, and bruises, and putrifying sores: they have not been closed, neither bound up, neither mollified with ointment (Isaiah 1:5-6).

Fundamentally corrupt, Judah defiled all her garments and made them filthy and vile in God's sight. Who would have thought that people so unclean could have been accepted by God? Surely the adversary would find a ready ear when he sought to press his charges before the throne of infinite holiness! But God had taken into account all Israel's failures when He first took them up in grace, so He would listen to no charge against them. He rebuked the devil with the declaration that He had chosen Jerusalem, and that Joshua, as the people's representative, was a brand plucked out of the fire. This is matchless lovingkindness, but what would we expect? For "the gifts and calling of God are without repentance" (Romans 11:29). He will discipline His failing people, but He will not allow Satan to bring a single indictment against them, for He has made provision for their moral fitness in His presence. Zechariah then heard Jehovah's voice saying to those who stood before Him, "Take away the filthy garments from him." While to Joshua this word was given, "Behold, I have caused thine iniquity to pass from thee, and I will clothe thee with change of raiment" (Zechariah 3:4).

At this the prophet's soul was stirred to its depths, and entering into the spirit of the occasion, he cried out, "Let them set a fair mitre upon his head" (5).

Immediately it was done as he requested, and as God had commanded. Joshua appeared no longer as a type or symbol of Judah, polluted by her failures and sins, but of the remnant that will be regenerated in the day of Jehovah's power. In that day she will be cleansed from all her pollution and God will be pacified toward her for all that she had done (compare Ezekiel 16:60-63).

No more beautiful gospel picture is found within the Bible than this. As aptly as Joshua stands for Judah, so does he represent the poor sinner coming into God's holy presence with all his guilt upon him. This is how every soul must meet Him for the first time. No one can put away his iniquity and thereby fit himself to face that righteous throne. But clad in his filthy garments, confessing fully his dreadful guilt, every repentant soul may approach God with the conscious knowledge that for all who come as he came there is mercy and cleansing.

The adversary will be there to oppose if he can. But Jehovah will not listen to him, for He has His eye on the work of the Lord Jesus Christ, accomplished on Calvary's cross, when "he [bore] the sin of many, and made intercession for the transgressors" (Isaiah 53:12). Against that mighty intercession no Satanic charges can succeed. Too loudly cries the blood in God's ear that speaks better things than the blood of Abel. Therefore, He delights to say of every believing sinner, "Is not this a brand plucked out of the fire?" (Zechariah 3:2)

Nor does this refer merely to a righteous position, but there will be moral fitness too. For those whom God justifies He likewise cleanses, purifying their hearts by faith, when they are born of the water of the Word and by the Spirit of holiness.

After Joshua had been justified, cleansed, clothed, and crowned, the angel of the Lord urged him to hear the word of Jehovah of hosts, so that he may walk in His ways and keep His commands. He assured Joshua that if he was faithful, he would judge God's house and keep His courts, having "places to walk among these that stand by" (7). That is, he would be given a place among those seraphic beings whose joy it is to obey the slightest command of the all-glorious and thrice-holy One. In the same way God's redeemed are called to serve Him whose grace has plucked them as brands from eternal fire. In the coming age, the restored and purged Israel will also delight to obey the voice of the Lord.

In verse 8, Joshua and his companions are said to be "men wondered at," or, more correctly, "men of signification," making clear that we have been correct in seeing in the high priest and his associates symbolic people.

Only in Christ will all these prophetic pictures be fulfilled; so at once we are told, "I will bring forth my servant the Branch." This ancient title for the Lord Jesus had been used many times by the prophets. Isaiah more than once foretold the day when "the branch of the Lord" would accomplish beauty and glory (Isaiah 4:2; 11:1). And Jeremiah twice spoke of David's righteous branch, who was to be called Jehovah-tsidkenu, "The Lord, Our Righteousness" (Jeremiah 23:5-6; 33:15-16). So Zechariah only amplified here and in 6:12 what God had long before made known.

The Branch of Zechariah 3:8 is identified with the stone of verse 9, which will be engraved like a signet with the sign of perfect intelligence—namely, seven eyes. This is the stone of salvation that was once a rock of offense. As such, it was rejected by the builders. Soon it will fall from Heaven, in accordance with Nebuchadnezzar's vision (Daniel 2), grinding to powder the enemies of the Lord, but removing the iniquity of the land of Palestine in one day. Then the spared remnant will enter into the blessing of Messiah's reign, in which each will call "his neighbor under the vine and under the fig tree."

This marvelous chapter ends rather abruptly but that is consistent with Zechariah's style. We see sudden terminations and quick transitions throughout his book.

ZECHARIAH 4: The Two Anointed Ones

The next striking vision, the fifth in the series, is of prime importance to any reverent student of the Word of God. Not only does it present precious and important truth regarding Israel as God's light bearer in the world, but it is the only instance where the symbolic meaning of oil is distinctly explained. It gives us therefore an unerring key to unlock many of the treasures of symbolic teaching throughout the Old Testament.

The prophet seemed to have fallen asleep after the interpretation of the previous vision; for we are told that the angel who had been speaking with him came again and woke him up, saying "What seest thou?" (1-2) Zechariah looked and saw a vision of great beauty and splendor. A golden lampstand, evidently somewhat similar to the one described in Exodus 25:31-37, appeared before his eyes. But in one marked respect it differed from those lamps the priest had to carefully fill daily lest they go out. Here, no human hand provided the oil nor was responsible to maintain the light of testimony. The stand and its lamps were a single unit, and the lamps were continually supplied with oil in a most remarkable way. On the top of the central shaft was a golden bowl or fountain. Seven pipes came out of this, which joined the seven lamps. On either side of the stand an olive tree was growing, the branches of which were represented as bending over the receiver-fountain and pouring their oil into it in a continual stream. Thus the light was always maintained in its beauty and power (Zechariah 4:2-3).

When Zechariah asked what this vision meant, the angel responded,

> This is the word of the Lord unto Zerubbabel, saying, Not by might, nor by power, but by my spirit, saith the Lord of hosts. Who art thou, O great mountain? before Zerubbabel thou shalt become a plain: and he shall bring forth the headstone thereof with shoutings, crying, Grace, grace unto it (6-7).

This was no meaningless oracle, like those of heathen prophets, but it was a plain declaration that just as the oil pouring into the golden bowl fed the lamps so the Holy Spirit would confirm and unfailingly supply Israel as Jehovah's testimony-bearer in the earth. He who had brought up a remnant from Babylon under Zerubbabel, the prince of David's line, would infallibly fulfill every promise made through His holy prophets. Human power and might could neither hinder nor help. The Holy Spirit alone could sustain them as His light in the world.

Thus we know what oil typifies: the Spirit of God, whether as anointer or earnest (see Ephesians 1:13-14). In His divine power alone any testimony can be carried on for God at any time. During the present dispensation of Israel's scattering, the church is the light bearer, even as her Lord was while here on earth. Shortly, when Israel will be restored in the saved remnant, she will once more become God's witness. But whether with the blessed Lord Himself, the church His body, or Israel His people, all true testimony resides in the energy of the Holy Spirit.

Empowered by the Holy Spirit, why should we fear people? To Zerubbabel and the feeble remnant in the land, though, Gentile authority might have seemed like a great mountain, hindering all progress in the special work committed to them. Only unbelief could regard the situation like this. Faith would say to the mountain of difficulty, "Become a plain," and it would be so. No weapon formed against them would prosper; no arm would be strong enough to obstruct them, until the temple was completed to the glory of Jehovah. Zerubbabel would bring forth the capstone amid the shouts of a rejoicing people, crying, "Grace, grace unto it" (Zechariah 4:7)!

Just like this, every promise made in the Word of God will be fulfilled to the letter. In this case the one who had begun the house would finish it (see Ezra 3:10-13; 6:14-18), proving that a prophet had been among them. It was a day of weakness, a day of small things; but they should not despise it, for it was the day of Jehovah's strength. The nations of the earth might be utterly indifferent to what was happening at the insignificant place where the Lord had set His name; but there He was, nevertheless, working in mighty power. There the plumb line of truth was in the hands of Zerubbabel, and the people worked as he told them. There too the eyes of the Lord rested after running to and fro through the whole earth (Zechariah 4:8-10).

In God's sight, a great work was going on in Jerusalem, for it was the fulfillment of His own word in regard to the coming of His Son into the world.

Zechariah wondered about one other thing—what the two olive trees signified. So he inquired boldly of the angel not once but twice before getting a response. The angel did not immediately reply, but questioned him again, as though spiritual intuition ought to have made all clear, saying, "Knowest thou not what these be?"(13) Confessing his ignorance, Zechariah was told that, "These are the two anointed ones, that stand by the Lord of the whole earth."

To him the two anointed ones could be no other than Zerubbabel, the prince, and Joshua, the high priest. So in kingly and priestly power the testimony of God was to be maintained. These were the agencies through which Jehovah would work.

In Revelation 11:4 the two witnesses are said to be "the two olive trees, and the two candlesticks standing before the God of the earth." The reference is clearly to Zechariah's vision; yet there is a noticeable difference. There we have two candlesticks; here, only one. The reason is plainly this: the two witnesses come on the scene before Israel is established as God's lampstand nationally. Therefore, in place of one seven-branched lampstand setting forth completeness of testimony, we have two witnesses described as two lampstands. They are also said to be the two olive trees; for they stand before God as His anointed sons of oil in the day when His name is denied and His Word despised. Coming in the spirit and power of Moses and Elijah, they prophesy in the energy of the Spirit until they are put to death by the beast and his adherents. Thus, for the moment, all testimony for God will seem to have been blotted out. But the word of the Lord will not fail, for the seven-branched lampstand will be set up when the Lord descends and delivers His people Israel out of the hand of all who oppress them.

ZECHARIAH 5: The Flying Roll and the Ephah

The visions of glory in the last two chapters are followed by others of a very different sort. Judah and Jerusalem would be blessed by sovereign grace alone; they did not merit any blessings. This is what the "flying roll" makes clear. It speaks of unsparing judgment according to their works—a judgment that must fall on all who refuse to judge themselves according to the Word of the living God. But it also lets us know that He, the Holy One, so grievously sinned against, has found a way to save in a righteous manner all who turn to Him and call on His name. Otherwise everyone would need to be cut off.

Zechariah 5:1-4 should be read with utmost care for it contains a solemn message that speaks loudly to every heart, both to Gentiles and to Jews. Primarily it refers to Judah because they will be restored to the land in unbelief when this prophecy is fulfilled. Note also that the general word *earth* in verse 3 (KJV) is better translated "land"—that is, Palestine—and is the word generally used in the books of the prophets. In studying the seventeen books that make up the last part of the Old Testament, it is of prime importance to remember that God is speaking of Israel as a people and Palestine as their land. That apparently insignificant strip of country is, for Him, the center of the earth and of all His ways with people on the earth. He gave it by inviolable covenant to Abraham and his descendants. There His blessed Son was born and lived and died. From there He ascended to Heaven. To that same land He will descend in person to usher in the kingdom long foretold.

For centuries, that land has been disgracefully trodden underfoot by the haughty Gentile conquerors, while its rightful inhabitants have, for their sins, been dispersed among the nations. But to that land they shall return—they have even now returned in large numbers, though still in darkness of soul and unbelief. There God will put them through a trial of unequaled fierceness, called "the time of Jacob's trouble" or "the great tribulation," separating the precious from the vile. God will destroy the sinners from among them and save the repentant subjects of His grace, who will form the nucleus of the kingdom in the day of His power.

This vision of the flying roll speaks of this preparatory judgment. Zechariah saw in the heavens a vast scroll moving swiftly through the air over all the land of Canaan. He saw that curses and judgments were written on both sides. On one side was God's word against those who wronged their neighbor, according to the last five of the ten commandments (this is mentioned first because man can best appreciate the wickedness of sin against his fellows). On the other side was the doom pronounced against those who were guilty of blasphemy, according to the first five commandments.

That law—in itself holy, and just, and good—became their condemnation; for "as many as are of the works of the law are under the curse; for it is written, Cursed is every one that continueth not in all things which are written in the book of the law to do them" (Galatians 3:10). The Jews boasted in that law; yet it spoke only for their condemnation.

The flying roll was the answer to the foolhardiness of the people who cried at Sinai, "All that the Lord hath said will we do" (Exodus 24:7). After a trial lasting long centuries, it is the witness against them, making obvious the solemn fact that they had failed at every point, with the result being their judgment.

The curse enters every house where the thief or the liar is found, bringing utter destruction in its wake. This is all that the law can do for any sinner. It can only condemn and curse the one who violates it.

And who has not violated it? Wherever it has been declared, it has found many who promise, but none who perform. No honest person can claim to have kept it; therefore since we do not have righteousness in ourselves, we cannot have salvation in ourselves.

But, blessed be God, He has found a ransom for men and women who have lost all right to His favor. "Christ hath redeemed us from the curse of the law, being made a curse for us: for it is written,

Cursed is every one that hangeth on a tree"(Galatians 3:13). On the basis of an accomplished redemption, grace now flows to all sinners who confess their lost condition and trust the sinners' Savior. On this same basis the flying roll will be averted from the houses of Judah's remnant in the last days. Those who turn to God in repentance, like their fathers on the Passover night, will find shelter beneath the blood of atonement. This is the truth conveyed in the wonderful vision of Zechariah 3.

In chapter 5 verse 5, we have another yet stranger symbol. Zechariah, evidently disturbed by the awful sign of the flying roll, was told by the interpreting angel to "lift up now thine eyes" to observe the next remarkable vision. He saw a great ephah, a vessel or basket for measuring merchandise, that had a heavy piece of base metal, like lead, on top of it. When the lid was lifted, Zechariah saw a woman who was thrown into the ephah, which was again covered with the lead. Two other women then appeared, with wings like those of a stork, who lifted the ephah between them and flew with it to the north. Zechariah asked, "Whither do these bear the ephah?" And the angel answered, "To build it an house in the land of Shinar: and it shall be established, and set there upon her own base" (5-11).

What is the meaning we can gather from this strange sign seen by the prophet? Notice that as we progress through the next visions in Zechariah, less interpretation is provided. It is as though the Lord had given enough in regard to the earlier visions to lay a solid foundation for understanding the later ones. So we need to carefully compare what we have here with what has already come before.

Various interpretations have been suggested, many of which seem to be extremely fanciful. One of the most common is this: The ephah is a symbol of commercialism, illustrating a stereotype of the Jewish race, who have often been regarded as a nation of keen bargainers. The woman symbolizes corrupt business practices. The carrying of the woman in the ephah to the land of Shinar indicates the revival of the ancient city of Babylon in great splendor as the commercial center of the coming day. Those who accept this interpretation view the commercial trade of the Mesopotamian region in our day as a sign that they are on the right track. But to my mind this is all pure speculation and absolutely unsupported by Scripture. Both Jeremiah and Isaiah make it clear, in my judgment, that Babylon has fallen to rise no more. It has been literally burned and destroyed, and God Himself has solemnly declared that for that wicked city there shall be no healing or revival.

Nor is there any solid reason for supposing that the ephah is in itself a symbol of great commercial enterprise. Is it not rather the recognized symbol of measurement, telling us that God will weigh Judah's sin and the sin of the whole house of Israel with unerring accuracy? When their iniquity cannot get any worse, in wondrous grace God will separate the wicked from the preserved remnant, dealing with it in connection with the place of its origin, the land of Shinar (Babylon). I believe that the woman in the ephah unmistakably represents wickedness of a religious nature, as in the woman Jezebel who corrupted the assembly at Thyatira (Revelation 2:18-29), paving the way for the awful blasphemy of the scarlet woman of Revelation 17.

Israel's great religious sin was idolatry. They had been separated from the nations to be Jehovah's witnesses to the unity of the Godhead. Instead of maintaining the testimony entrusted to them, they turned to the practices of the heathen, provoking their Rock and causing Him to fall on them in wrath. Babylon was the mother of idolatry. It is the home of all that is false in a religious way. When the end comes, this spirit of wickedness will be separated from Judah and carried by stork-winged women—who most likely symbolize the unclean energy of the human mind, femininely lovely, but propelled by the energy of the prince of the power of the air—to the land of Shinar, where its house will be built. That is, there its home will be, and there it will be judged.

In mystical Babylon, literal Babylon finds her identity continued and her sin fully dealt with. All nations have been deceived by her sorcery, and in her will be "found the blood of prophets, and of saints, and of all that were slain upon the earth" (Revelation 18:24).

In this manner Israel will be purified, and idolatry of every form will meet its just and final doom. All this prepares the way for our God and His Christ to establish His kingdom.

ZECHARIAH 6: The Four Chariots, and the Crowning Day

The sixth chapter concludes the first division of the prophecy, and is itself divided into two parts. Verses 1-8 give us Zechariah's final vision. Verses 9-15 present the glorious symbolic climax of all prophetic instruction—the crowning of Joshua the high priest, which represents the coronation of our Lord Jesus Christ when He will be revealed to Israel as "a priest forever after the order of Melchizedek," who combined in himself the kingly and priestly offices (Hebrews 5:6).

The vision is simple, yet comforting, and requires only a little explanation. Zechariah saw four chariots drawn respectively by red, black, white, and speckled bay horses. No mention is made of drivers. It would seem as though the horses were directed by an unseen agency, which is fully in keeping with the explanation given afterward.

The chariots and their horses were seen coming out from between two mountains of brass (Zechariah 6:1-3). The prophet asked what the symbols meant and was told by the angel,

> These are the four spirits of the heavens, which go forth from standing before the Lord of all the earth. The black horses which are therein go forth into the north country; and the white go forth after them; and the grisled go forth toward the south country. And the bay [translated in some versions as "the red" or "the strong"] went forth, and sought to go that they might walk to and fro through the earth (5-7).

Then the angel addressed the restless steeds directly, telling them, "Get you hence, walk to and fro through the earth."

At once they started on their mission, and the angel turned again to Zechariah and said, "Behold, these that go toward the north country have quieted my spirit in the north country" (8).

The vision clearly depicts God's control of all destructive agencies used by Him in the punishment of the nations that have deserved His wrath. This vision was intended to impart peace and confidence to the remnant, reassuring them that the God of Israel was also the Lord of all the earth. "All things serve His might." In His own way and time, therefore, He would send the chariots of His sovereign rule against the nations that had made a prey of His people. The mountains of brass represent power in righteous judgment. From between two such mountains the chariots go forth.

God's providential instruments may seem to unbelievers like restless, untamed horses rushing here and there according to blind chance or their own uncontrolled energy. But people of faith, though they cannot always see the hand that guides the reins, know that divine wisdom orders everything according to righteousness.

The special prophetic application of what Zechariah had seen was at that moment connected with the kingdom of Babylon on the north and Egypt on the south. Between these two powers God would sustain His feeble flock, checkmating every effort to destroy them until the Messiah would appear. Tragically, when He came they knew Him not! So they were driven from their ancestral home and scattered among the Gentiles. But in the last days, they will again be found in a similar, though more serious, state than before. Then the lesson of this vision will be for their comfort and encouragement, directing them to look up in confidence to the One who controls every power that seeks to overthrow them. Compare Revelation 7:1-3, where four angels are seen holding the winds, or spirits of destruction, in check until the remnant preserved for the coming kingdom are sealed.

So far, we have studied the apocalypse of Zechariah, seeking to understand his visions in their prophetic and moral bearing. They harmonize perfectly with those of Daniel and the Revelation and also with the unfolding of God's ways in Hosea. Now we will turn our attention to Zechariah's symbolic action, which illustrates the glorious crowning day—the coronation day of the once-rejected Jesus as Priest-King over all the earth.

Zechariah was told to go to some of the returned exiles, and take from them gifts of silver and gold to make crowns. One of these crowns was to be set on the head of Joshua, the son of Josedech, the high priest. But in doing so, he was to speak of a greater than Joshua, saying,

> Behold the man whose name is The Branch; and he shall grow up out of his place, and he shall build the temple of the Lord: Even he shall build the temple of the Lord; and he shall bear the glory, and shall sit and rule upon his throne: and he shall be a priest upon his throne: and the counsel of peace shall be between them both (12-13).

Zechariah also placed crowns on Joshua's companions, which represented the dignity of restored Israel when they will all be a kingdom of priests. This was done "for a memorial in the temple of the Lord" (14). Then he declared, "they that are far off shall come and build in the temple of the Lord, and ye shall know that the Lord of hosts hath sent me unto you. And this shall come to pass, if ye will diligently obey the voice of the Lord your God" (15).

Those directly addressed by Zechariah did not diligently obey Jehovah's voice, so they forfeited the promised blessing. But in a future day, an obedient remnant will be found who will be born again and in whose hearts and minds will be written the law of God so that they will delight in His testimonies. Then the Branch of Jehovah will be glorious throughout the whole earth. And then the crown will be placed on the brow that was once pierced with the mock crown of thorns when Pilate led Him forth, uttering unconsciously the very words of the prophet, "Behold, the man!" (John 19:5) There he stopped, for the hour had not yet come when that lowly Man was to be invested with His regal glories. But when God brings His first-begotten into the world again, He will call on all created intelligences, human and angelic, to pay Him homage. Then the promise of Psalm 110 will be fulfilled, and His Melchizedek priesthood, in relation to Israel and the earth, will be ushered in.

The words, "He shall build the temple of the Lord," in Zechariah 6:13, together with the prophecy of verse 15, make it clear that another and more glorious temple than the one Zerubbabel built was in mind. That house, "exceeding magnifical," (1 Chronicles 22:5) is fully described in the last nine chapters of Ezekiel. It will be built when the long-awaited King has come, and in His person the two offices of priest and ruler combine.

"The counsel of peace shall be between them both," we are told

(Zechariah 6:13). That is, the new covenant will rest, not on an agreement entered into by man and God, but on the grounds of "the counsel of peace" made between Jehovah of hosts and the Man whose name is "The Branch." He, the Man of God's purpose, settled every question regarding sin when He died on the cross. And now, "having made peace through the blood of his cross," He is the agent through whom the reconciliation of all things in Heaven and earth will be effected (Colossians 1:20).

We have been carried in spirit from the days of Judah's first restoration to her final blessing in the land, when "this man shall be the peace" (Micah 5:5) and "in his times he shall show, who is that blessed and only Potentate, the King of kings, and Lord of lords" (1 Timothy 6:15).

This is the ultimate goal of prophecy, and it closes the first division of our book.

ZECHARIAH 7: The Need of Reality

When we reach the second division of Zechariah's prophecy a little more than two years have passed since chapter 6. In the meantime, royal permission had been given for the completion of the temple, and the work went on energetically (see Ezra 5). There had been some effort to revive the ancient feasts and keep the more modern fasts. Concerning the latter, a delegation of Jews came to consult Zechariah and the elders. Their Babylonian names tell that they had been born in captivity. As representatives of the people, "Sherezer and Regem-melech, and their men," came to "pray before the Lord, And to speak unto the priests which were in the house of the Lord of hosts, and to the prophets, saying, Should I weep in the fifth month, separating myself, as I have done these so many years?" (Zechariah 7:2-3)

This seems to be an appropriate question. For the fast of the fifth month—as well as the fasts of the fourth, seventh, and tenth months (8:19)—there was no direct authority in the Word of God. The returned remnant, then, had been learning to inquire, "What saith the Scriptures?" concerning both commands and teaching.

During their Babylonian exile they had kept these four fasts to commemorate various events in their past sad history, all connected with punishment for their sins. None need doubt the piety that prompted the observance of these special seasons of humility before God.

The only trouble was that formality quickly took the place of reality and genuine self-humbling in the presence of the Lord. On the tenth day of the fifth month, Nebuzar-adan burned the temple and the city of Jerusalem. On the yearly anniversary of that solemn event the Jews fasted and wept, begging the Lord to have mercy and restore the house and the city. Naturally, now that they were again in the midst of Jerusalem's ruins and their prayer seemed answered in that the house of God neared completion, the question of the righteousness of continuing the self-appointed fast of the fifth month came before them.

The word of the Lord of hosts came through Zechariah in reply. But there was no legislation regarding the fast at all: He neither forbade nor commanded it. In itself, such a fast was without positive Scriptural authority. On the other hand, it was in full keeping with the general tenor of the Word. It was extrascriptural, rather than unscriptural. If the people met in true self-examination and brokenness of spirit before God on that day, or any day, it would have been acceptable. If they met simply as legally observing a fast which, after all, He had never appointed, it was a burden to the flesh and worthless in His sight. Therefore Zechariah stressed the need of reality. What had been their aim and condition of soul as they kept the fasts in the past? When they commemorated the burning of the temple in the fifth month (see 2 Kings 25:8-9; Jeremiah 52:12-13) and the death of the faithful Gedaliah in the seventh month (2 Kings 25:25; Jeremiah 41:1-2), did they truly fast to Jehovah all the years of the captivity?

On the other hand, when they kept the appointed feasts in place of the fasts, was it God's glory they sought? Or did they simply come together for social enjoyment, eating and drinking, without one thought of honoring Him whose power and grace they were supposed to be remembering? (Zechariah 7:6)

Surely, if everything before had been empty and unreal, now, with such marked evidences both of divine grace and rule before them, they should turn to God with all their hearts. They should remember the words that God had cried by the former prophets, who had testified to their predecessors before Jerusalem was destroyed, when they dwelt in peace, and prosperity in the land (7).

This is all the answer that was given for the moment. It was left to them to decide whether they should keep the fast or not. This is most significant and speaks to us today, emphasizing the fact that mere formality will never do for God. He must see a true turning to Himself if He would delight in the gathering together of His people. There may not always be chapter and verse for every practice, but God will graciously accept all that springs from true contrition—as long as it is not opposed to the plain letter of His Word. It has become the fashion in some places to ask for the Scripture commanding formal times of Bible study, or where the direct verse is for gathering the young together to teach them the knowledge of the Bible and thus lead them to Christ. We need not be troubled by such coldhearted questions as these. Rather, let the Sunday school worker ask himself or herself, "Why do I work with the children? Is it only a duty that has become legal drudgery, which I continue because such work is now customary? Or do I seek to glorify the Lord Jesus Christ? Is my purpose to reveal Him to the young so that their tender hearts may be drawn to Christ before they become hardened by the deceitfulness of sin?" If this is the case, let there be no further question, but go on joyfully with your service, doing it heartily as unto the Lord.

The same principle applies to Bible study meetings among believers. There is no direct Scripture that says such meetings should be held at stated intervals. There is, however, plenty in Scriptural examples to make it clear that when such meetings are held by earnest, loyal-hearted saints, who come together hungering for the precious truth of God and desiring to apply it to their ways, it is truly pleasing in His sight. Otherwise, it is but a work of the flesh—religious flesh, no doubt, but flesh still, for all that.

This principle is equally true of the assembly meeting in 1 Corinthians 14 and the meeting for the breaking of bread in 1 Corinthians 11 and Acts 20:7. It is quite possible to sit down at the Lord's table, where the bread and wine speak of Jesus' body given and His blood shed for us, and yet not eat the Lord's supper at all because the mind is so occupied with other things that there is no true remembrance of Christ. One may go from church relieved in conscience for not neglecting the table of the Lord, when all the time there has been nothing for God in it at all. The whole thing was only a perfunctory and empty ceremony, detestable in God's eyes, if indeed there has not been an actual eating and drinking of judgment to oneself (see 1 Corinthians 11:27-29).

But if there is to be reality when saints are gathered together, there must be righteousness in their daily lives. So Zechariah again spoke the word of the Lord, saying,

> Execute true judgment, and show mercy and compassions every man to his brother: And oppress not the widow, nor the fatherless, the stranger, nor the poor; and let none of you imagine evil against his brother in your heart (9-10).

Solemn words are these! Would that they had been more often called to mind by the people of God in all ages! God has said, "Woe unto them that decree unrighteous decrees" (Isaiah 10:1)! Yet how frequently ecclesiastical authority has been invoked to enforce the most clearly cruel and unholy decisions! Oh, the crimes that have been committed in the name of the Lord and His truth! The cruelties of those who have claimed to know the exclusive mind of the Lord will produce a terrible and humiliating record at the judgment seat of Christ. When will saints learn that nothing unholy is of God; that nothing unrighteous is right; that nothing unjust is approved by the just One! Nothing has divine sanction if it outrages the mercy and compassions of Christ.

Because Israel had continually forgotten all this and "made their hearts as an adamant stone," the earlier prophets had been sent to warn them. They would not listen, however, so great wrath came upon them. As they were indifferent to the cry of the distressed and calloused to the sorrows of the needy, so God gave them over to learn in bitterness of soul what distress and need really meant. In the day of their anguished cry, He refused to hear, just as they had refused to hear His voice of pleading and warning. They had been scattered with a whirlwind among all the nations (Zechariah 7:11-14).

Would their children learn from the sad experience of the past? Or must they too be broken and driven forth because of indifference to the commands of the holy and true One?

To Christians of the present day the same questions may well be posed. May God give us grace to profit by the failures of the past and to walk humbly and in love, according to truth, in this time before the Lord Jesus returns.

ZECHARIAH 8: Future Light on the Present Path

The value of studying future prophecy is strikingly displayed in this chapter. Here we find God, through His servant, drawing back the veil that hides the coming glory so that His people may comprehend in some measure their hope and live accordingly.

It might have been better to have no break between chapters 7 and 8 because it all seems to be part of Jehovah's answer regarding the fifth-month fast.

Chapter 8:1-8 forms a lovely millennial picture, describing the conditions that will prevail when "Jerusalem shall be called a city of truth; and the mountain of the Lord of hosts the holy mountain." Because of their idolatrous ways the Lord had been "jealous for Zion with great jealousy." And with great wrath He had delivered Judah into the hands of their enemies, so that they might learn in the strangers' land the folly of trusting in idols and sacrificing to the demons behind the symbols (2). Their exile in Babylon had cured them of this for the time; though our Lord Jesus showed that they were really like an empty house, swept and furnished, to which the unclean spirit who had gone out returns, bringing with him seven demons worse than himself (Matthew 12:43-45). This will be fulfilled when idolatry of a worse kind than ever before is established among them—even the abomination of desolation standing in the holy place. But all this is passed over here, for God's purpose is our focus, and not the people's failure.

It is clear that the latter half of Zechariah 8:3 could never have been properly applied to Jerusalem and mount Zion after the return from Babylon. Yet the first half of verse 3 fits that context, "I am returned unto Zion, and will dwell in the midst of Jerusalem." All the subsequent failure, even the rejection of Messiah Himself and their consequent dispersion, is passed over in silence, and the future glorious estate of Jerusalem is linked with the remnant then in the land. Only when the Lord has been manifested in power will the words that follow be fulfilled. Then there will be old men and women living in the restored city, while "the streets of the city shall be full of boys and girls playing in the streets thereof" (4-5). The street was now the place of danger. But then the children will play in them with perfect safety. It is touching to see how the eternal God concerns Himself even with the innocent pastimes of little children. It would be beneficial to strict and legalistic parents to ponder this fifth verse, for I fear that boys and girls are often made to feel that their simple pleasures are, if not displeasing to God, at least without value.

The fulfillment of this prophecy is marvelous indeed in the eyes of puny humans; but it is only a small thing with the One who hurled worlds into space and directs the movements of the minutest of His creatures. God's omnipotent hand will surely perform what His mouth has spoken. From what He said next we surmise that He definitely had a future return in mind:

> Behold, I will save my people from the east country, and from the west country; And I will bring them, and they shall dwell in the midst of Jerusalem: and they shall be my people, and I will be their God, in truth and in righteousness (7-8).

This is the universal testimony of the prophets. The restoration from Babylon was only temporary in order that what had been written concerning the Messiah might be fulfilled. When Jesus was cut off, those who refused Him were driven forth into all the ends of the earth. From there, in God's appointed time, they will return again to that country, which is still to them the land of promise, where all that the prophets have spoken shall come to pass.

In verse 9 the practical application is stressed. In view of the glory that is coming, their hands may well be strong. Why should they be downcast and discouraged with such a future assured? So the people were urged to work and hope, encouraged by the promises of rich reward. God was caring for their interests, and He wanted them to be earnest about His too. When Haggai first spoke to them, famine threatened and disappointment clouded all their sky. But when they willingly and cheerfully gave themselves to the work of building the Lord's temple, He had declared, "From this day will I bless you" (Haggai 1:9-11; 2:18-19). He had been as good as His word and would still watch over them for blessing, giving prosperity and increase while they put first things first, making His glory their object (Zechariah 8:10-12).

But in all these promises it is clear that God had something more in mind than the returned remnant. He was looking to the fullness of blessing in the millennium. This is why He declared that Israel, once a curse among the nations, would be saved and made a blessing, according to His covenant with Abraham. This did not occur in any significant way for the returnees or their descendants, to whom Zechariah spoke; for less than six hundred years later we hear the Holy Spirit declaring that through them the name of God was blasphemed among the Gentiles (Romans 2:24). But God's Word abides nevertheless, and in a future remnant every promise will be made good (Zechariah 8:13).

The Lord had no delight in afflicting His people; but their ancestors had provoked Him to wrath. Let their children take heed to their ways, therefore, and obey His voice, and all would be well.

> These are the things that ye shall do: Speak ye every man the truth to his neighbour; execute the judgment of truth and peace in your gates; And let none of you imagine evil in your hearts against his neighbour; and love no false oath: for all these are things that I hate, saith the Lord (16-17).

Practical righteousness and true morality are the same in all dispensations. Christians would do well to examine their hearts as we read these verses and note what is abhorrent in God's sight. Truth and judgment according to truth: in these He delights. Evil conjecturing (a most fruitful source of trouble in all ages) and false oaths: these He hates. May God give us the grace to cleave to the former and refuse the latter!

The question regarding the fasts (Zechariah 7:3) is referred to again in verses 18-19. The fasts of the fifth and seventh months we have already examined. The fast of the fourth month commemorated the taking of Jerusalem, while that of the tenth called to mind the beginning of its siege. If the restored remnant earnestly sought to walk with God, truly turning away from the sins of the past, these fasts would be transformed into cheerful feasts. "Therefore love the truth and peace," they were told (19). Notice that truth comes first, then peace, as in 2 Timothy 2:22. Believers there are challenged, in a day of confusion and distraction, to follow righteousness first of all. Then faith, love, and peace would rightly follow.

Zechariah 8 concludes by portraying the happy spiritual condition that will prevail in the day when Messiah's kingdom is established. When Israel is at last a regenerate and sanctified people, they will gather to the Lord not out of compulsion or cold, formal obedience, but out of joy. Each city will compete with the other to "provoke unto love and to good works" (Hebrews 10:24), saying one to another, "Let us go speedily to pray before the Lord, and to seek the Lord of hosts: I will go also" (Zechariah 8:20-21). His service will be their joy and delight. Psalm 122 will be fulfilled, and the voices of the restored remnant will sing with exultation, "I was glad when they said unto me, Let us go into the house of the Lord."

It is always like this when Christ Himself is before the soul. The gatherings of the children of God become foretastes of Heaven when His own people regard Him as altogether lovely. There would be no dry, listless meetings then; but every heart would thrill with a supernatural joy as He fills the vision of the enraptured soul. If we were truly right with God, we would always enjoy this holy freshness and fervent longing for His presence. But when we permit sin to do its deadly work, the Holy Spirit is grieved, Christ is hidden, and what would have been a delight becomes a weariness of the flesh.

When the saints of God are enjoying Christ, others are attracted to Him and to them. Likewise, when Israel will finally gather around Him, dwelling under His shadow and happy in His love, there will be a great stirring of hearts among the nations who will not have been destroyed when the stone falls from Heaven. "Many people and strong nations shall come to seek the Lord of hosts in Jerusalem, and to pray before the Lord" (Zechariah 8:22). The Jew, so long despised and hated, will be looked at as the ambassador of the Lord, and ten men of all languages shall hang onto one who is of Judah, saying, "We will go with you: for we have heard that God is with you" (23). It is impossible, by any principle of honest interpretation, to make these words fit any revival of the past or present. They apply only to the day when Jerusalem will be the spiritual metropolis of the whole earth, and when the term Jew, so often used in contempt, will proclaim one who is truly a son of praise, joyfully worshiping the Lord of hosts as he stands on redemption ground. (*Jew* is a contraction of *Judah,* which means "praise." Note how Paul interprets the name in Romans 2:28-29.) Then indeed shall all the nations know that "salvation is of the Jews" (John 4:22).

The spiritual application, once more, is this: When the people of God, in any age, proceed in happy fellowship with their Lord and Savior, the unsaved will be attracted to Him. They will seek out His disciples, saying, "We would see Jesus" (John 12:21).

ZECHARIAH 9: The Coming King

We have already seen that the book of Zechariah divides into two parts. The second division encompasses chapters 7–14, which further divides into three more sections: chapters 7–8, chapters 9–11, which show the coming of the Messiah and His rejection by Judah, then chapters 12–14, which reveal Jesus' second coming and His acceptance by the repentant remnant.

The rejection of Christ when He came in grace is morally connected with the state the people had fallen into long before. The cross was merely the culmination of a course of willful hardening that had been going on from the days of the wilderness. This was the reason for the various captivities and many afflictions they had experienced. When these resulted in repentance, the peaceable fruit of righteousness followed. The remnant had been called to this in chapters 7 and 8. Now the prophet pointed them to the coming Savior-King so that they could prepare their hearts for His reception. But Chapter 11 closes with the solemn prediction of the selling of the true Shepherd for thirty pieces of silver and the consequent acceptance of the idol-shepherd, the antichrist.

Chapter 9:1-8 is occupied with the destruction of the Syrian power in "the land of Hadrach," along with all Israel's enemies bordering on the land of Palestine, in preparation for the extension of the promised kingdom. These verses evidently have a double application. First, they set forth the past overthrow of the kingdoms before the first coming of the Lord (which would have been final had He been received and owned as the Anointed of Jehovah). Second, they reveal the future doom of the powers that will be in those lands when the final triumph of the King of kings comes. In that day, God will "encamp about [His] house," becoming like a wall of fire to protect His own. Every enemy will be destroyed so that "no oppressor shall pass through them any more" (8).

Through all these lands the victorious armies of Alexander the Great passed, overthrowing all of the cities mentioned, in strict accordance with the prophetic Word. Damascus, Hamath, Tyre and Sidon, and the strongholds of the Philistines were all subjugated, and some were utterly ruined to rise no more. Yet Judah and Jerusalem were spared, as if by direct divine intervention, and the Grecian armies became the protectors instead of the destroyers of Abraham's seed. The temple and city were preserved so that in them would be carried out all that the prophets had spoken concerning the coming of the just One, who was to suffer and die there.

In verse 9 we have the words that Matthew 21:4-5 and John 12:14-15 tell us were directly fulfilled when the Lord Jesus Christ rode into Jerusalem amid the welcoming cries of the disciples, the children, and the people. Zechariah wrote, "Rejoice greatly, O daughter of Zion; shout, O daughter of Jerusalem: behold, thy King cometh unto thee: he is just, and having salvation; lowly, and riding upon an ass, and upon a colt the foal of an ass." He came as the Prince of Peace, only to be eventually despised and considered nothing. When He comes the second time, it will be as the Warrior-King on the white horse of victorious judgment (see Revelation 19).

Between Zechariah 9:9 and verse 10 this present dispensation of grace comes in, for it is obvious that the latter part of the chapter has not yet been fulfilled. The King came but was rejected. His cross became the sign of salvation for all who trust Him, while He Himself has taken His seat on the Father's throne in Heaven. Never for one hour has He occupied the throne of David which is yet to be His. He will take that throne when He descends from the heavens with power and great glory. Then He will cut off all the enemies of Jerusalem, and "He shall speak peace unto the heathen: and his dominion shall be from sea to sea, and from the river even to the ends of the earth" (10). Only when He appears in person will these words come to pass. There can be no millennium without Christ.

At His glorious revelation Jesus will deliver Judah's prisoners out of the waterless pit through the blood of the covenant confirmed in His death. He will bring salvation to these prisoners of hope, and they will find in Him a stronghold and a defense from all their enemies—but only after He has rendered to Israel double for all their iniquities (Isaiah 40:2; 61:7). Then Judah will be like a strong bow in His hand, and Ephraim like a polished shaft. And the nations will then bow before the Lord, confessing the excellency of the God of Jacob (Zechariah 9:11-13).

Again we have to notice a secondary application of this prophecy. Verses 13-16 seem to refer in part to the Maccabean conflict with Antiochus Epiphanes, a type of the antichrist of the last days. Jehovah raised up the sons of Zion against the sons of Greece, and made the army of Judah "as the sword of a mighty man." However, the fuller interpretation is undoubtedly that which refers to the conflicts of the great tribulation. Then, in their darkest hour of trial, "the Lord shall be seen over them, and his arrow shall go forth as the lightning," He will blow the trumpet to signal the defense of those who, in their distress, will turn to Him with all their hearts.

He will "save them in that day as the flock of his people," when they will become the jewels of His crown, brilliantly shining on Immanuel's land (16). What a day of glory for the people so long hated and oppressed! They who have been accounted by many as the very offscouring of the earth will shine in unparalleled brilliancy in the diadem of the crucified One when they cry, "Blessed is he that cometh in the name of the Lord!" (Matthew 21:9) No longer will Jesus be to them "without form or comeliness," and bereft of all beauty that would cause them to desire Him (see Isaiah 53:2). On the contrary, as they gaze astonished on the head once crowned with thorns and the face once marred more than any man, they will cry, "How great is his goodness, and how great is his beauty!" Then He will feed them bountifully, providing them with every blessing so that "corn shall make the young men cheerful, and new wine the maids" (Zechariah 9:17). Fasting and sorrow will have ceased forever. The joy of an unending feast in the banqueting house will have begun with the banner of love waving over all.

ZECHARIAH 10: The Gathering

Chapter 10 pursues the same general subject as chapter 9, detailing the glory that might have been enjoyed by Israel if they had accepted Messiah's claims. Since they rejected Him, however, their blessings have been suspended during the present church age, and they will only be realized when His people receive Him whom they once spurned as the Anointed of Jehovah.

Notice that all Israel is included, not merely Judah (10:6-7). At the appointed time, a remnant from all twelve tribes will be brought into blessing and settled in their ancestral land, never again to be uprooted by an enemy's hand.

Without the latter rain (see Joel 2:23 and notes) Palestine becomes little better than a wilderness; though in our day water conservation and irrigation serve to a certain degree in its place. But under natural conditions, the former and latter rains are required to ensure plenty and prosperity. Therefore we need not be surprised to find the prophets using the rains in a figurative sense. Spiritually, Israel has had her former rain, but a long season of drought has since come in. Now they are urged to look up in hope, and ask the Lord for "rain in the time of the latter rain" (Zechariah 10:1). In response He pledged Himself to give showers of blessing. This is undoubtedly the outpouring of the Spirit predicted by Joel, which will surely take place at the time of the end.

Until then spiritual famine prevails. They had found no comfort in their idols, so at the captivity they put them away. Since then, however, they have been like an unshepherded flock, taking their own course and wandering in a dry, desolate land. The undershepherds and the leaders of the people, "the goats," have caused them to stray, thus incurring the Lord's anger. He is about to visit His flock, limited here to the house of Judah, for it was they who crucified the Lord of glory. Once He brings them under His control again, they will become "as his goodly horse in the battle" (2-3).

Out of him—that is, Judah—came forth the Cornerstone and the Nail. Both of these names I take to refer to Christ. He is the Head of the corner, and "it is evident that our Lord sprang out of Judah" (Hebrews 7:14). He is also the Nail on whom will hang all the glory of His Father's house (see Isaiah 22:23-24).

But the Battlebow and every oppressor will likewise spring from Judah. The bow seems to be used symbolically of the Lord when He rides forth in His might to overthrow all His enemies. The rulers of Judah will be associated with Him when the first dominion returns to the royal tribe.

Victorious over all who have sought their destruction, the once feeble remnant will become like mighty men treading down their enemies when led to certain triumph by the Lion of Judah (Zechariah 10:5).

With every enemy finally overthrown, Jehovah will strengthen the house of Judah and save the house of Joseph. He will bring them again in mercy to their land and make them one people, restoring them to His favor as though He had never cast them off (6). In this way He will repeal the Lo-ammi sentence of Hosea 1:9. The Jews, first brought back to their land in unbelief, will pass through the sorrows of the great tribulation, which will separate the remnant from the apostate mass. The ten tribes will be gathered later and added to Judah and Benjamin when Messiah Himself has appeared in glory. The ten tribes had no direct part in the crucifixion of God's Son, so the special hour of trial is not for them.

The restoration will be far more than political or national—or even giving them back Palestine, their ancestral home. There will be a divine work in the souls of the long blinded people so that the veil of unbelief will be taken away and they will rejoice in the Lord. This will be the fulfillment of the feast of tabernacles, the happiest season of all the year (Zechariah 10:7). Rejoicing in conscious redemption, they will be fruitful and increase as in the days of old.

The manner of their ancient deliverance is used as a figure of this future one (9-12). They will be gathered from all the lands to which they have been dispersed and returned to the land of promise. They will be the center of the nations, in accordance with the word of the Lord concerning Jezreel, the seed of God (see Hosea 2:22-23 and notes). Passing in triumph through the sea of affliction (not "with affliction") and the river of sorrow, they will find in the Lord their God strength and victory and will walk in freedom in His name.

This is the universal testimony of Scripture regarding the future glory of the nation now scattered and despised. Their blindness will pass away; and with the eyes of their heart enlightened, they will see the beauty of the One who was once abhorred and crucified.

In this way their whole history becomes a lovely illustration of the precious words of Psalm 76:10, "Surely the wrath of man shall praise thee: the remainder of wrath shalt thou restrain." God will permit only as much evil as will ultimately glorify Him. Anything beyond that He holds in check. How comforting this is for the afflicted saint in any dispensation! How often the spirit is overwhelmed and the soul cast down. But faith can look up in the hour when all seems hopeless and darkness overspreads the scene, knowing that,

> God sits as Sovereign on His throne,
> And ruleth all things well.

He can make a way for His redeemed through the sea. His power can dry up the rivers and make His people pass over on dry land. What will be true for Israel nationally will be true for every child of God to enjoy personally.

Zechariah 10:9-12 coalesces with Isaiah 43:1-7:

> But now thus saith the Lord that created thee, O Jacob, and he that formed thee, O Israel, Fear not: for I have redeemed thee, I have called thee by thy name; thou art mine. When thou passest through the waters, I will be with thee; and through the rivers, they shall not overflow thee: when thou walkest through the fire, thou shalt not be burned; neither shall the flame kindle upon thee. For I am the Lord thy God, the Holy One of Israel, thy Saviour: I gave Egypt for thy ransom, Ethiopia and Seba for

> thee. Since thou wast precious in my sight, thou hast been honourable, and I have loved thee: therefore will I give men for thee, and people for thy life. Fear not; for I am with thee: I will bring thy seed from the east, and gather thee from the west; I will say to the north, Give up; and to the south, Keep not back: bring my sons from far, and my daughters from the ends of the earth; Even every one that is called by my name: for I have created him for my glory, I have formed him; yea, I have made him.

What human words could compare with this divine declaration of God's unchangeable purpose in regard to His earthly people. And by what perverse system of interpretation can such words be made to find their fulfillment in the present work of grace going on among the Gentiles? The latter is an instance of the high-mindedness the apostle rebuked in Romans 11. Such passages as Isaiah 43:1-7 and Zechariah 10:9-12 are wrested altogether from their true context by unspiritual spiritualizers and applied to the church, whose heavenly calling is lost sight of, while Israel's hope is denied.

As one learns to rightly divide the Word of truth, its various lines fall into order and its happy distinctions become plain to the anointed eye. The confusion will then be seen to exist, not in God's perfect Word, but in man's bewildered mind, controlled by tradition and often clouded by self-sufficiency. Truth is learned in the conscience. If that is being exercised, the Holy Spirit, who is the Spirit of truth, can be depended on to make plain the mind of the Lord to even the simplest person.

ZECHARIAH 11: Thirty Pieces of Silver

The scenes briefly depicted in the preceding chapters have been surpassingly lovely. But the glory promised there is withheld during the present time because of the rejection of the One on whom it all depends. So we now have a sorrowful account of the scornful refusal of the Good Shepherd and the acceptance instead of the anti-shepherd, who seeks only his own exaltation and does not care about the devastation and scattering of Jehovah's flock.

The two opening verses sound an alarm, speaking of woe and

disaster. "Open thy doors, O Lebanon, that the fire may devour thy cedars. Howl, fir tree; for the cedar is fallen; because the mighty are spoiled: howl, O ye oaks of Bashan; for the forest of the vintage is come down." This is the somber pronouncement of wrath coming on the land and people because of the tragedy of the cross. Fire, in Scripture, speaks of God's holiness exercised in the judgment of what is unholy. It has been fiercely burning against Judah for centuries, since the day they cried, "His blood be on us, and on our children" (Matthew 27:25). He had come in grace as the Shepherd of Israel to gather and feed the poor of the flock. He came to His own, but His own did not receive Him; so desolation and dispersion ensued. The undershepherds should have cried out in dismay, for they were the ones who had led the revolt against Him—the One whose love would have been like a rod and staff in the hour of need. Their glory was spoiled, and so was the pride of Jordan. No longer was there a barrier to prevent the invasion of the lions of the wilderness, seeking to prey on the flock of slaughter (Zechariah 11:3).

Zechariah was directed to act the part of the shepherd. He was to feed the flock whose buyers slew them and held themselves guiltless. Unpitied by their own shepherds, they were appointed to death; but a remnant was reserved—even the poor of the flock previously mentioned (4-7).

Obediently, Zechariah took two symbolic staves and fed the flock. One staff was called Beauty; the other, Bands or Concord. These represent the pastoral care Israel will know in the future when, with the beauty of the Lord her God upon her, she will dwell in unity and concord as one nation in the land covenanted to Abraham. Then she will sing with joy, "[Jehovah] is my shepherd; I shall not want. He maketh me to lie down in green pastures; he leadeth me beside the still waters" (Psalm 23:1-2).

They could have been enjoying all of this now if they had had ears to hear and a heart to understand when He spoke to them yearningly, "Come unto me, all ye that labour and are heavy laden, and I will give you rest" (Matthew 11:28). But they turned a deaf ear and hardened their hearts to the voice of God's loving plea. So they would have to experience the bitterness of forsaking the only One who could meet their need, both nationally and spiritually. Zechariah then (in a vision, I take it) cut off the hireling shepherds who loathed him, and whom he loathed because of their unprincipled conduct. Three in one month were judged. But the flock did not recognize his tender care, so he gave them up also to desolation both by their enemies and strife among themselves (Zechariah 11:7-9).

To signify the breaking of Jehovah's covenant, which was forfeited by their sin, Zechariah destroyed the staff called Beauty—for all their loveliness was gone, and they were unclean in His sight. But still a feeble remnant was set apart, for God always preserves an election of grace. So we read, "The poor of the flock that waited upon me knew that it was the word of the Lord" (10-11).

Then, as a striking type of the Messiah, Zechariah said to them, "If ye think good, give me my price; and if not, forbear." They needed no time to consider. All was settled in their minds. His rejection was fully determined before he spoke. At once they weighed for his price "thirty pieces of silver" (12). This was, of course, the very sum for which Judas sold the true Shepherd of Israel (see Matthew 26:14-16).

Notice, not only was the prophet's value estimated at this sum, but the potter's was too: "Cast it unto the potter: a goodly price that I was prised at of them." By referring to Exodus 21:32 we see the irony of this expression, "a goodly price." Thirty pieces of silver was the value the law set on a slave who had been gored and slain by an ox. Such was the "goodly price" man put on the Savior.

The money was thrown to the potter in the house of the Lord; and the other staff, Unity or Concord, was broken, displaying the breach between Judah and Israel (13-14).

All this was fulfilled to the letter in the Lord Jesus. Sold for thirty pieces of silver, the wretched betrayer cast down the money in the house of the Lord. But in blind obedience to the Word, which they seemed too dull to comprehend, the chief priests gave it to the potter to purchase a field to bury strangers in. Such a potter's field has Palestine been ever since.

Before His rejection, though, our Lord said to the Jews, "I am come in my Father's name, and ye receive me not: if another shall come in his own name, him ye will receive" (John 5:43). He spoke, undoubtedly, of the willful king, the personal antichrist of the last days, who will be received by the Jews as the Messiah when he comes with power and signs and lying wonders.

Zechariah next shifts his attention to this dreadful person. He was directed by the Lord to take the instruments of a foolish shepherd and impersonate one who would be raised up in the land, in whom Judah would vainly hope for deliverance. Devoid of compassion for the flock, he will seek only his own ends, and "he shall eat the flesh of the fat, and tear their claws in pieces." The indignant judgment of Heaven will fall on this impious wretch: "Woe to the idol shepherd that leaveth the flock! the sword shall be upon his arm, and upon his right eye: his arm shall be clean dried up, and his right eye shall be utterly darkened" (Zechariah 11:15-17). His final doom is given in Revelation 19, where we see the false prophet cast alive into the lake of fire.

In our days of great achievement and marvelous advancement, we hear much of the coming man, the fully developed, cultivated man of the twentieth century. The expression refers, of course, to the boasted progress of the race, not to any single individual. But it may well remind us of the two coming men spoken of in Zechariah 11 and elsewhere in the book of God, though both are usually forgotten by people.

God has His coming man—the man Christ Jesus. In speaking so of Him, we should not lose sight of His dignity. He is indeed God "over all, God blessed forever" (Romans 9:5). When He returns in glory to this world that killed Him and turned, Cain-like, to building cities and making advancement in the arts and sciences, we will be shown to be quite forgetful of the blood shed on Calvary's cross, which cries out to God still (compare Genesis 4:8-10). We do not notice as often as we should the two aspects of Christ's death brought before us in the Bible, with widely different results. Viewed as offering Himself a sacrifice to God for sin, and suffering at the hand of God for guilt not His own, the result is free salvation and complete justification for all who believe in Him. On the other hand, viewed as the One rejected by humanity, and suffering at the hands of wicked people, the result is dire judgment on the world that cast Him out. (These two aspects and results are especially presented to us in Psalms 22 and 69.)

When He returns the second time, it will be "without sin unto salvation" (Hebrews 9:28) for all who have trusted Him as their Savior, who will be "in the twinkling of an eye" changed and caught up together in the clouds to meet Him in the air (1 Corinthians 15:51-52; 1 Thessalonians 4:16-17). Shortly after, however, He will be revealed from Heaven in flaming fire to take vengeance on all who have rejected His grace (2 Thessalonians 1:7-10).

He will be judge of both living and dead (2 Timothy 4:1; 1 Peter 4:5). The living who have spurned His offer of mercy will be judged when He comes to institute the kingdom long promised by the prophets (Revelation 20:1-6; Isaiah 32, 63). This is the premillennial judgment of the sheep and goats depicted in Matthew 25. The wicked dead will be judged by Him when He sits on the great white throne at the close of the ages of time.

Of the day or hour of His return no one knows or can know. Speculations are useless. "In such an hour *as ye think not* the Son of man cometh" (Matthew 24:44, emphasis added). It is fitting then, to be ready to meet the coming Man and not be ashamed in His presence.

There is only one way by which anyone born in sin and a transgressor by practice can be ready to face Him, the holy and the true One. All who trust Him are instantly cleansed from every sin by His precious blood. His work, finished when He was here before, is of such infinite value and so thoroughly met all the requirements of God's holiness that all who believe are made fit "to be partakers of the inheritance of the saints in light" (Colossians 1:12). If you, reader, have rested your soul in Him as Savior, you will be ready to meet Him and will be raptured away to be forever with Him, if spared until He comes.

But Satan also has his "coming man," of whom our Lord spoke in John 5:43. In the interval between the rapture of the church and the appearing in glory of the Savior, this monster of infamy, in himself a very incarnation of the devil, will arise to dazzle the eyes of the world by his unhallowed brilliancy and power. He will be Satan's masterpiece of deception, the false Christ, who will sway the minds and consciences of those who reject the love of the truth. He is called "the son of perdition," linking him in character with that awful apostate who sold his Master for thirty pieces of silver (2 Thessalonians 2:3; John 17:12).

Think of people, those of the greatest culture and learning, bowing down before this vile creature and acknowledging him as their Lord! He is aptly called a "beast" in Revelation 13:11, though in appearance he is the counterfeit of the Lamb of God. His speech is that of the dragon, "that old serpent, which is the Devil and Satan" (Revelation 20:2). This is the coming man of the earth, and the Lord Jesus is the coming Man from Heaven.

Which, dear reader, will have your heart and your allegiance? If you are left behind unsaved at the Lord's coming, you will worship antichrist. For God will send those who did not obey the truth strong delusion so that they will believe the lie of "the man of sin" to their eternal condemnation (2 Thessalonians 2:8-12).

May you then, if still out of Christ, turn "to God from idols to serve the living and true God; And to wait for his Son from heaven" (1 Thessalonians 1:9-10). Then your portion will be with the blessed Man in glory forever. If you turn away from Him, your doom will be horrible, shared with the man of the earth and all the lost in the lake of fire for eternity.

ZECHARIAH 12: Judah's True Day of Atonement

The last three chapters of Zechariah relate almost entirely to the period called the great tribulation, or the time of Jacob's trouble, with the establishment of the kingdom following. Our attention has already been directed to that short but severe season in what we have noticed about the antichrist. This grave time is the moral result of the rejection of the Lord Jesus, and it will be the final governmental display of Jehovah's wrath because of Judah's colossal error.

The Lord speaks of Himself in the first verse of Zechariah 12 as the One "which stretcheth forth the heavens, and layeth the foundation of the earth, and formeth the spirit of man within him." The last clause deserves our careful attention.

Since God forms the human spirit within a person, the spirit then is an entity existing distinct from the body. It is not to be confused with the breath, nor is it merely the same as the mind. Mind is one of the functions of the spirit, for it is the seat of intelligence. "What man knoweth the things of a man, save the spirit of man which is in him? even so the things of God knoweth no man, but the Spirit of God" (1 Corinthians 2:11). It is logically impossible to deny the personality of man's spirit and not likewise deny the personality of the Spirit of God. The spirit is the real person who inhabits the body during life. At death, it puts off the tabernacle of flesh and goes out unclothed into the unseen world, called by the Jews *Sheol*, by the Greeks *Hades*. This is not the grave but the condition of departed spirits, whether saved or lost. The spirit of the believer is "absent from the body, and...present with the Lord" (2 Corinthians 5:8). That of the unsaved is "in torment," but awaiting the final judgment when death and Hades will be "cast into the lake of fire" (Revelation 20:14).

Sadducees of every era deny the true personality of the spirit as an unseen entity formed within the outward person we see. God, however, links this special creation with the heavens and the earth:

> Thus saith God the Lord, he that created the heavens, and stretched them out; he that spread forth the earth, and that which cometh out of it; he that giveth breath unto the people upon it, and spirit to them that walk therein (Isaiah 42:5).

Here breath and spirit are clearly distinguished. The one is fleeting; the other exists forever. True, this passage is not specifically and deliberately teaching about the spirit of humankind; but the passage is nevertheless all-important and a distinct guard against Sadduceeism, if carefully considered.

In Zechariah 12:2 Jerusalem, the center of all God's ways in the earth, is introduced; and a siege is foretold that will evidently take place in the last days. Jerusalem will at that time be a cup of trembling or reeling—that is, an intoxicating drink—to all the nations. Possessed with an almost insane desire to control the ancient city (a city that is recognized by all as the key of the East), they will make desperate attempts to obtain rule over it. But Jerusalem will turn out to be, as it has always been down through the centuries, a burdensome stone. Every nation burdening itself with it will be destroyed, even though a coalition formed for its destruction were made between all the people of the prophetic earth (3).

A number of powers, however, will each act for itself, in the time of the tribulation. The Roman empire will be revived in the form of ten kingdoms, freely allied, that will give their support to the blasphemous beast in the first part of Revelation 13. Its seat will be in Rome, proudly called the Eternal City. In Jerusalem itself the antichrist will reign, having made a league, offensive and defensive, with the beast. He is the second beast of Revelation 13, and he simulates the Lamb of God. His dragonic speech, however, betrays his real character.

As prophesied in Daniel 11, two rival powers will set themselves against him, trying to obtain Jerusalem and destroy him and each other (namely, the kings of the north and the south). This means that Egyptian power will gain some prominence and try to capture Palestine in that time of trouble, but it will be opposed by a northern power inhabiting the territory now called Turkey, in Asia. This is identical with the Assyrian so frequently mentioned.

Farther north will be the great empire of Gog, the last enemy to come against Jerusalem. This is undoubtedly Russia, ever the inveterate enemy of the Jews who grasps eagerly after their land. The end of this power is foretold in Ezekiel 38 and 39.

Another confederacy is mentioned in Revelation as "the kings of the east" (16:12) or, "the sun-rising"; but it would seem as though the hordes of these nations barely reach the land before the judgment falls. It is significant that Japan is called the kingdom of the rising sun.

In the endtimes mighty armies will be gathered from all quarters against Jerusalem just before the Messiah appears in glory. They will clash in the great battle of Armageddon, long since predicted by the prophets and briefly depicted in Zechariah 12:4-5 (but more fully described in chapter 14 and in Revelation 19).

Following the utter defeat of all Israel's enemies, government will be established firmly in Judah; and Jerusalem will be rebuilt in unequaled splendor, inhabited by a redeemed and happy people (Zechariah 12:6).

The ten tribes will be regathered after the kingdom is set up. The tents of Judah will be saved first. Then the house of David will be distinguished from them, and one taken from there will act as prince-regent on earth for the true Son of David who will reign from Heaven. Afterward, the ten tribes will ask the way to Zion and will return from all the countries to which they have been scattered.

And so that ideal state which the prophets had long yearned for will have been reached. The Lord Himself will defend His people, and the weakest among them will be like David, the heroic defender of the liberties of Israel. His house will be in direct communication with Heaven, establishing a pure theocracy on earth—where every enemy will be destroyed and peace and goodness will everywhere prevail (7-8).

The chosen people might have enjoyed all this ages ago if they had only obeyed the Spirit's call to repentance, recorded in Acts 2. That was a summons to self-examination and humbling in Jehovah's presence because of their national crime—the crucifixion of the Messiah. All their blessings wait for this act, which will mark their acceptance of the atoning value of Jesus' work. Only then will they in spirit have reached the great feast of the seventh month, the true day of atonement.

Leviticus 23 gives us important instruction regarding the feasts, providing the yearly calendar of all seven great feasts. The sabbath is introduced as the symbol of the rest that will follow all the dispensations when the course of time has come to a close, as declared in Hebrews 3:10–4:11.

The Passover prefigures the cross, even as we are told that "Christ our passover is sacrificed for us" (1 Corinthians 5:7). This is immediately followed by the feast of unleavened bread, both in Leviticus 23:6-8 and 1 Corinthians 5:8, which says: "Therefore let us keep the feast, not with old leaven, neither with the leaven of malice and wickedness, but with the unleavened bread of sincerity and truth." This sets forth the call to repentance that is now extended to Jew and Gentile alike. Resting beneath the sheltering blood of the slain Lamb, they must be holy and separate from all evil, waiting for the time of their full redemption.

The next feast in Leviticus 23 is the feast of firstfruits, which was to be held the day after the feast of unleavened bread had ended.

This feast of firstfruits points to Jesus' resurrection—and ultimately our own (see 1 Corinthians 15:20-23).

After Christ's resurrection, His church experienced Pentecost, which is the next feast mentioned in our Leviticus passage. The day of Pentecost, or the feast of weeks, required that a new meal-offering be presented before Jehovah (Leviticus 23:15-22). This pictured the present mystery, which was not made known until Israel's final rejection of the testimony of the Lord and His apostles. Note that this was in the third month.

Then there is a long break, until the seventh month. Now, since Pentecost clearly includes the calling out of a people from among the nations for the Lord's name, then all the feasts of the seventh month obviously refer to Israel when the fullness of the Gentiles will have been reached, when God will summon with His holy trumpet His earthly people to the land of their fathers. That trumpet will blow when the church has been caught up to Heaven. This the feast of trumpets beautifully pictures. It is the awakening of Israel, when the veil will begin to be taken away (see Romans 11). Then they will be called to self-abasement and repentance for their fearful sin—manifested in the cross and consummated in the rejection of the Holy Ghost. This is, for them, the great day of atonement. Long centuries have passed since the Lamb of God bled, but they have not yet kept the day of fasting and affliction of soul that God joined with the sacrificial offering to make atonement for their sins.

That day of mourning will come in the hour of their deep distress, just prior to the appearing of the crucified One in the glory of His Father and all His holy ones with Him. This, therefore, is the weeping referred to in Revelation 1:7, and Zechariah 12:10-14. In the Apocalyptic passage we read, "Behold, he cometh with clouds; and every eye shall see him,...and all kindreds of the earth shall wail because of him." This is not wailing in terror, but the anguished mourning of the awakened remnant when they realize the dreadful sacrilege their fathers were guilty of in crucifying the Lord of glory.

God Himself will pour upon the house of David and the inhabitants of Jerusalem the spirit of grace and humble prayer, and "they shall look upon me whom they have pierced, and they shall mourn for him, as one mourneth for his only son, and shall be in bitterness for him, as one that is in bitterness for his firstborn" (Zechariah 12:10). The word *look* might be rendered "contemplate." It implies intense attention, perceiving deeply so that every contour of His face may be imprinted on their souls. His once-marred face, His pierced hands and side—all will be indelibly impressed on them. When they learn in this way that He who was spurned as a criminal and a blasphemer was really the Lord of glory, their grief and repentance will know no bounds.

We have two New Testament pictures of this scene. First, Thomas the apostle, called Didymus (the twin), believed when he saw. In the remnant of Judah, the other twin (may I say) will come to the front, equally unbelieving until the marks of spear and nails will prove conclusive.

Second, in Saul of Tarsus we have a pre-eminent picture of the same remnant. Hating the name of Jesus, he went on his way, zealously persecuting all who loved that name until he was arrested by a light from Heaven. His eyes, blinded to earth's glory, peered into the holiest. And there he saw on the throne of God, the Nazarene! In this way he was one born before the time—that is, before the time when, by a similar sight, the remnant will be brought to cry as he did, "Lord, what wilt thou have me to do?" His days and nights of darkness correspond to the period of mourning set forth in Zechariah 12. "In that day shall there be a great mourning in Jerusalem, as the mourning of Hadadrimmon in the valley of Megiddon" (11). This verse alludes to the great grief that fell on Judah when Josiah was slain, in the same valley where the Lord will yet appear to judge the armies of those who hate His earthly people. Megiddon is, of course, Armageddon, the valley of slaughter in Revelation 16:16.

In Zechariah 12:12-14 the people are divided into various classes. The family of the house of David, the royalty of Judah, mourn separately. The house of Nathan, the very prophet who once reproved David for his sin, also mourn separately. Then there are the families of Levi and of Shimei or Simeon, once joined in iniquity, now each separately join in common confession because of sin. Every family will participate in the affliction of soul when they see the One who long ago entered into the heavenly sanctuary by His own blood, coming in glory.

Another feast closes the series in Leviticus 23, which relates to Zechariah 14. So I will leave it until we reach that portion.

ZECHARIAH 13: The Fountain Opened and the Shepherd Smitten

The fountain that provides cleansing from all defilement is immediately linked with the true day of atonement (Zechariah 13:1). When the Spirit of God has produced repentance in the remnant, the Word of God will at once be applied in cleansing.

It is *to* (not *in*, as people often attempt to quote it) the house of David and to the inhabitants of Jerusalem that the fountain is opened. They will be morally cleansed from all sin and uncleanness, in fulfillment of the testimony of Ezekiel:

> For I will take you from among the heathen, and gather you out of all countries, and will bring you into your own land. Then will I sprinkle clean water upon you, and ye shall be clean: from all your filthiness, and from all your idols, will I cleanse you. A new heart also will I give you, and a new spirit will I put within you: and I will take away the stony heart out of your flesh, and I will give you an heart of flesh. And I will put my spirit within you, and cause you to walk in my statutes, and ye shall keep my judgments, and do them (Ezekiel 36:24-27).

The day of atonement brings them to the cross. The next step is the laver, depicted by the fountain. Note carefully, it is not, as Christian poets have sung, "a fountain filled with blood," but of living water—the Word of God applied in the Spirit's power to their consciences. The same truth is taught in the Lord's washing His disciples' feet; it is the laver of regeneration and the washing in the water of the Word, but all in connection with the present dispensation. So from the side of the crucified Savior flowed both blood and water: blood to *expiate* sin before God, and water to *cleanse* the ways and keep the saint free from defilement.

When the power of the truth is brought home to the remnant, it will lead them to judge all sin and to put away all uncleanness.

Idolatry will be like a bad dream when it is past, and deceivers of all kinds will "pass out of the land" (Zechariah 13:2).

Also, since all prophecy will have reached its glorious fulfillment, the office of the prophet will cease. Anyone assuming that role will be judged even by their own parents (3-4).

But there is One who is opposite of the false prophets in every way—the One over whom they will mourn when they see how they sinned against Him. "He shall say, I am no prophet, I am a husbandman; for man taught me to keep cattle from my youth" (5). Some have followed the rabbis in applying these and the following words to the deceivers. But it seems far clearer and more in keeping with the context to apply them to the Lord Jesus Christ. He was a servant from His youth, and, like the devoted slave of Exodus 21:5-6, for the love of His own He would not go out free. To Him the wondering remnant cry, "What are these wounds in thine hands?" He replies, "Those with which I was wounded in the house of my friends." What grace, that He should speak this way of Judah, who did not know Him when He so humbly came among them.

But He could never have been wounded by them, had it not been God's purpose for Him to be a sin offering. This is why we read next, "Awake, O sword, against my shepherd, and against the man that is my fellow, saith [Jehovah]: smite the shepherd, and the sheep shall be scattered: and I will turn mine hand upon the little ones" (7). Clearly, the shepherd who is struck here is the wounded One of the preceding verses. In verse 6 man's treatment of Him is emphasized. Here in verse 7, God's judgment has fallen on Him for our sins. On the cross, as the Good Shepherd, He gave His life for the sheep and endured divine wrath in our place, so that all who trust in Him might be forever safe from the well-deserved vengeance of Jehovah's insulted throne. The words are directly applied in Matthew 26:31; the Shepherd was smitten by Jehovah Himself, and the sheep were for the moment scattered. God's hand, however, is turned in grace to the little ones who humble themselves and confess their guilt, trusting in Him whose precious blood cleanses every stain of sin. The remnant will know the value of His work when their blindness passes away, and they will be numbered among the poor in spirit who cast themselves on redeeming grace.

Not all Israel, however, nor all of Judah will be saved. But of those restored to the land after the church has been taken to Heaven, two parts will be cut off in death during the time of Jacob's trouble. The third part will be brought through the fiery trials of the great tribulation and will be refined like silver and purified like gold. They will call on Jehovah's name, and He will respond to them in grace and lovingkindness. To them He will say, "It is my people," thus reversing the Lo-ammi sentence of Hosea 1:9. While they in turn will cry out with hearts uplifted at the thought of such abounding mercy, "[Jehovah] is my God" (Zechariah 13:8-9).

Their salvation then will be of a double nature, as it was for their fathers of old: wherever faith was exercised, people were both brought to God and saved from Egyptian bondage.

Zechariah 14 gives us the details of their deliverance from their enemies, and it does not leave them until they are keeping the happiest feast of all the year—the feast of tabernacles—with the assured sense of God's favor.

ZECHARIAH 14: The True Feast of Tabernacles

How darkly this chapter opens, but how gloriously bright it closes!

Of all Jerusalem's sieges, none was more severe than the one depicted in these first two verses. They describe conditions beyond any past destruction of the city and can only apply to something yet future.

> Behold, the day of the Lord cometh, and thy spoil shall be divided in the midst of thee. For I will gather all nations against Jerusalem to battle; and the city shall be taken, and the houses rifled, and the women ravished; and half of the city shall go forth into captivity, and the residue of the people shall not be cut off from the city (1-2).

From east, west, north, and south, the armies of the nations will advance on Jerusalem, hating the people and the city of God, but also hating each other.

Antichrist will be embraced by the apostate Jews within the city as the Messiah and King of Judah. But against him the Assyrian (or the king of the north) and the king of the south (terms used relative to Palestine) will pour their hordes into the land in one last desperate effort to wrest from this wicked king his brief authority. Behind the Assyrian power will be Gog, the last prince of Rosh, Meshech, and Tubal—undoubtedly the head of the vast Russian empire. Allied with him will apparently be the kings from the sunrising, or the far east, whose armies will hurry to join him in his assault on Jerusalem.

On the other hand, the beast, the elected emperor of the confederacy forming the revived Roman empire, will be the sworn foe of all these hostile powers, and the arm on which antichrist will lean. From every part of western and southern Europe he will draw his vast armies, who will be imbued with equal hate against both the faithful remnant of Judah and the Assyrian coalition.

Between these conflicting powers, Jerusalem's position will be a most pitiable one. Unable to maintain the dreadful struggle, the city will be taken, and the horrors of ravaging conquest will be undergone again.

But when it seems as though no power, human or divine, could prevent the city's total extinction, the Lord will go forth as a mighty warrior, staining His robes in the blood of His people's adversaries (3). He will appear in glory before the eyes of the world's astonished armies. And He "shall stand in that day upon the mount of Olives," from which He ascended to Heaven when He had made purification for sins.

As His feet touch that sacred spot, a great earthquake will split the mountain in two. One part will fall east, the other west, opening up a deep valley through which the remnant of His people will flee for refuge. They will head for Azal (a spot now unknown), just as Lot fled Sodom for Zoar (see Genesis 19), when judgment is about to sweep over the scene. In this way they will be hidden in the day of the Lord's anger, until His indignation is past.

This section closes, if properly punctuated, with the declaration, "Yea, ye shall flee, like as ye fled from before the earthquake in the days of Uzziah king of Judah." Here there should be a full stop. We have no specific record about this earthquake in Uzziah's day, though many believe it is the same one referred to in Amos 1:1. The reference to it here completes the dramatic account of the siege and the deliverance.

A new beginning is made in the last clause of verse 5, which introduces an orderly account of the Lord Jesus' appearing in glory with all His heavenly saints and the blessed results that follow: "The Lord my God shall come, and all the saints with thee." This is how that glorious kingdom, so long predicted, will be ushered in. This event will not happen through the preaching of the gospel and the conversion of the world. Nothing less than the personal presence of the Son of God will ever bring in the millennium. The holy ones who will come with Him include all the heavenly hosts—angels and redeemed sinners transformed into glorified saints. First Thessalonians 4 and 1 Corinthians 15:51-57 make it plain that prior to the beginning of the time of trouble for Israel, all the saved of every past dispensation will be caught up to meet their Lord in the air.

> Dead and living, changed and rising,
> In the twinkling of an eye.

They will appear at His judgment seat to be rewarded according to the services rendered to Him during their lifetimes. Then the church as the bride, and all Old Testament saints as the called and chosen guests, will participate in the marriage supper of the Lamb, which will be celebrated in the Father's house. After the happy nuptial rites, the Lord Jesus, accompanied by all His holy ones, will descend to take His earthly kingdom and deliver the remnant of Israel and Judah from their adversaries.

This will take place on "one day which shall be known to the Lord," a day that no human method of calculating can determine. The exact meaning of Zechariah 14:6-7 has puzzled the most scholarly, but this much seems clear: that day will be different from every other, beginning in deepest gloom and darkness but brightened by the shining of the Sun of Righteousness—"at evening time, it shall be light." And so the morning without clouds will have dawned on this poor world, where night has held sway so long.

The great earthquake predicted in verses 4-5 will probably cause the phenomena of verse 8. According to the Word of the Lord given in Ezekiel 47:1-12 and Joel 3:18, living waters will go out from Jerusalem as a perennial stream of refreshment. They will divide into two parts, half going toward the eastern sea and half toward the western. Spiritually speaking, this image presents the river of God's pleasure, the Holy Spirit's testimony to the glories of Christ, which will be a stream of life and joy to the saved nations.

Remarkable physical changes will also take place in Palestine. With the valleys raised, and the mountains leveled, the country will be like a great tableland from Geba on the north to Rimmon, south of Jerusalem. The sacred city will be inhabited in security, and her day of fear will be forever past. For the Lord will be King over all the earth and be acknowledged everywhere as the one Jehovah: "and his name one" (9-11).

The nations that showed no mercy to Jerusalem will be likewise judged without mercy—a plague consuming their flesh and civil feud causing them to destroy each other. Satan himself was an anarchist in the beginning. His kingdom is a kingdom of anarchy, knowing neither love nor pity (12-13).

Judah will be like the battle-ax of the Lord in that day of His power, victorious over every enemy, and enriched by the spoil of those who would have spoiled them. Retributive justice will be visited on all oppressors when righteousness no longer suffers, but reigns triumphant (14-15).

Then, finally, the last joyful feast of the Levitical calendar will actually be reached—the feast of tabernacles. This was to be observed after the ingathering for a full week, culminating in the holy convocation of the eighth day—which pointed to eternity (Leviticus 23:33-43). With the sowing and the long period of waiting for the harvest over, the reaping time will have come—when joy and praise will fill every heart, and songs of thanksgiving will be in every mouth.

Israel will not keep her feast alone, but all the nations that are left will go up from year to year to Jerusalem to worship the King, the Lord of hosts, and to join with His people. They will even be numbered among God's people celebrating the glorious ingathering, dwelling in booths of palms as of old. It will be a sweet and lovely ending after centuries, even millennia, of bitter strife and bloody warfare. The noise of battle will never be heard again, national hatreds will be done away with, and the era of peace on earth and God's good pleasure in men will have arrived.

Verses 17-19 seem to hint that at the beginning there might be dissidents who will dare to refuse to worship the great King. If that should happen, immediate judgment will fall on them. The heavens will be closed and their lands parched for lack of rain so that they may know that the time when God directly governs the world has at last arrived. If the family of Egypt will not go up—those who depend not on rain but on the yearly inundation of the Nile for the fertilization and maturing of their crops—then a special judgment will be theirs: a plague "wherewith the Lord will smite the heathen that come not up to keep the feast of tabernacles."

In this age people may defy God and seem to prosper. In that coming time, however, godliness and prosperity will be inseparably linked together. That day will be the dispensation of the fullness of the seasons, when all things will be under the headship of Christ. Every knee must bow to Him—and people will no longer walk by faith, as now, but by sight, seeing everywhere the evidences of direct divine intervention in human affairs.

The last two verses of Zechariah form a fitting climax to the chapter and the book.

> In that day shall there be upon the bells of the horses, HOLINESS UNTO THE LORD; and the pots in the Lord's house shall be like the bowls before the altar. Yea, every pot in Jerusalem and in Judah shall be holiness unto the Lord of hosts: and all they that sacrifice shall come and take of them, and seethe therein: and in that day there shall be no more the Canaanite in the house of the Lord of hosts.

No longer will a distinction be made between sacred and secular. Instead, everyone will have learned that anything worth doing at all should be done for the glory of God. The articles for temple service (used in the rebuilt temple of Ezekiel 40–48) will be sacred to Jehovah. But so will every vessel used in Jerusalem and in Judah; and the very bells on the horses will tinkle His praises. This is the lovely ideal the Holy Spirit portrays for Christians living in the present age; as it is written:

> Let the word of Christ dwell in you richly in all wisdom; teaching and admonishing one another in psalms and hymns and spiritual songs, singing with grace in your hearts to the Lord. And whatsoever ye do in word or deed, do all in the name of the Lord Jesus, giving thanks to God and the Father by him (Colossians 3:16-17).

Also in 1 Corinthians 10:31 we are told, "Whether therefore ye eat, or drink, or whatsoever ye do, do all to the glory of God." Those who always set God's glory before them, even in the smallest details of life, anticipate the millenium and already enter into what will one day be true of restored Israel under the reign of the Lord Jesus Christ.

There will be no drudgery then, no mere working for wages, for the *Canaanite* will have disappeared from the land in that day. Undoubtedly, the name refers to the ancient enemy who always challenged Israel's possession of the promised inheritance. But it also bears the meaning of "merchant" or "bargainer," to which the sons of Jacob are compared (see Hosea 12:7). When bad feelings between Abraham and Lot were so narrowly avoided only because of Abraham's generosity, it is significant that Scripture records, "the Canaanite . . . dwelled then in the land" (Genesis 13:7). When all conflict and bitterness is done away with in Abraham's redeemed seed, the Canaanite will have passed out of the scene forever.

This is Israel's hope: the possession of the land pledged to their fathers, under the righteous rule of our adored Lord Jesus Christ. In His own time, He will show that He is the blessed and only Potentate, King of kings, and Lord of lords. Ours is a higher and holier destiny—to be the bride of Him who is then to reign. We look to Heaven, not to earth, for our inheritance. And we expect that very soon now,

> the Lord himself shall descend from heaven with a shout, with the voice of the archangel, and with the trump of God: and the dead in Christ shall rise first: Then we which are alive and

> remain shall be caught up together with them in the clouds, to meet the Lord in the air: and so shall we ever be with the Lord (1 Thessalonians 4:16-17).

So the two callings are clearly distinguished in Scripture. Israel is the wife of Jehovah, now divorced because of her sin, but who will be brought back to Him in grace and will live in her former land in the day the kingdom is displayed. The church of the present dispensation is the bride of the Lamb, whose nuptial hour is drawing near, and who will be one with her Redeemer throughout all the ages to come. Old Testament saints and tribulation saints who died before the kingdom is set up will be, as was John the Baptizer, friends of the Bridegroom. They will be "called" to the marriage supper of the Lamb to participate in their Lord's rejoicing, and they will also share in Jehovah's joy when the earthly bride returns to His arms of love and compassion. In Heaven their position will be similar to that of those who were spared of the nations, those who will rejoice with Israel when they see the place she will have in the millennial kingdom.

There are distinct groups, then, and varied glories in Heaven and on earth. But when the Lord Jesus' authority is confessed in both spheres, and every enemy has been banished and rendered powerless, all redeemed creation will delight to ascribe blessing and honor and glory and power to our God and to the Lamb that was slain, world without end. Amen.

MALACHI

A PROFILE
MALACHI
THE GATHERING GLOOM

BY JOHN PHILLIPS

Malachi's voice is heard in the gathering gloom. It is the last prophetic call (436-416 B.C.) before a long silence of four hundred years descended upon mankind. Malachi's name means "my messenger," and he has been called "the unknown prophet with the angel's name."

Era of Malachi's Prophetic Ministry

Malachi prophesied possibly a whole century later than Haggai and Zechariah. At any rate it was long enough after those prophets for a sharp decline to have set in, both religiously and morally. Sacrilege and profanity characterized the religious attitude: witchcraft, adultery, perjury, fraud, and oppression were prevailing moral sins; disregard of family responsibility highlighted social conditions; and "robbing God" reflected the gross materialism of the age. The attitude of the people was one of sneering self-defense. The formalism and skepticism of Malachi's day are seen in full bloom in the Pharisaism and Sadduceeism of the time of Christ.

Themes of Malachi's Ministry

Malachi's ministry dealt with the Lord's complaints against the nation Israel and the coming of the Lord to deal with judgment and justice.

- I. The Lord's Complaint (1–2)
  - A. The Nation's Spiritual Sins (1:1–2:9)
    1. Denying God's Love (1:1-5)
    2. Despising God's Name (1:6)
    3. Defiling God's Altar (1:7-14)
    4. Disregarding God's Law (2:1-9)
  - B. The Nation's Special Sins (2:10-17)
    1. Their Detestable Worship (2:10-13)
    2. Their Deserted Wives (2:14-16)
    3. Their Distorted Words (2:17)
- II. The Lord's Coming (3–4)
  - A. To Deal in Judgment with Sinners (3:1-15)
    With their:
    1. Ungodly Actions (3:1-5)
    2. Ungodly Attitude (3:6-12)
    3. Ungodly Arguments (3:13-15)
  - B. To Deal in Justice with Saints (3:16–4:6)
    The righteous are to be:
    1. Remembered (3:16-18)
    2. Rewarded (4:1-4)
    3. Revisited (4:5)
    4. Revived (4:6)

Malachi not only cataloged the sins of the nation (sins that were never fully arrested but which took deep root and produced the conditions that climaxed in the murder of the Lord Jesus). He also spoke emphatically of the Lord's coming. He pointed back to Moses, the great representative of the law, and to Elijah, the great representative of the prophets. Then he foretold the coming again of Elijah, a coming which had, at least, an initial fulfillment in the ministry of John the Baptist. The last word of Malachi, the last word of the Old Testament, and the last word before a long silence fell, was the solemn, sobering word "curse." With that fearful word ringing in his ears, the Jew came to the chronological end of his Bible.

The New Testament begins where the Old Testament ends. Without the New Testament, the Old Testament tells of a beginning without an ending, relates hundreds of promises and predictions without any lasting fulfillments, and begins with blessings and ends with a curse. Gratefully we now acknowledge that the silence of God has been broken. God has spoken to us in these last days in His Son.

CHAPTER TWELVE

THE PROPHECY OF MALACHI

We know nothing whatever about the writer of this book. His name, Malachi, meaning "my messenger," occurs in verse 1; but we read of him nowhere else in Scripture, and we get no particulars concerning him here. He was the last of the prophetic band, and his book appropriately closes the Old Testament canon. Until the advent of John the Baptist, of whose coming Malachi prophesied, no other messenger was directly sent to Judah from God.

The conditions Malachi described fit well with the state of the returned remnant in the latter period of Nehemiah's governorship. So it is quite likely that he lived and proclaimed the word of Jehovah either during that time or a little later.

The divisions of his book are not very pronounced. From 1:1 to 2:9 the prophet gives a message to the priests. The balance of the book addresses the people, but it includes more than the remnant and really amounts to an indictment of all Judah. Chapters 3 and 4 tell of the coming day of the Lord. This will be preceded by the one who, like Malachi himself, will in a distinctive sense bear the title "my messenger."

A striking feature of the prophecy is the eightfold complaint Jehovah had against His people (1:2,6,7; 2:14,17; 3:7,8,13). Again and again Malachi solemnly charged them with turning away from God in their hearts while outwardly professing to serve Him. And each time, with brazen insolence, they dared to contradict God's testimony and asked for proof, thus disclosing an utterly calloused conscience.

All this provides us with a serious warning, particularly if we are moving in their same direction in any way. They had shown an outward return to God and His Word, but their hearts were still far from Him. The people became occupied with *place* and *position* rather than with vital godliness. This resulted in the gross Pharisaism of Jesus' day, which was simply the outgrowth of the conditions described by Malachi.

MALACHI 1: The Failed Remnant

Sad as Judah's state had become, it was love, not judgment, that opened the first chapter. "I have loved you, saith the Lord." What could be more tender, more calculated to touch the hearts of His people—if indeed they had any heart left and were not altogether hardened and indifferent! Unchanging was that mighty love of His, however wayward His people were. Yet they responded to Him with contempt: "Wherein hast thou loved us?" They looked for temporal prosperity and worldly glory as the proof of His love. Lacking both, they called His affection into question, utterly ignoring their own prolonged course of carelessness and infidelity, for which He had chastened them. Patiently, He accomodated their caustic question: "Was not Esau Jacob's brother? saith the Lord; yet I loved Jacob, And I hated Esau." Then He illustrated that statement by describing the desolations of Edom, declaring that they would never recover because the descendants of Esau were "the people against whom the Lord hath indignation for ever." On the other hand, though Israel's blessings seem delayed, they will surely come at last so that all nations will confess, "The Lord will be magnified from the border of Israel" (1-5).

Centuries later, the apostle Paul made clear what God's dealings with Jacob and Esau meant. He quoted the phrase "Jacob have I loved, but Esau have I hated" in Romans 9:13 to prove the wisdom of God. For the Lord made His choice before the children were born, when He said, "The elder shall serve the younger" (12). Carefully observe, there is no hyper-Calvinistic question here of condemnation to Hell and predestination for Heaven. The apostle contended for Jehovah's inalienable right to dispose of His creatures as He wills. And He declared with holy joy that He *wills* to show mercy to those who deserve only wrath. Jacob and Esau are cited as illustrations. Before either was born, God chose Jacob to be superior to Esau, nationally. The elder was to serve the younger and thus demonstrate the superiority of God's choice. When the whole of Old Testament history had come to a close, He summed it all up, saying, "I loved Jacob, and I hated Esau." The grace first extended to Jacob, the poor heel-catcher, was shown to his descendants to the very end.

But what had He received from Israel in return for all this? It is clearly a duty for a son to honor his father, and a servant his master; but what honor had God received as a Father, or what reverence as a Master? Even the priests in the newly restored temple despised His name. But when the charge was brought, they disdainfully replied, "Wherein have we despised thy name?" (Malachi 1:6)

Solemnly He brought their sins before them. They had offered defiled bread on His altar, failing to honor His holiness and ignoring His laws. Again they were ready to answer back, as if the reply to their previous question was not enough. "Wherein have we polluted thee?" What amazing patience and grace God showed; what incomprehensible apathy and flippancy they revealed. They said in essence, "The table of the Lord is contemptible"; for they offered blind, lame, and sick animals to Him in sacrifice, and kept the best for themselves. Would they dare do this to their governor or any other earthly ruler? Yet He, the great King, they treated so unworthily. Still He pleaded with them to repent and come to Him for the grace that they were ignoring yet needed so much. Covetousness was the root sin that led them daily farther astray. The priests would not so much as shut the temple doors save for wages, nor kindle the altar fire except for gain. True love for God was absent; and their holy office had been denigrated to a mere worldly profession, used as a means of profit. Because of this, God could have no pleasure in them nor accept an offering at their hands (9-10).

It seems almost unnecessary to draw attention to the similar state prevailing in so many places today. It is obvious to even the least spiritual that worldliness and covetousness characterize the professing church, with godliness and true devotion being the exceptions. Even where there has been a measure of revival and return to what is written in the Word of God, the same evil principles have crept in insidiously and are doing their deadly work in many quarters. Nothing but a spirit of prayerfulness, coupled with watchfulness, will keep any from being carried away by the unholy current.

But it is good to know that, whatever the failures of the present church, God will still be fully glorified, as Malachi wrote,

> From the rising of the sun even unto the going down of the same my name shall be great among the Gentiles; and in every place incense shall be offered unto my name, and a pure offering: for my name shall be great among the heathen, saith the Lord of hosts (11).

It is not the present work of grace among the Gentiles that is spoken of here; rather this prophecy points to that wonderful era of blessing which is still in the future—the time when everything the holy prophets have said will reach their total fulfillment. Then Jehovah's name will be honored and His word obeyed throughout the whole earth, when all nations will bask in the sunshine of His favor. We wait in faith for brighter and more glorious hopes to be consummated.

In the next verse, the prophet returned to the Lord's charges against His people. Judah profaned the table of the Lord, characterizing it as polluted and its meat, contemptible. They declared the service of His altar a weariness. And they made light of what should have been both sacred and precious. Their unsuitable offerings disclosed the thoughts of their hearts. And the Lord would not accept either. Instead, He invoked a curse on the deceiver who brought Him that which was corrupt while keeping the better part for himself. How dare they treat the King of kings this way, whose name was to be reverenced among the Gentiles (13-14)! They who had known so much of His power and grace had proven themselves unworthy of His love. But the nations who had been passed by during the time of Israel's special favor would yet bow at His feet and confess His greatness and glory.

Let us be ashamed if we in any way resemble those depicted in this solemn chapter we have so briefly gone over!

MALACHI 2: The Sin of the Priests

In a fuller and more pointed manner, the sins of the priesthood were brought home to their consciences in Malachi 2. Anointed for temple service, set apart to holiness, and devoted to the most sacred of all offices—"ordained for men in things pertaining to God, . . . [to] offer both gifts and sacrifices for sins" (Hebrews 5:1)—they had proved unfaithful to their sacred trust and thought only of their own profit. "Supposing that gain is godliness" (1 Timothy 6:5), they lost no opportunity to serve their own desires while neglecting their holy calling.

In this present dispensation, we have no similar official priestly order. However, we do have the priesthood of all believers, holy and royal, with immediate access to the holiest by virtue of the blood of Jesus. As worshipers we go in to God to offer up spiritual sacrifices. As royal priests separated to Himself, we go out to show His praises to a needy world. And as holy priests we are appointed to intercede on behalf of those who do not pray for themselves. What cause for shame and humiliation, then, when our feet stumble and our paths are crooked! All that Malachi said to the earthly priesthood is applicable to us, the heavenly company, as we search our consciences to find whether we too have not failed grievously as they did.

"O ye priests, this commandment is for you" (Malachi 2:1). Clearly and distinctly the priestly hierarchy is addressed in this verse. If they refused to hear and heed this solemn word, the Lord would send a grievous curse upon them: He would curse their blessings, as He had already begun to do. Their seed would be rejected—the family of Levi set aside from their appointed place of privilege. This is how it has been, in fact, since the rending of the temple veil, though only visibly since Jerusalem's destruction by the Romans under Titus. Their solemn feasts would also be polluted, and they themselves would be rendered ceremonially unclean to illustrate the uncleanness of their hearts and hands (2-3).

God's covenant of life and peace had been with Levi from ancient times, when Levi was set apart from his brothers to find his all in God. Because of the fear he showed Jehovah when Israel made the calf in the wilderness (Exodus 32:25-29), God had established an everlasting covenant with him. But this covenant would not stop God's wrath during the season of Israel's dispersion because of their sins. The Levites no longer reverenced His name, as they had in those days of the wilderness. Back then "the law of truth was in [their] mouth[s], and iniquity was not found in [their] lips." In singleness of heart they had walked with God in peace and equity and were His honored instruments in executing judgment on evil (Malachi 2:4-6).

This is a lovely description of true devotion to the Lord. Only when we, as believer-priests, in this same way keep our hearts and guard our ways will God be glorified in our lives. To talk of separation and keeping the truth while neglecting what Malachi sets forth here is mere sham and hypocrisy.

Believer-priests' lips should impart knowledge and people should seek the law from their mouths. This is how we prove ourselves messengers of the Lord of hosts (7). This is also why we need earnest, prayerful study of the whole Word of God, aiming toward bringing our whole life into practical subjection to God's will. The servant of God in the New Testament is exhorted to "study to show thyself approved unto God, a workman that needeth not to be ashamed, rightly dividing the word of truth" (2 Timothy 2:15). It is not a question of following some favorite teacher or clinging to a particular interpretation of doctrine. Rather we are to give the Holy Scriptures, in their entirety, the honored place God intended them to have as the complete guide for His people and the suitable food for their souls. Nor are we merely summoned to Bible study— we are called to be "doers of the word" (James 1:22). We should allow no portion of it to be a dead letter to us, but we must give it all its due weight and authority over our hearts and consciences so that we walk in all that is written there.

The priests utterly ignored Malachi's instruction. Having left the path of obedience themselves, they caused the simple to stumble and go astray from the Word of the Lord. Therefore, the covenant of Levi had become corrupted. They had shown themselves to be anything but the moral seed of Phinehas, whose javelin had stopped the plague and whose faithfulness would be remembered to all generations (Numbers 25:7-13). Despising the law, these faithless priests had been made contemptible themselves, and they would be despised by the people they had misled. Their ways testified against them, so the Lord rejected their service (Malachi 2:8-9).

The tenth verse begins the second division of the book, which goes on to the end of the prophecy. Malachi now addressed the people of Judah as a whole—in the last message they would ever get directly from God until the coming of the just One, the Amen, the faithful and true Witness. The coming of His forerunner to public ministry, John the Baptist, is predicted in the first verse of chapter 3.

The Jews had all sprung from one common father, Abraham, and were created by one God, Jehovah of hosts. Why, then, should they deal treacherously with each other by profaning the covenant of their fathers (verse 10)? It is not the so-called "Fatherhood of God" that is here declared. There is little evidence that "one father" refers to the Deity. Only in a national sense could Israel say, "Doubtless thou art our father" (Isaiah 63:16). Individually they all had one father, Abraham, in whom they gloried and whose seed they all were. Thus they were a nation of brothers. But, sadly, how unbrotherly they had acted!

What can be more shocking than to be called by a name so suggestive of love and tenderness (as Abraham himself said to Lot, "We be brethren," Genesis 13:8), and yet to treat one another with a callous indifference and coldheartedness that amounted at times to enmity and even hatred. "Who are these brethren?" one is reported to have asked, concerning certain companies of factious saints. "They are people," was the reply, "who are very particular about breaking bread, and very careless about breaking hearts!" What a shame that such a testimony concerning any Christians should ever be more than slander originating from the father of lies. "Let brotherly love continue" is God's admonition to us all (Hebrews 13:1). And let us bear in mind that, since our Head has gone back to Heaven, we reveal our love to Him by loving His members here on the earth.

The feeble remnant, returned to the land of God's name and separated from the nations, surely needed the strength that comes from unity and mutual love, and brotherly encouragement. Outside, the wolves raged and snarled. Inside, the sheep were biting and devouring one another! It is a pitiful picture. (Tragically, this picture has often been duplicated by Christ's sheep since.) The outside opposition did not wound Nehemiah's heart; but when he found the consecrated people exacting usury of one another and treating their countrymen with cruelty and greed, his great soul was moved to its depths (Nehemiah 5). That this evil had never truly been abandoned but only temporarily checked is clear from Malachi's rebuke.

Since they treated one another so treacherously, it was only to be expected that they would prove traitors to their God as well. This is the prophet's next charge against all Judah and Israel (Malachi 2:11). They had profaned the holiness of Jehovah, that holiness "which he loved" (how striking the expression), and had married the daughters of strange gods. These mixed marriages are also mentioned in Nehemiah and Ezra, which helps us to pinpoint the time of Malachi's ministry. Neither true to each other nor to the Lord, the people defiled themselves by forming unholy alliances with the idolatrous people around them. When brotherly love is lacking, true godly separation will soon be in name only. And we need not be surprised that the next generation would turn to the world for their companions if all they have seen from those professed to be united in God's name is bickering and strife. God's face, however, is against all those who act this way, and He will cut them off. As Malachi showed, God could not accept offerings from a people so indifferent to His holy character, whatever the outward expression of grief and penitence (12-13).

Their response to such grave words—"Wherefore?" (or "Why?")—shows the actual state of their souls. And God was not slow to reply, for He was the witness to all their evildoing. God had forbidden them to enter into marriages with the heathen so that He could make of two people one flesh among His own people. But they had violated their covenant pledges by taking foreign and idolatrous wives who were leading them away from the Lord. God's plan had been to seek a godly seed; that's why He had made this decree concerning their family relationships. But leniency toward divorce and mixed marriages were fast corrupting the seed of God (14-15).

The practice of setting aside their wives (so tragically common in our own degenerate times) to gratify a passing whim was detestable in God's eyes. He hates divorce. Hidden violence would all be searched out and could not remain forever covered. Everything must come to light in due time. "Therefore take heed to your spirit," was His word, "that ye deal not treacherously" (16).

We need only to turn to Matthew 19 to see what little impact this admonition had on them. Divorces were granted on the most trifling and absurd pretenses, while all their lawlessness was covered with a cloak of extreme rigidity in outward religious observances. How easy it is to make much of externals while being habitually careless about true piety and sincere obedience to the weightier matters of the Word of God!

The Lord was wearied with their empty religiosity—mere words from the lips, not the genuine utterance of the heart that is acceptable in His sight. But again they answered with the brazen question, "Wherein have we wearied him?" He replied, "When ye say, Every one that doeth evil is good in the sight of the Lord, and he delighteth in them; or, Where is the God of judgment?" (17) They were setting aside His revealed Word and congratulating themselves on being Abraham's seed and therefore in the line of promise. They thought the merits of their fathers would cover all possible deficiencies in their own lives. It could not be, thought they, that God would judge those in whose veins flowed the blood of Abraham, Isaac, and Jacob. So they lived in a fool's paradise, having already forgotten the lesson of the Babylonian captivity.

And it has not been much different with the church. Ruin and disaster came in early because of departure from the living God. For centuries, spiritual Babylon held sway over the consciences of God's children and kept them in bondage and ignorance. At last, through the recovery of the Word of God, deliverance and blessing came. But not long after, even in the lifetime of the reformers, there crept in a lifeless orthodoxy, coupled with relaxation of morals and indifference to that Word so graciously entrusted to them. Since then, there have been various revivals in which the Spirit has emphasized practical godliness and devotion to Christ. Each successive movement has begun with more or less loyalty to God and to His Word. But decay and disintegration have soon followed. When the truth of the mystery of Christ and the church was brought to light, the name of Jesus became the rallying standard for many of

His people, who were tired of the failing systems of men. But, again, pride and self-will wrought sad havoc. It now remains to be seen how close judgment is for marring the lovely testimony of the peerless name of the Lord.

The hour is late. The Judge is at the door. The coming of the Lord draws nigh. Humble self-examination is fitting for us all. May we have the grace to discern the signs of the times and to bow our hearts to His Word.

MALACHI 3: Preparation for the Messenger

As we have already noted, the name *Malachi* means, "my messenger." It was through him that Jehovah declared,

> Behold, I will send my messenger [using the same word as the prophet's name], and he shall prepare the way before me: and the Lord, whom ye seek, shall suddenly come to his temple, even the messenger of the covenant, whom ye delight in: behold, he shall come, saith the Lord of hosts (1).

This is the prediction of the coming of John the Baptist to herald the King, the Messiah. He would do so in such a way as to make it plain that Messiah Himself was identified with Jehovah; for the prophecy is, "He shall prepare the way before me" (see Matthew 11:10; Mark 1:2; Luke 1:76; 7:28).

It is also important to notice that *angel* and *messenger* are the same word in Hebrew. So John was the angel of Jesus, but Jesus Himself was the Covenant-Angel of whom Jehovah had said long ago, "My name is in him" (Exodus 23:20-21). To the temple so recently rebuilt by Zerubbabel, though later enlarged and beautified by Herod, He would suddenly come as the Nazarene—only to be despised, rejected, and crucified. But another coming is clearly foretold in Malachi 3, for when this future coming takes place, the unholy will not be able to endure it or stand in His presence. As a refiner and purifier God will purge the Levitical family and set apart for Himself the sons of Zadok (Ezekiel 48:11). They will have turned to Him, confessing their guilt and judging themselves for their share in the sins of the priesthood. On the rest, judgment must burn like fire (Malachi 3:2-3).

It seems plain from verse 4 (see also Ezekiel 43) that in the days when the kingdom is established over all the earth, sacrifices and offerings will be reinstituted in Jerusalem and the land of Judah. However, they will only be commemorative of the one great sacrifice of the cross. In this way the millennial saints will have the same relationship to the sacrifices as Christians do to the Lord's supper today.

Sinners will be weeded out from among the people, and a righteous remnant alone will be preserved, "For I am [Jehovah], I change not; therefore ye sons of Jacob are not consumed" (5-6).

The Jews had never kept God's ordinances in a completely Scriptural manner. From the days of their ancestors, they had departed from what He had written for their guidance. So, in view of the advent of the Messenger of the covenant, God bid them to return to Him so that He could return to them with blessing and loving favor. But, as so often before, they arrogantly asked, "Wherein shall we return?" (7) There was no sense of need or of failure. Quite the contrary, they were self-satisfied and content. As long as outward forms and ceremonies were attended to, they saw no reason to examine their ways.

Their sinfulness, therefore, had to be pressed on them more strongly still. "Will a man rob God?" Yet they had deliberately robbed Him. With amazing audacity, they asked, "Wherein have we robbed thee?" He replied, "In tithes and offerings," and declared that the curse of the violated law rested on the whole nation. Conscience seemed completely gone; and when a good conscience has been set aside, anything can be indulged in with a degree of self-assurance that seems inexplicable (8-9).

Still, terrible as their failure had been, it was not too late to repent. God told them to bring all the tithes into the storehouse, which would acknowledge their stewardship under Him and provide for the needs of those who served in the temple. It would also release them from the grasp of carnal things and open the way to God's promise of abundant blessing if they would heed His voice. He would have them prove Him and see if He would not open the windows of

Heaven and pour out such a shower of spiritual refreshment that they would be hard-pressed to find space to store it. He would rebuke the devourer too for their sakes, stopping their enemies from persecuting them so that in peace and quietness they might enjoy the abundant fruits of their labor. Blessed with all that their hearts could desire, both spiritually and temporally, all nations would call them the happy people, and theirs would be a land of delight (10-12).

All this will be literally fulfilled when the spirit of grace and supplication is poured out on the future repentant remnant and they return to God with their whole heart. Everything waits on this, just as the Lord Jesus Himself declared, "Ye shall not see me henceforth, till ye shall say, Blessed is he that cometh in the name of the Lord" (Matthew 23:39).

But for saints of every dispensation, an important principle is here enunciated—blessing depends on true, wholehearted devotion. Let all that is due the Lord, all that has been long withheld because of our selfishness, be rendered to Him. Let all the tithes be brought in, and He will gladly pour down showers of blessing on His waiting and expectant people. God delights to give; but our low, earthly-minded state frequently hinders His visiting us with a gracious revival. "Let us search and try our ways, and turn again to the Lord" (Lamentations 3:40) is a word in season at the present moment in the church's history.

For Judah, the era of blessing had not yet dawned—nor has it ever really come since, because they did not recognize God's judgment on them. Their words were strong against God. When He challenged them about this, for the eighth time they brazenly challenged Him in return: "What have we spoken so much against thee?" (Malachi 3:13) No appeal, request, or warning seemed to move them or turn them in the slightest degree from their self-complacency and egoism.

They had said, "It is vain to serve God," for they blindly estimated things by the standard of worldly prosperity. As they contrasted their humble lot with the proud surrounding nations, they decided that there had been no profit in keeping Jehovah's Word and seeking to obey His voice. What they did not take into account was that they were part of a failed nation and were still reaping the sad fruit of their fathers' evil sowing. So they stumbled at the prosperity of the wicked, but they did not, like Asaph, enter the sanctuary with unshod feet so that they might understand the end of the enemies of the Lord (see Psalm 73).

Not all the people, however, were so calloused and cynical. Verses 16-18 distinguish a remnant that is a shining example to us. In the midst of all the degeneracy and coldheartedness of the majority, a few feared Jehovah and sought God's light together in the surrounding darkness. They spoke often with each other about the precious and serious things of God. And the Lord took pleasure in this feeble company, listening to their discussions and confessions, and entered their names in a book of remembrance. This book will soon be opened at the judgment seat of Christ: "And they shall be mine, saith the Lord of hosts, in that day when I make up my [peculiar treasure]"; for as they had found their treasure in *Him,* so He found His in *them.* In the day when He will visit on the wicked their iniquities, He will spare the remnant, discerning between those who truly served Him and those who had no heart for His Word. It is a striking and beautiful passage, rich in comfort and cheer to the tried and tested ones who value fellowship with God above all else.

Focusing our thoughts on the evil only weakens the hand and distresses the spirit. But centering our thoughts on Him who sits in peace above the mists of earth will strengthen and refresh, proving that the only real power for practical holiness and victory over all the might of the enemy lies in Him.

MALACHI 4: The Sunrising

The break between chapters 3 and 4 seems unfortunate, because it diverts the mind from what has just been presented. Verse 1 of chapter 4 is a continuation of what has gone before. The Lord is going to discern between the righteous and the wicked. When? In the coming day that will burn like an oven—the day of the Lord toward which all prophecy points as the time when all the wrongs of all the ages will be put right.

"The day," remember, is not a brief period of twenty-four hours but a day that will embrace the entire millennium, concluding with the passing away of the earth and the heavens. It will introduce the day of eternity, or "the day of God," as Peter wrote in his second letter (3:10-12). This present time is called "man's day," for it is a time of undefined duration when people will do their own will (1 Corinthians 4:3; alternate reading of "day" in place of "judgment"). For the heavenly saints, "the day of Christ" will immediately follow, and we will be caught up to meet the Lord in the air and brought before His judgment seat (Philippians 1:6,10). The "day of the Lord" will then begin for Israel and the nations. That day will encompass the judgments to be visited on the earth and the reign of righteousness and will end when the kingdom is delivered up to the Father. God (Father, Son, and Spirit) will at last be all in all throughout the never-ending "day of God"—the eternal state.

Malachi 4:1, then, speaks of the day when the Lord Jesus will return in glory to judge all who have refused the everlasting gospel. That day will "burn as an oven; and all the proud, yea, and all that do wickedly, shall be stubble: and the day that cometh shall burn them up, saith the Lord of hosts, that it shall leave them neither root nor branch." All humanity will know the wrath of the Lamb when He is revealed from Heaven in flaming fire, taking vengeance on those who have rejected God.

But in that day of thick darkness and gloom, a light will break forth in overwhelming glory for a preserved remnant.

> Unto you that fear my name shall the Sun of righteousness arise with healing in his wings; and ye shall go forth, and grow up as calves of the stall. And ye shall tread down the wicked; for they shall be ashes under the soles of your feet in the day that I shall do this, saith the Lord of hosts (2-3).

This is very different from the hope of the church. We wait for the shining forth of the Morning Star, not the rising of the Sun of righteousness, which is distinctively Israel's hope. The morning star heralds the dawn, and rises before the sun is yet visible. So it is with the Lord Jesus, the Morning Star. He will descend from Heaven with a shout, and translate Christians into the Father's house prior to the time of Jacob's trouble, the great tribulation. This terrifying time occurs on the earth in a brief interval between the coming of Christ for the church and His appearing with His holy ones in glorious majesty. He will give relief to the remnant of Judah and Israel in the day of their trial, which has come because of their rejection of the Lord when He came before in grace. This latter deliverance is the shining forth of the Sun of righteousness, whose beams will bring healing for His own but will consume the wicked with their intensity. It will not be the church, but Israel, who will then tread down the evildoers as ashes beneath their feet, in accordance with the universal testimony of the prophets.

It should be plain to all thoughtful students of the Word of God that this passage completely nullifies the theory of a converted world at the coming of Christ. Where, then, would be the wicked who are to be trodden down? The fact is that Scripture knows nothing of this prevalent modern doctrine. There will be no millennium until Christ appears, for He must first act in power for the destruction of all who have refused to accept His claims, thus purging the scene for the establishment of His kingdom.

Annihilationists of every school have made much of these three opening verses of Malachi 4. They suppose that the prophet refers to the final day of judgment and the ultimate destruction of the lost in the lake of fire. Their argument is that since the wicked will be burned up root and branch and be ashes under the feet of the righteous, they will have ceased to exist—they will have been effectually blotted out of God's universe.

They make their mistake by failing to observe that it is *temporal* judgment that is foretold here, with Sodom and Gomorrah's judgment being an example. Fire from heaven will consume the *bodies* of the wicked before the millennial kingdom is set up; that is what becomes ashes under the feet of the righteous. But there is no hint here as to what will become of their souls and spirits. We learn elsewhere in Scripture of judgment after death, even though the body is burned to ashes. Our Lord tells us that it will be more tolerable for Sodom and Gomorrah in the day of judgment than for certain of the cities in which His mighty works had been performed but He Himself had been rejected (Matthew 11:20-24).

Nearly forty centuries have passed since Sodom and Gomorrah

were burned up root and branch. Had Abraham or Lot walked over the sites of those destroyed places a few days after the fire fell from heaven, the wicked would have been ashes under the soles of their feet. But were they then annihilated? Far from it. They have yet to stand before the great white throne for judgment, where they will be dealt with in accordance with the light they had and which they refused.

The same may be said of "the proud, yea, and all that do wickedly," spoken of here by Malachi (4:1). Their bodies and place on earth will be destroyed utterly, yet they will continue to exist in the world of spirits and will prove that "it is appointed unto men once to die, but after this the judgment" (Hebrews 9:27). For, as our Lord Jesus said, God "is not a God of the dead, but of the living; for *all* live unto him" (Luke 20:38, emphasis added). If you, dear reader, are unsaved, do not be lulled to sleep by the devil's gospel of final extinction. Abiding wrath and eternal judgment are terrible realities from which the precious blood of Christ alone can deliver.

In Genesis 1:16 the sun is first introduced as a type of the Lord Jesus, from whom His church gets all her light, just as the moon reflects the glory of the sun. Before Malachi closed the Old Testament canon, he returned to that first type and presented the same glorious person as "the Sun of righteousness."

In view of all this, the last three verses take on a most solemn tone. Judah is exhorted to remember the law of Moses, which God had commanded for all Israel but which they had violated from the start, and were now filling up the cup of their iniquities. To call them back to Himself, He would send them Elijah the prophet before the coming of that great and dreadful day of the Lord we have been considering. We know from Matthew 17:10-13 and Mark 9:11-13 that, for certain, John the Baptist was that Elijah. The nation did not accept him as such; therefore the ministry Malachi refers to is yet future. As Moses and Elijah are linked in these verses (the lawgiver and the restorer), so we see the signs of each performed by the two witnesses of Revelation 11. This would clearly indicate the type of ministry that would arise in Jerusalem at the end time.

Elijah will turn the hearts of the fathers to the children, and the hearts of the children to the fathers. In this way, he will bring all the remnant into subjection to the revealed will of God so that He will not have to come and smite the earth with a curse.

And so with this solemn word, *curse*, the Old Testament abruptly comes to a close. The law had been violated in every particular. On the grounds of the legal covenant, the people had no hope whatever. Wrath like a dark cloud was lowering over their heads. The awful *curse* of that broken law was all they had earned after long ages of trial. But a Redeemer had been promised; and where there was faith in any who felt the seriousness of their condition, there would be seen the coming of the Seed of the woman who was to bruise the serpent's head. He Himself would be made a curse so that all who put their trust in Him might be redeemed from the doom they had so long and fully deserved. "To him give all the prophets witness, that through his name whosoever believeth in him shall receive remission of sins" (Acts 10:43). Through Him alone can guilty men, who confess their lost condition and trust His grace, be delivered from the *curse*.

AUTHOR BIOGRAPHY

HENRY ALLAN IRONSIDE, one of this century's greatest preachers, was born in Toronto, Canada, on October 14, 1876. He lived his life by faith; his needs at crucial moments were met in the most remarkable ways.

Though his classes stopped with grammar school, his fondness for reading and an incredibly retentive memory put learning to use. His scholarship was well recognized in academic circles with Wheaton College awarding an honorary Litt.D. in 1930 and Bob Jones University an honorary D.D. in 1942. Dr. Ironside was also appointed to the boards of numerous Bible institutes, seminaries, and Christian organizations.

"HAI" lived to preach and he did so widely throughout the United States and abroad. E. Schuyler English, in his biography of Ironside, revealed that during 1948, the year HAI was 72, and in spite of failing eyesight, he "gave 569 addresses, besides participating in many other ways." In his eighteen years at Chicago's Moody Memorial Church, his only pastorate, every Sunday but two had at least one profession of faith in Christ.

H. A. Ironside went to be with the Lord on January 15, 1951. Throughout his ministry, he authored expositions on 51 books of the Bible and through the great clarity of his messages led hundreds of thousands, worldwide, to a knowledge of God's Word. His words are as fresh and meaningful today as when first preached.

The official biography of Dr. Ironside, *H. A. Ironside: Ordained of the Lord*, is available from the publisher.

THE WRITTEN MINISTRY OF H. A. IRONSIDE

Expositions

Joshua
Ezra
Nehemiah
Esther
Psalms (1-41 only)
Proverbs
Song of Solomon
Isaiah
Jeremiah
Lamentations
Ezekiel
Daniel
The Minor Prophets
Matthew
Mark
Luke
John
Acts
Romans
1 & 2 Corinthians
Galatians
Ephesians
Philippians
Colossians
1 & 2 Thessalonians
1 & 2 Timothy
Titus
Philemon
Hebrews
James
1 & 2 Peter
1,2, & 3 John
Jude
Revelation

Doctrinal Works

Baptism
Death and Afterward
Eternal Security of the Believer
Holiness: The False and the True
The Holy Trinity
Letters to a Roman Catholic Priest
The Levitical Offerings
Not Wrath But Rapture
Wrongly Dividing the Word of Truth

Historical Works

The Four Hundred Silent Years
A Historical Sketch of the Brethren Movement

Other works by the author are brought back into print from time to time. All of this material is available from your local Christian bookstore or from the publisher.

LOIZEAUX

A Heritage of Ministry . . .

Paul and Timothy Loizeaux began their printing and publishing activities in the farming community of Vinton, Iowa, in 1876. Their tools were rudimentary: a hand press, several fonts of loose type, ink, and a small supply of paper. There was certainly no dream of a thriving commercial enterprise. It was merely the means of supplying the literature needs for their own ministries, with the hope that the Lord would grant a wider circulation. It wasn't a business; it was a ministry.

Our Foundation Is the Word of God

We stand without embarrassment on the great fundamentals of the faith: the inspiration and authority of Scripture, the deity and spotless humanity of our Lord Jesus Christ, His atoning sacrifice and resurrection, the indwelling of the Holy Spirit, the unity of the church, the second coming of the Lord, and the eternal destinies of the saved and lost.

Our Mission Is to Help People Understand God's Word

We are not in the entertainment business. We only publish books and computer software we believe will be of genuine help to God's people, both through the faithful exposition of Scripture and practical application of its principles to contemporary need.

Faithfulness to the Word and consistency in what we publish have been hallmarks of Loizeaux through four generations. And that means when you see the name Loizeaux on the outside, you can trust what is on the inside. That is our promise to the Lord...and to you.

If Paul and Timothy were to visit us today they would still recognize the work they began in 1876. Because some very important things haven't changed at all...this is still a ministry.